LIVING WITH

Elbie Lebrecht

GRAFTON BOOKS

A Division of the Collins Publishing Group

LONDON GLASGOW
TORONTO SYDNEY AUCKLAND

Grafton Books
A Division of the Collins Publishing Group
8 Grafton Street, London W1X 3LA

A Grafton Paperback Original 1989

ISBN 0-586-20106-8

Printed and bound in Great Britain by
Collins, Glasgow

Set in Sabon

CONTENTS

Acknowledgements *vii*
Introduction: the sugar in our lives *1*
Living Without *23*

1 Breakfast *41*
2 Breads and Scones *49*
3 Spreads and Toppings *75*
4 Biscuits, Bars and Sweet Nothings *83*
5 Drinks *107*
6 Sweet and Sour Main-Course Dishes *115*
7 Salads *137*
8 Chutneys and Spiced Fruit *145*
9 Pastry, Pies and Tarts *153*
10 Cold Fruit Desserts *191*
11 Hot Fruit Desserts *203*
12 Cakes *221*
13 Sauces *253*
14 Mousses, Jellies and Creams *261*
15 Ice Cream *279*
16 Children's Parties *293*

Natural Sugar and Fibre in Food *303*
Bibliography *307*
Index *313*

ACKNOWLEDGEMENTS

Jasmine Challis, senior dietitian at St Bartholomew's Hospital, has validated the carbohydrate and calorie counts in this book, compiled the food table and helped me with accurate nutritional information. I am very grateful for her expert advice and practical experience.

Material from Drs Kenneth Heaton, Erik Millstone and Michael Weitzman helped clarify points that arose in the Introduction.

For discussions and recipe ideas I am indebted to Eva Burke, Aviva Cohen, Judy Dangoor, Diana Dantes, Elizabeth Heayberd, Arlene Howard, Judy Jackson, Vicky Philosoph, Stephanie Segal, Millicent Sherman, Rachel Simon, Richard Simon, Rosalind Solomon, Ron Somekh, Mark Spivack, Erna Weiss and Pam White. Anne Freeman provided constructive editorial suggestions.

Lorraine and Freddy Isaac and Marion and Nigel Scott volunteered to test and taste some of the recipes. Yonatan Kahn was a valuable judge of sweetness levels.

My husband has been a source of counsel and concern and, with my girls, Naama and Abigail, played an essential role in the creation of this book.

INTRODUCTION

One fifth of what we eat is made up of sugar, a plant extract that gives your body nothing nutritious and can harm your health.

This book defines the dangers of sugar, examines its invasion into our way of life, and demonstrates how each of us can live a full, vigorous, enjoyable life without it – and without even missing it.

Sugar started exercising its spell on Western society as an exotic spice and medicine used by the very wealthy in the Middle Ages. In the 20th century it has become a staple foodstuff. In the past two hundred years, sugar production has increased 400 times from ¼ million tonnes in 1800 to 100 million tonnes in the 1980s. The average British adult consumes around 37 kilos (82 pounds) of sugar every year. And this figure does not include sugar-based sweeteners such as glucose used in manufactured foods. These bring the total close to 45 kilos (100 pounds) a year – almost 1 kilo (2 pounds) per person per week. Even if sugar were totally harmless these figures would be cause for concern as healthy nutrients in our daily diet are replaced by an alien intruder.

But sugar is not harmless. At the point of entry to your body it interacts with the plaque coating on the teeth to produce an acid that eats into tooth enamel, causing steady damage and intermittent agony. Once inside you, sugar has been identified as one of the main causes of excess weight, of increasing the risk that you will develop heart disease, high blood pressure and diabetes. Links between sugar and gallstone formation and the development of cancer of the bowel have been indicated by recent research.

The root of the problem is that sugar is a highly refined, low-fibre carbohydrate. In the long process of producing sugar, which involves crushing the plant, clarifying the juice, boiling it down and evaporating the water, separating off and removing impurities from the final sugar crystals, 90 per cent of the plant is discarded. That 90 per cent contains whatever fibre, vitamins, minerals, trace elements and proteins nature may have bestowed. All the remaining 10 per cent does is to sweeten; it provides calories and nothing else for the body.

Even the Sugar Bureau, the promotional and political lobby set up by the producers, concedes that 'it is true that refined sugar contains no vitamins, minerals or proteins'. It argues that sugar's function is 'to make foods palatable and help keep our diet varied'. But sugar makes up 20 per cent of the average person's diet – an alarmingly high amount for a mere flavour enhancer.

The complete removal of fibre from sugar results in a very concentrated sweetener called table sugar which is 99.9 per cent sucrose. Fibre slows down the absorption of food. Without it, sugar is absorbed very rapidly and causes a sharp rise in blood sugar levels. Extra insulin is pumped out by the pancreas to bring the sugar level back to normal. The rush of insulin leads to a swing down to low blood sugar. These ups and downs of sugar levels have a direct impact on moods and behaviour.

When sugar is introduced into a nation's diet, certain patterns develop that have been repeated all over the world. As the country becomes wealthier, more sugar is eaten and the traditional staples such as bread, flour and rice decline. The staples become identified with poorer times, and sugar represents the promise of the modern and wealthier era – cake rather than bread within everyone's grasp becomes the ideal. Sugar becomes cheaper. Before the creation of the sugar plantations one pound of sugar in the England of 1400 was the cost equivalent of 29 pounds of butter – today the same weight of sugar costs less than half a pound (225 grams) of butter. As sugar edges out the old foodstuffs, their dietary contributions are gradually eroded. The nation's health suffers with the depletion of minerals, vitamins and fibre.

The extent of the international sugar addiction confers great power on a few producers. Only two firms supply the 2.4 million tonnes of sugar consumed annually in Britain. 'That does not mean I can control European policy,' Paul Gardini, head of the Feruzzi group which owns 45 per cent of the Italian sugar market, 33 per cent of the French and which narrowly failed to acquire British Sugar's 50 per cent share of the UK market, was reported in the *Financial Times* as saying. 'But it does mean I can have a stronger voice in Brussels in order to influence quotas . . . My profitability is tied to quotas – the more quotas, the more profits.' In plain English, this means that the EEC has built up a 3 million tonne glut of sugar that someone will have to pay for. Each tonne of sugar produced in the EEC has a guaranteed sale price higher than prices on the world market, paid for by unwitting citizens. With so much sugar to get rid of and so many sugar farms to keep sweet,

European governments dare not take serious steps to reduce dependence on sugar and protect the well-being of their citizens.

The sugar industry promotes medical conferences, research and publicity with the aim of vindicating sugar from any connection with poor diet or ill-health. 'The sugar industry is winning the publicity battle against the health faddists,' trumpeted a recent sponsored feature in the trade journal *Supermarketing*.

'Our sugars,' proclaims a manufacturer's advertisement aimed at young women readers in *Cosmopolitan*, 'are just as natural as the humble sugar beet they're removed from.' Yet the fat bulbous beets are far removed from the shiny white crystals in the sugar bowl. 'Sugar has the purity of a chemical,' states I. I. Brekhman, the Russian researcher. 'Table sugar is one of the purest chemicals produced in large quantities by modern industry,' wrote R. Passmore and M. A. Eastwood in *Human Nutrition and Dietetics*.

Why we have become so dependent for daily sustenance on a chemical is a matter for historians and sociologists to answer. This book offers an alternative lifestyle in the form of over 200 different recipes using fresh fruit, dried fruit and whole vegetables as alternative sweeteners. Natural sugar is present in all these foods, but it comes as a complete package with all the nutrients intact.

Sweet Sugar Blues

'Sugar is a good source of energy' thought nearly 70 per cent of the people questioned in a survey conducted by the University of Bradford in 1986.

But there is no physiological need for pure sugar. Our body can extract all the sugars it needs from foods such as fruit, vegetables and grains. When refined sugar is eaten it gives a raw burst of energy very shortly after being swallowed. It bypasses the body's elaborate digestive machinery and rushes into the bloodstream, raising the blood sugar level. The automatic response is for the pancreas to produce a lot of insulin to lower the sugar level, but the resulting sudden drop can leave a feeling of tiredness and low spirits.

These observations are not recent.

> *I'm so unhappy, I feel so bad*
> *I could lay me down and die.*
> *You can say what you choose*
> *but I'm all confused,*
> *I've got the sweet, sweet Sugar Blues*
> *More Sugar!*
> *I've got the sweet, sweet Sugar Blues.*

That lyric, written in 1923, beats out the message that eating sugar creates a need for more sugar. Back in the 16th century Leonhard Rauwolf, a German botanist and traveller in the Middle East, observed that the Turks and Moors had become so addicted to sugar that they 'cut off one piece after another and so chew and eat them openly everywhere in the street without shame . . . and in this way accustom themselves to gluttony and are no longer the intrepid fighters they had formerly been'.

Concentrated energy can be obtained far more usefully from dried fruits. Sultanas do not explode into the body as sugar does because their concentrated sweetness comes in a complete package with fibre and water and is slowly released into the bloodstream. They contain 250 calories per 100 grams against sugar's 394 calories.

Sugar and Spice and all things nice . . .

The major users of sugar are the confectionery, soft drinks, packaged cakes and biscuits industries of which confectionery is the largest by a considerable margin. Manufactured foods account for two-thirds of UK sugar sales; in the USA they form 75 per cent of sugar sales.

More sweets are consumed in Britain than in any other country – 254 grams (9 ounces) worth per person each week. And only the Swiss eat more chocolate – just 15 grams (½ ounce) more weekly.

The *confectionery industry* in 1986 sold £3 billion worth of its wares, an increase of £1 billion in only six years. It paid out as much in VAT to the government as the combined revenues from sports equipment and children's toys. It spent £87 million on advertising – much of it targeted at children.

'Demographic factors indicate the child population will continue to grow into the 1990s, which will favour modest growth, especially in the sugar confectionery sector,' predicts an internal confectionery industry market research report. Today's babies are being groomed as tomorrow's sugar-junkies. The message of TV commercials is re-inforced in the sale of sugar and chocolate models of popular figures like Postman Pat and Thomas the Tank Engine. Children under 16 make up one third of all sweet and chocolate consumers, but purchase only one tenth of manufacturing output. In other words most sweets are bought for children by misguided adults.

The confectionery industry, concludes the report, 'would seem to have little to fear from dietary awareness gaining more ground, even from consumer groups who to date have shown little interest in health issues, and who are amongst the heaviest users'. Nevertheless it has sought to exploit 'dietary awareness' as a marketing opportunity by creating products with a supposedly 'nutritious and health promoting image'. Among these, Rowntree's Novo snack bar was introduced to compete with health food bars. This 'nutritious' bar contains the following ingredients: milk chocolate, rolled oats, demerara sugar, raisins, crisped rice, cornflakes, vegetable fat, honey, coconut, malt extract, glucose syrup, treacle, sugar, sesame seeds, modified starch, emulsifier (lecithin). In terms of dietary benefit a bar like this is as nutritious as a cheeseburger is vegetarian.

In-depth studies of different groups provide a more detailed picture about who eats sugar. Families on low incomes spend more proportionately on table sugar than wealthy families. This also means that more of the poorer family's diet consists of pure sugar.

The heaviest sugar consumers, as shown by recent UK studies, are men and teenage boys. Teenage boys eat theirs in sweets, chocolates and in soft drinks while men pour a lot of it into their tea and coffee. In one Cambridge village, men ate three times as much table sugar as women, some eating more than 225 grams (8 ounces) every day.

Dietitians are a group who would be expected to be careful about what they eat. A survey found they averaged 35 grams (1½ ounces) of sugar a day while some 'heavy consumers' of 50 grams (2 ounces) daily relished the same sweet food as the teenage boys and men – confectionery, soft drinks and table sugar. It seems to be a case of physician, heal thyself.

What heavy sugar eaters had in common was that they did not eat different foods from anyone else but more of the ones containing concentrated sugar – three bars of chocolate a day instead of one, three teaspoons of sugar in their tea instead of none.

Elaborate techniques have been developed by the confectionery sector to combat the growing perception of health risks in sugar. By sponsoring the London Marathon each year, Mars promoted the message that its bars provide the energy needed to run 26 miles. Less resoundingly, Christine Cross, sports nutritionist for the National Coaching Foundation, considers that a balanced diet for a sportsperson should contain little or no sugar, a lot of carbohydrates and a limited amount of fat. 'Athletes,' she says, 'need bread and carbohydrates to build up the energy to train and create muscles.' All sugar does is give sudden artificial bursts of energy, followed by lethargy.

Even more insidiously the £10,000 Smarties' prize for children's books suggests to parents and kids that reading and eating sweets are of equal educational value. The author Alan Ahlberg refused to accept the prize when his publishers entered one of his books for this award without consulting him. Other authors were less principled.

Advocates of sugar have always been ready to attack those who try to resist its use. In the 18th century, Dr Frederick Slare found sugar to be a cure-all and wrote vigorously against its detractors, particularly against Dr Thomas Willis who had made a detailed study of diabetes and raised questions about sugar and its relation to health. His wrath was also directed against concerned mothers, or, as he called them, 'Ladies of Better Rank, who read Books of some learned Persons, condemn Sugar and denied it to their Babes very injuriously.' He insisted that 'water-pap' or 'cow's-milk' would not satisfy a baby unless sugar was added. This same philosophy has been applied by the soft drinks industry.

Over a quarter of a million tonnes of white sugar was poured into the *soft drinks* produced in Britain last year – principally cola drinks, lemonade and orange and lemon squashes. Soft drinks consumption has increased more than five times in the last 35 years, from 52 ml (2 fl oz) per person a day in 1950 to 260 ml (9¼ fl oz) in 1984. The increase in America has been sevenfold, from 40 bottles a year per person to 300 bottles in 1980 – nearly a bottle a day. 'You go to supermarkets and there's just aisle after aisle of junk – avenues 50 feet long with soft drinks on both sides,' warns Michael Jacobson, director of the Washington-based lobby Center for Science in the Public Interest.

The sugar content in a bottle is more heavily concentrated than one would imagine: tonic water contains 3 teaspoons of sugar, an average can of cola contains 7 teaspoons, and Lucozade, which is promoted as an energy-giving drink, contains 8 teaspoons of sugar per glass. Ribena, the popular children's drink, contains 5 teaspoons of sugar per glass. Undiluted, it consists of 60 per cent sugars – the rest is water.

High Fibre and Sugar

The flood of high-fibre cookery books being published over the last ten years has underlined the importance of whole grains, recommending wholewheat instead of white flour, brown rice and spaghetti in place of white. When it comes to sugar, however, there has been a suspension of logic. Most health cookery writers use it but advocate raw cane or muscovado sugar. The message is: brown is beautiful; any brown food has to be healthy; therefore brown sugar is good for you in the same way as brown or wholewheat bread. This is wishful thinking. Wholewheat flour is milled from the whole grain. Brown sugar, like white sugar, has had 90 per cent of the original plant removed. It is nutritionally identical to white sugar in that it is a concentrated carbohydrate which contains no fibre at all.

Countless gullible housewives believe they are helping their family by purchasing and using vast amounts of brown sugar: they might as well be taking four lumps of white in their tea. Fibre is removed from sugar cane at an early stage of refining. Sugar juice is extracted from the crushed canes and is concentrated, crystallized and purified.

Raw cane brown sugar contains some minerals because it has not been purified to the same degree as white sugar. However, the amount of mineral salts it contains is limited, and is about 0.5 per cent. Light brown sugar is usually made from white sugar, often sugar beet, which has been coloured with caramel or molasses. Neither has any fibre. Sugar of any hue has no place in a high-fibre lifestyle.

Wholefoods and whole grains are beneficial because their fibre and nutrients are intact and not discarded. Fibre in wheat is the wrapping around the kernel which protects the oil, minerals, vitamins, carbohydrates and protein.

The great advantage of fibre is that it fills you up and prevents overeating. Foods that contain fibre require a good deal of chewing and the effect of this is to slow down the amount of food you can eat at one go. Volunteers who were asked to drink apple juice containing 60 grams (2⅓ ounces) of carbohydrate did so in 90 seconds flat. When they had to eat the same amount of carbohydrate by chewing four apples, it took them over 17 minutes. 'Most of them,' says a report, 'found this rather heavy going and would gladly have given up after two apples, whereas drinking the juice was easy.' Fibre-rich apples leave a full feeling; juice, or sugar-sweetened beverages, leave you unsatisfied. To satiate the hunger more food has to be eaten, a surplus of calories is consumed and the body's system is overloaded, and the excess energy is stored as fat.

Fibre also aids the speedy transit of waste from the body. It absorbs water and swells up to add bulk to the residue food passing through the intestine, hastening its removal. That is why a high-fibre diet, or a bran supplement, is prescribed for constipation. 'Browne bread . . . having much branne . . . fylleth the belly with excrements, and shortly descendeth from the stomacke,' observed Thomas Cogan some four hundred years ago.

Fibre is thought to absorb toxins that can be harmful if they stay in the body for too long, including potentially cancer-forming toxins. Research in Holland shows that diets containing less than 37 grams (1⅓ ounces) of fibre a day are linked with an increased risk of cancer. This may be good news for vegetarians in the West who average 40 grams (1½ ounces) of fibre a day, but worrying for carnivores on 20 grams (¾ ounce) a day. In rural societies in parts of Africa which show virtually none of the common degenerative Western diseases the average daily fibre intake is 70–100 grams (2¾–4 ounces).

One of the first people to consider the effects of white sugar and white flour was Robert McCarrison, a British doctor working in India at the turn of the century. He carried out extensive research into deficiency diseases and, in a famous experiment, compared the typical English working man's food with the Sikh diet. A group of rats on foodstuffs 'commonly used by the poorer classes in England' were fed white bread, margarine, over-sweetened tea with a little milk, boiled cabbage, boiled potatoes, cheap tinned meat and tinned jam. Rats on the Sikh diet ate wholewheat flour chapatis, butter, 'whole' milk, dhal (lentils), raw vegetables, and meat once a week. The Sikh-diet rats flourished, put on weight, and lived happily together. The rats on the English diet showed stunted growth, did not put on weight and their coats lacked gloss. They were nervous and quarrelsome. By the sixtieth day of the experiment, they had begun to eat the weaker members of the group. Post-mortem examinations showed the English-fed rats to have a high incidence of gastro-intestinal and lung diseases; the Sikh-fed rats died healthy.

As a result of his many experiments, McCarrison launched a fierce attack on the European diet, urging people to eat fresh vegetables, dairy produce and eggs. He blamed 'the extensive use of vitamin-poor white flour and the inordinate use of vitamin-less sugar' for lack of vitamin B1 in the diet. Fibre, which he called roughage, had an important role to play: 'food must also contain a certain amount of innocuous, indigestible material, or roughage as it is called, to stimulate intestinal movement.'

In *The Saccharine Disease*, a concept first developed by Surgeon-Captain T. L. Cleave in 1966, the cumulative role played by sugar and refined cereals in chronic illnesses common in Western societies was closely examined. Cleave evolved the idea of a 'single master-disease' that caused such conditions as diabetes, coronary disease, haemorrhoids, appendicitis and diverticulitis. These conditions, said Cleave, were due to the refining of carbohydrates, especially sugar, but also white flour. Because of refining, the body absorbed more than it was designed to handle. Over a period of time, this led to chronic health conditions.

Cleave showed a strong correlation between the rapid increase in consumption of refined sugar and flour in industrialized societies and the development of chronic illnesses. He argued that Africans living with their tribes in rural areas rarely had diabetes while those in towns were succumbing in the same numbers as whites. Yemenite Jews when they moved to Israel increased the amount of sugar they ate – from virtually zero to 20 per cent of their carbohydrate intake. Twenty-five years later this community had begun to suffer from diabetes and heart disease – conditions which had hitherto been very rare.

Cleave's arguments and those of his many successors have been taken up by a variety of institutions such as the Royal College of Physicians; Oliver Gillie, medical editor of *The Independent* newspaper, cites 'at least 50 national and international committees' having recommended a reduction in sugar consumption. In 1983 the Health Education Council issued a discussion paper known as the NACNE (National Advisory Committee on Nutrition Education) Report, urging an increase in national fibre intake to 30 grams (1⅛ ounces) a day, and cuts of 50 per cent in sugar consumption and 34 per cent in fats. Although these recommendations do not go nearly as far as Cleave wanted they provoked an outcry from the food industry, which brought pressure to delay publication. When the report finally appeared it was relegated to the status of a discussion paper rather than a policy statement, and disowned by the Department of Health and Social Security which had instigated the process. Even this half-suppressed report was chided as too tame by Cleave's successors D. Burkitt, H. Trowell and K. Heaton in their important book *Dietary Fibre, Fibre-depleted Foods and Disease* which appeared in 1985. They condemn the NACNE guidelines as 'inadequate' and urge 'much greater reductions in fat and sugar and for that matter greater increases in starch and fibre'. Minimal changes, they stress, will achieve only minimal results.

Early in 1987 a government-appointed advisory committee met to investigate sugars and their links with disease; a sub-committee of COMA (Committee on the Medical Aspects of Food), its conclusions were due to be published at the end of 1988.

The recipes in this book do not use sugar at all. They are full of fibre, while fat is either omitted from recipes or used at a very low level. All the flours used are wholegrain.

How Much Fibre in . . .?

	amount of fibre per 100 grams (4 ounces)		amount of fibre per 100 grams (4 ounces)
Sugar	0 grams	Prunes	16.1 grams
Glucose	0 grams	Raisins	6.8 grams
Honey	0 grams	Sultanas	7.0 grams
Dried dates	8.7 grams	Bananas	3.4 grams
Dried apricots	24.0 grams	Apples	2.0 grams
Dried figs	18.5 grams	Carrots	2.9 grams

(McCance and Widdowson, *The Composition of Foods*, 1979)

Honey

Honey is made by bees, as everyone knows. The bees remove a dilute solution of sugar from plants and concentrate it, resulting in a substance that is 76.4 per cent sugar.

Honey has never been eaten as a basic food, but always used sparingly. Nature made it so difficult to obtain that we must assume it was never intended for large-scale consumption. This particular sweetener came with a sting. King Solomon warned, 'It is not good to eat much honey' (Proverbs 25,27). Honey is not as concentrated as sugar, but like it contains no fibre and very few nutrients; consequently it is not used in my recipes.

Although many people extol the virtues of honey and mistakenly describe food made with it as sugar-free, it contains no B vitamins or any other vitamins. It has very small amounts of minerals, including some trace minerals.

In the early Middle Ages honey was used for its medicinal powers and today royal jelly, or honey from the queen bee, is sold in many chemists as a putative health aid.

16th-century beekeeper

Sugar canes

Sugar – a plant and its power

Sugar has been growing for thousands of years: it was cultivated in Polynesia more than 10,000 years ago. The Old Testament refers to the 'fragrant reed' (Jeremiah 6,20, Isaiah 43,24), but there is doubt whether this was sugar cane or if it had yet reached that part of the world. It is only in the last two centuries that it has been cultivated commercially. Today one-tenth of the world's calories are eaten as sugar.

It originates from the Pacific, where it features prominently in creation folklore. In Polynesian mythology woman emerged full-grown from a sprouted cane which had been netted by fishermen. In Solomon Islands legends both 'Adam' and 'Eve' arose from sugar cane to become mother and father of mankind.

Sugar cane spread into south-east Asia and India six to eight thousand years ago. In India a technique for removing the juice from the plant was developed at least 350 years before the birth of Christ. In a Sanskrit grammar of this time frequent mention is made of sugar in combination with food such as rice pudding with milk and sugar. Crystallization of the juice into sugar in India is traced back to the first century. The name 'sugar' originates from the Sanskrit 'sakara' meaning gravel or grit – probably a reference to its coarse texture.

The technique of sugar-refining spread in the 6th century to Persia where the Arabs picked it up as the sword of Islam extended eastwards. They carried it militarily west into North Africa and the Mediterranean lands of Sicily, Cyprus, Malta and Spain, and their outstanding scientists worked on ways to improve cultivation of cane and its conversion into sugar.

Northern Europe discovered sugar during the Crusades. 'In the fields of the plains of Tripoli can be found in abundance a honey reed which they call Zuchra; the people are accustomed to suck enthusiastically on these reeds, delighting themselves with their beneficial juices, and seem unable to sate themselves with this pleasure in spite of their sweetness,' wrote Albert van Aachen in reminiscences of the First Crusade (1096–99). It was a Crusader who sent the first large cargo of sugar to England from Venice in 1319 in exchange for a shipment of wool.

Sugar was still a rarity in the Middle Ages and was confined to the very wealthy who used it as a spice and a medicine. Arab physicians prescribed it in powder form, as a thick syrup, an infusion and a concoction called a 'rubb' which was the immersion of flower petals and fruits in hot water and sugar which was boiled down until it became concentrated. An 11th century court doctor applied 'rose sugar' for breaking a fever, and a 12th century treatise recommended sugar for dry coughs, chapped lips and stomach diseases. It was one of the futile remedies swallowed to combat the Black Death.

Columbus carried sugar cane on his second voyage to the New World in 1493, and it was first grown by settlers in Hispaniola (the Dominican Republic). As the Arabs were driven from Spain sugar growing declined in Europe and spread to a climate and soil that suited it ideally.

Imperial, military and economic activities were also now motivated by the acquired sweet tooth of Europe's rulers. Spain and Portugal colonized the Caribbean, Mexico and Brazil. The Dutch, French and English fought over the rest of the Americas and Caribbean, inter-mittently gaining and losing territories.

To work the new sugar plantations, whose indigenous populations were often completely wiped out by disease and war, Europe went into Africa to round up slave labour. The Portuguese were the first to ship captives from the coast of West Africa in 1445. Although not all slaves were put to work on sugar, Noel Deerr, in his definitive *The History of Sugar*, estimates that it is 'no exaggeration to put the tale and toll of the slave trade as twenty million Africans, of which two-thirds are to be charged against sugar'. Sugar was therefore responsible for the con-quest of two continents and the criminal enslavement and relocation of entire cultures. Sugar is one of the main causes of the oppression of the black peoples of America and of the prevailing animosity between black and white.

Cheap slave labour brought down the price of sugar and accelerated its invasion of Europe's diet. The colonies, meanwhile, became rich and spent their sugar profits on more and more products from the mother country, hastening the process of industrial revolution. This flourishing import-export trade made great ports of Bristol and Liverpool, whose newly prosperous merchants had spare capital to invest in industrial developments and leisure pursuits. Sir Henry Tate, of the famous sugar family, ploughed part of his profits into London's Tate Gallery, along with several paintings.

This immoral interaction did not proceed entirely without protest. Helvétius, the polemical 18th century French philosopher, declared: 'No cask of sugar arrives in Europe to which blood is not sticking. In view of the misery and sufferings of the slaves anyone with feelings should renounce these wares and refuse the enjoyment of what is only to be bought with the tears and death of countless unhappy creatures.' Dr Johnson proposed a toast at an Oxford College to 'success to the next revolt of the negroes in the West Indies'. Adam Smith, the English philosopher, wrote, 'From the experience of all ages and nations I believe that the work done by slaves is in the end the dearest of any.' It took a century of courageous campaigns before slavery was finally abolished: slaves in the British Empire were emancipated in 1838, and American slaves in 1865.

The structure of the sugar plantations provided an important agro-industrial model for the huge industries that arose during the later industrial revolution. The combining of agriculture and processing under one roof, along with the organization and discipline of a large labour force working to fulfil schedules dictated by the nature of the material, were translated from the slave settlements to the factories of Europe. The poverty, overcrowding and misery of the new industrial cities were a pale-faced reflection of life on the plantations.

And it was not only slaves who were making sugar more accessible. In 1747 a Prussian chemist, Andreas Marggraf, succeeded in extracting half an ounce of sugar from half a pound of white beet and pointed the way to cultivating sugar in a temperate climate. His pupil, Franz Carl Achard, continued this work with the support of the King of Prussia and built a sugar beet factory in 1802.

Napoleon encouraged the production of sugar beet during his Wars to make France independent of sugar shipments from the English colonies. Benjamin Delessert personally received a medal from him in 1812 for setting up the first French sugar beet factory. By the next year 334 factories had been established in France. Today sugar beet accounts for 40 per cent of world sugar and is the principal source of sugar in Europe. Sugar beet production has become so widespread that the EEC is plagued with a glut of three million tonnes of surplus sugar each year.

An incidental colonial contribution to the sugar explosion was the tea-drinking habit that took root in the 18th century. Consumption of Chinese tea rose from 20,000 pounds in 1700 to more than five million pounds in 1760. Its interrelationship with sugar was underlined by Duncan Forbes, a Scottish jurist and theologian: 'Sugar, the inseparable Companion of Tea, came to be in the possession of the very poorest housewife, where formerly it had been a great Rarity.' By 1840 over 400 million pounds were shipped annually by the East India Company. Tea eventually became cheaper than beer.

By the 18th century cookery books began to appear devoted entirely to sugar confectionery. And in 1825 Brillat-Savarin, author of the gastronomic classic *Physiologie du goût*, wrote that 'there is not a woman, especially if she be well-to-do, who does not spend more for her sugar than she does for her bread.'

The final repeal of taxes on sugar in Britain in 1874 resulted in a product that was cheap enough for even the working classes and could be produced in sufficient quantities for all. From being the preserve of the very wealthy in the Middle Ages, sugar became one of the mainstays of the poor, a convenience food for the first industrialized nation.

Mothers working factory shifts could quickly provide a meal of bread spread with jam accompanied by hot sweetened tea. In the eyes of the anthropologist Mintz, 'the diet of a whole species was gradually being remade'.

Artificial Sweeteners

Sales of artificial sweeteners doubled in Britain between 1980 and 1985 and, although this amounts to £21 million-worth of sales, their share of the sweetener market is small compared to sugar. Yet these intense sweeteners are a rapidly growing industry, finding their way into more and more manufactured foods. Research studies and reports have linked artificial sweeteners with serious health problems and this excludes them from being a viable alternative to sugar. Artificial sweeteners only prolong the dependency on unhealthy, oversweet food.

The most popular sweeteners are saccharin and aspartame.

Saccharin – my daughter returned home from a party with a packet of American chewing gum in her party bag bearing the slogan, 'Use of this product may be hazardous to your health. This product contains saccharin, which has been determined to cause cancer in laboratory animals' – a nice going home present, I thought.

This warning is the result of a compromise by the USA Food and Drugs Administration which had announced a proposal to ban saccharin from all processed foods, soft drinks and as a table-top sweetener in April 1977. This decision followed research studies which showed that saccharin caused bladder cancer and had led to its total banning in Canada. Tremendous pressure was brought by the food, drink and additive industries and by autumn of 1977 the US Congress passed a temporary Moratorium which prevented the Food and Drugs Administration from banning saccharin and only required that products containing it carried a warning label.

Saccharin was invented in 1879 and by 1890 the Commission of the Health Association of France banned its manufacture and import. In Germany in 1898 saccharin was banned from food and drink, and in the USA saccharin was banned in 1912 from food and soft drinks. It regained acceptance during the two World Wars when sugar was in short supply, and the restrictions were not reimposed after the wars.

Recent research indicates that rats fed saccharin eat 15–20 per cent more food than normal. This confounds the implicit sales message that it provides a way of avoiding extra calories.

Saccharin is extensively used in Britain in such products as soft drinks and pickles, and in products marketed as low calorie or diabetic. Food Regulations specify that it may not be used in baby foods.

Aspartame is a sweetener that has only recently exploded on the British food market and is sold under the name of NutraSweet or Canderel. At the beginning of 1984 it was used in four products but by 1986 it had reached more than 160. The main foods in which it is found are soft fizzy drinks, soft drink concentrates, slimmers' yogurts and desserts.

Permission for its use in fizzy soft drinks in the USA was only granted by the Food and Drugs Administration in 1983. Prior to this there had been considerable controversy over the validity of safety tests conducted by the manufacturer. Millstone and Abraham argue in *Additives, a Guide for Everyone* that 'we cannot be certain that the tests to which Aspartame has been subjected are adequate, even by the relatively poor standards of current best practice, and so we cannot be confident that Aspartame is safe.'

Research has been carried out at Massachusetts Institute of Technology which concentrates on the effects this chemical has on the biochemistry of the brain. Large doses have resulted in epileptic seizures. There are restrictions on its use in Austria, Belgium, France, Greece, Italy, Holland and Portugal. The UK government has issued warnings about its use by sufferers from phenylketonuria who require a diet low in phenylalanine.*

Sorbitol is used in ice cream, confectionery, chewing gum and soft drinks. It has been used for a long time in foods intended for diabetics. Large doses produce diarrhoea, although in children small doses have a similar effect. When my daughter, a diabetic, first went to school the kind-hearted cook used to make special sugar-free versions of crumbles and pies for her. She loved them. It took me a little while before I linked this with her doubling up over the toilet when returning home.

There is also some evidence that high doses contribute to the formation of bladder tumours.

Sugar and your health

'Everyone is at risk, child or adult.'†

Sugar has been linked with several illnesses and conditions in more

---

* Phenylketonuria is an inborn defect of protein metabolism causing an excess of the amino acid phenylalanine in the blood which damages the nervous system and leads to severe mental retardation.

† A Health Education Council spokesman in response to the food industry funded British Nutrition Foundation's report *Sugar and Syrups* which tried to pinpoint the effects of sugar on certain high risk groups.

than 2000 research papers. These connections are resisted by the sugar barons and disputed by scientists funded by the sugar industry. However, one physical consequence of sugar that no one can challenge is its degenerative effect on human teeth.

Tooth decay

Health reports are unanimous in connecting sugar with tooth decay – even a special report commissioned by the US government's Food and Drug Administration in 1986, *Health Aspects of Sugar*, which exonerated sugar from any other ill-effects, agreed with this. The risks of sugar consumption were suspected long before the 20th century. In 1598 a German writer, Paul Hentzner, recorded in his journals that Queen Elizabeth I's black teeth were 'a defect the English seem subject to, from their too great use of sugar'. In James Hart's 17th century *Klinike or the Diet of the Diseases* he wrote that sugar 'rotteth the teeth, maketh them look blacke, and withall causeth many time a loathsome stinking-breath. And therefore let young people, especially, beware how they meddle too much with it'. Today 95 per cent of British adults have tooth decay, and £400 million is spent each year on filling over 30 million teeth.

Tooth decay is caused by the bacteria in plaque, the transparent film that collects on teeth, reacting with sugary foods to form acids which dissolve the enamel of the teeth to produce decay.

The more sugar snacks are eaten between meals the greater the likelihood of damage to the teeth. Continual snacking leads to the bacteria multiplying and converting more sugar to acid. A Northumbrian study of 405 11- to 14-year-olds found they ate about seven times a day, and many of these meals were 'snacks rich in added sugars, and frequent eating of sugary foods is considered to be the habit most conducive of caries' (tooth decay). While sucrose – table sugar – 'the arch criminal of dental caries', has been found to have a more detrimental effect than any other sugar.

Despite this overwhelming evidence the Sugar Bureau, the promotional arm of the sugar industry, produced a video for schools claiming that sugar was not the main cause of tooth decay. The British Dental Association urged health and education authorities not to show the film which it described as 'a deliberate attempt to minimize the dangers done to teeth by sugar'.

Societies which have changed from a high fibre diet to a Western style diet high in refined carbohydrates show an increased incidence of dental decay. Research studies in Israel show that Bedouin youths who retained nomadic habits had fewer dental problems and less of a sweet tooth than those who settled in towns, where they became acclimatized to sweetness, developed a preference for sweet tastes and consequently suffered more from tooth decay.

A famous instance of the Western diet's attack on teeth occurred on the Atlantic island of Tristan da Cunha when in 1932 a ship brought in sugar, white flour, jam and other processed foods for the first time. Examining the 162 inhabitants the ship's doctor found that 83 per cent were free of tooth decay and no child under five had a bad tooth. Between 1933 and 1937 ten ships docked delivering sugar, white flour and toothbrushes. By 1937 50 per cent of the islanders were afflicted with dental decay, with the rise most marked amongst young children. By 1955 88 per cent had bad teeth as average sugar consumption reached 900 grams (2 pounds) per person a week.

Some dental researchers consider that refined starches can also cause dental decay, although not to the same degree as sugar. On the other hand high-fibre food, which requires considerable chewing, is thought to stimulate the production of saliva which neutralizes the acid content in the mouth and provides some protection for the teeth.

Obesity

One in three British adults is unhealthily overweight. 'Sugar,' said the 1983 report *Obesity* by the Royal College of Physicians, is 'an unnecessary source of energy in a community with such a widespread problem of overweight.'

Several other UK reports over the past fourteen years link obesity with high sugar consumption and in 1986 the British Medical Association, in their report *Diet, Nutrition and Health*, urged a halving of present sugar intake 'in an attempt to avoid obesity'.

The US government's Food and Drug Administration report on sugar played down this equation by arguing that sugar was not the 'unique' cause of obesity. It is, however, an important cause. Dr K. Heaton of Bristol University Medical School, commenting on the report, said, 'Sugars by their very nature tend to be consumed to excess.' Fats – which include butter, oils, margarine and lard – contain more calories than sugar but sweets are more noshable than chips. Even after a large meal most people can manage to squeeze in a little sweet extra. If fat and sugar come mixed together, as they often do, then sugar makes the fat palatable and the calorie load is multiplied.

Overweight people, whether they are slightly or dangerously obese, suffer the same symptoms to varying degrees. High levels of blood pressure and cholesterol and low glucose tolerance – when the body has difficulty handling sugar or glucose in the blood – frequently arrive with obesity. Low glucose tolerance can establish a basis for diabetes and high blood pressure, and cholesterol levels pave the way to heart disease. <u>There is no such thing as being slightly obese, any more than you can be slightly pregnant.</u>

Heart disease

Heart disease is the number one killer in Britain. It is killing more people than the great plagues of the Middle Ages, according to Dr Michael Scott, consultant cardiologist at Belfast City Hospital. At the turn of the century only two people in every 100,000 died each year of cardiac ailments. Today the figure has rocketed to 243 in England and Wales and 298 in Scotland and Northern Ireland.

'The people who are at risk from heart disease are those who are obese and those who are diabetic. Sugar is clearly associated with both these conditions,' warned Anne Dillon, Director of the Coronary Prevention Group. She was responding to the BNF's 1987 report *Sugar and Syrups* which contested any link between sugar and heart disease. Obesity increases the risk factors. Studies show that as a person's weight increases beyond a certain limit, the long term risk of heart disease grows. The Coronary Prevention Group urges a massive reduction of sugar and fats and an increase in fibre-rich foods.

Doctors estimate that two-thirds of the annual 180,000 deaths from heart conditions could have been avoided by effective prevention campaigns. Where these have taken place there have been marked improvements; for example, in the USA the death rate has plummeted by nearly 50 per cent to 230 per 100,000.

High blood-fat levels, a factor in heart disease, can be raised in men by high sugar consumption. 'In our first experiments with nineteen young men the sugar-rich diet produced an increase in blood tri-glycerides in all of them after two weeks,' reports Dr John Yudkin, the veteran anti-sugar campaigner, in his book *Pure, White and Deadly*.

There is a suggestion that eating too much sugar depletes the level of chromium in your body. Low chromium is associated with increased hardening of the arteries, which can lead to heart disease, and with an impaired handling of glucose, which can lead to diabetes. Stephen Davies, a nutritional doctor, notes that 'it is interesting that practically all the chromium found in sugar cane is removed in the refining process'. Refined flour also has low levels of chromium compared to wholewheat flour.

Diabetes

Overweight people are more susceptible to non-insulin-dependent diabetes – what used to be known as maturity-onset diabetes – particularly if there is a history of it in the family. Diabetes occurs when insufficient insulin is produced by the pancreas and as a result the sugar level in the blood becomes dangerously high. Diabetics are advised to watch their weight and to stick to a high-fibre diet. Since high fibre is digested more slowly by the body it keeps blood glucose levels at a more stable level.

Diabetes is one of the oldest known diseases, referred to in the *Ebers Papyrus*, an ancient Egyptian text. In this century, however, it has spread more rapidly than ever before. The National Commission on Diabetes in the USA estimated in 1975 that one in five Americans born in that year would develop diabetes if they lived an average 70 years. In Britain and Western Europe 1 to 2 per cent of the population are diabetic. For every case known, there is at least one undiagnosed sufferer. The causes of diabetes have not been isolated, but nutritional elements are believed to play an influential role. During the Second World War, when sugar supplies were severely restricted in Britain and the National Loaf was mandatory, figures for diabetes fell sharply. In the early 1950s when food rationing was gradually removed they were on the rise again. Whatever causes diabetes, current medical opinion holds that eating an excess of refined foods, including sugar, increases your susceptibility to the disease – especially if you are already over-weight and have an incidence of diabetes in your family.

Gallstones are linked to obesity and to high calorie consumption. 'A low fibre diet may accentuate a tendency to gallstone formation,' states the *Obesity* report of the Royal College of Physicians. Low carbohydrate slimming diets based on eating small amounts of bread and cereal can actively promote gallstones in people who are already overweight.

The *kidneys* in certain groups of people are at risk from sucrose. It is one of the factors that increases the possibility of a certain type of kidney stone called the idiopathic renal stone.

A high sugar intake is also linked with other conditions:
– A study of patients at the Royal Bristol Infirmary suffering from *cancer of the large bowel* discovered that they ate 41 per cent more refined sugar than people in a control group. Since the sugars were often eaten with fats, doctors concluded that a combination of excess sugars and fats encouraged a predisposition to this type of cancer.

– There are some people who are naturally *sensitive* or allergic to sugar. When they eat it they get a bloated stomach and diarrhoea. Sufferers usually avoid it.

– Adults with *Crohn's disease*, a serious dysfunction of the intestine, eat an excess amount of sugar for many years before the symptoms develop. Doctors have been unable to find a mechanism to explain the relevance of this phenomenon.

– *Spots and pimples* are often the result of eating sweets, chocolates, ice cream and cakes. These are all foods that are particularly high in sugar or combinations of sugar and fat and are usually eaten at the expense of fruit and vegetables.

Sugar and white flour together are often indicted for promoting certain conditions. One of these is *hypoglycaemia*, which is the production of too much insulin. Since the brain cells need glucose to function normally this can lead to faintness, hunger, irritability and sudden mood swings. One of the basic approaches in treating this condition is the total exclusion of refined foods and the introduction of complex carbohydrates such as pulses and wholegrains. Alcoholics often suffer from hypoglycaemia.

Diverticular disease is when small inflamed pockets form in the bowel due to chronic constipation and straining. It is a condition that has become more common since the beginning of the century, triggered off by the increasing amounts of refined flour, cereal and sugars in our diet. This unpleasant condition, resulting in abdominal discomfort and pain, is usually relieved by a high-fibre diet.

Excess sugar can affect *mood and behaviour*, especially in children and adolescents. B. F. Feingold found that sugar when eaten together with certain synthetic additives was a cause of hyperactivity. Alexander Schauss, a former American probation officer who studied the effects of diet on his clients, came to the conclusion that diet was the cause of much anti-social behaviour. High on his list of suspect foods was 'excess refined carbohydrate intake'. He found that 'in some institutions, the quantities of these (sugar added) substances is limitless'. American juvenile detention centres which applied his theories to their menus experienced an improvement in inmates' behaviour. A secret reduction of sugar over three months at a US juvenile-delinquents' home resulted in a 45 per cent reduction in anti-social or violent behaviour. But when Stephen Schoenthaler repeated his experiment with a group of female delinquents no change was shown. Similar research is currently taking place in a centre for disturbed adolescents in Durham, in which half are being given a diet free of refined sugar and additives and containing plenty of fibre and the other half are eating the usual diet.

In many individual researches sugar has been blamed for a variety of other conditions: Dr John Yudkin, Emeritus Professor of Nutrition at London University, links it to breast cancer, enlargement of the liver, the adrenal glands and the kidneys. Dr Stephen Davies, who specializes in nutritional medicine, believes it weakens the ability of white blood cells to fight infection and recommends it should be cut out as part of a package of measures to deal with migraine and thrush. In his latest book Yudkin writes: 'If only a small fraction of what is already known about the effects of sugar were to be revealed in relation to any other material used as a food additive, that material would promptly be banned.'

This section is not meant to read like a catalogue of horrors, but to encourage readers to think more about what they eat and the possible long-term effects. Maimonides, the 12th century philosopher-physician, took the remarkably sensible view that 'no illness which can be treated by diet should be treated by any other means'. Although medical intervention nowadays is less painful and risky than it was then, the principle remains attractive. A slice of wholewheat bread spread with peanut butter is more palatable than swallowing a laxative medicine. Eating fresh fruit salad rather than a chocolate mousse for dessert could save you from becoming a regular visitor to the dentist or to the hospital dietitian.

LIVING WITHOUT

Sugar is not – contrary to what the producers want you to believe – a daily necessity. In fact, it is not necessary at all in your diet, but if you have become used to the taste, you will want to be weaned off it gently.

Your decision to start giving up sugar will have an eventual bonus – the gradual adjustment of your taste-buds to the natural sweetness in the foods you eat. At the end of the first year without sugar I suddenly noticed that sweet corn really was sweet, and so were onions and carrots. When the cake that used to make your life complete tastes cloyingly sugary you will know that your taste-buds have begun to sort out the natural sweetness from the chemical.

Finding alternatives can be a slow process. A couple of women students in my cookery class complained of suffering from terrible sugar cravings, finding themselves getting up in the middle of the night, raiding cupboards for sugar or chocolate. I consulted two doctors on their behalf: they both diagnosed a hormonal or metabolic imbalance, disagreeing sharply about its causes, but both prescribing treatment of a high-fibre diet of wholewheat bread, jacket potatoes, plenty of fruit and vegetables and no sugar or white flour.

Eating healthily is pointless if it makes you feel awful. A regime that forbids cakes and sweets quickly becomes oppressive and encourages the feeling that the forbidden food is the most attractive. Sweet treats are part of our culture and it is difficult to sidestep them. The purpose of this book is to provide tempting alternatives which satisfy at the same time as altering perceptions of sweetness. The recipes for cakes are intentionally light rather than the familiar wholefood slabs that sink to the bottom of the stomach. The emphasis is on fibre, but this includes a lot of fruit as well as whole grains.

The balance of recipes in this book is unusual. The bulk of it is devoted to cakes, biscuits, pies and sweets – food that is not an essential part of our diet. Even the main courses are sweet and sour. The reason for this balance is that the overriding concern is how to enjoy sweet flavours without using sugar.

How to shake off sugar – stage by stage

1. Cut it out of *tea and coffee*. This is often the hardest step and you may only be able to do it after reducing sugar in the rest of your diet. Avoid artificial sweeteners – they will not re-educate your taste-buds to appreciate the taste of natural sugar.

2. Adopt the *cake and biscuit* recipes in this book and adapt your favourite recipes to sugar-free ingredients (see the introductions to Pastry, Pies and Tarts, Sweet and Sour Main-course Dishes, and Salads).

3. Eat your meals with *fresh fruit* or fruit-based pies and compôtes.

4. If you need *snacks* to keep you ticking over between meals, make sure they are high-fibre ones such as fruit bars, but not laced with honey or any kind of added sugar. Try sunflower seeds sprinkled with soy sauce and baked in the oven until dry, or cooked chickpeas sprinkled with freshly ground black pepper and salt. These make scrumptious bites, are high in energy and very nutritious.

5. For *soft drinks* either buy the apple-based fizzy drinks from Whole Earth and other health food firms or make your own with fizzy mineral water and fruit juice.

6. Look out for *sugar-free foods*. They are increasingly available in supermarkets and health food shops (see Pick of the Sugar-Free Packaged Foods, page 28).

Spot the Sugars

To avoid sugar when shopping requires all your ingenuity and skill because it is so pervasive in manufactured foods. Sausages, salami, smoked salmon, pickled herrings, soups and mixed savoury spices are usually sugared. There is one teaspoon of sugar in every tablespoon of tomato ketchup. Vegetables, in most manufactured brands, are canned in a solution of water, sugar and salt. Most packaged bread contains dextrose. Many brands of tinned sauces, such as bolognese and curry, contain sugar, as do packets of soup. Sugar is used with these foods not always for its sweetening powers, but as a flavour enhancer, preservative or bulking agent – individual properties which manufacturers could find in other ingredients.

Sugars appear in such a wide range of foods that careful reading of the small print on the packet is essential. The position of an ingredient on the list indicates the amount used in the food. If sugar appears second on the list, as it does with tomato ketchup, then it is the second main ingredient. The word 'sugar' does not always appear on labels, but instead there might be one of the many equivalent chemical compounds known as 'sugars', all of which are highly refined, containing virtually no fibre, vitamins or minerals. Look out for them:

– _Sucrose_ is the name given to table sugar and is found in sugar beet and sugar cane. It is made up of the two sugars, glucose and fructose.
– _Glucose_ accounts for 15 per cent of the sugar used in manufactured goods – a threefold rise since the 1950s. It occurs naturally in fruits such as grapes. Carbohydrates we eat are broken down by the digestive system into glucose.
– _Dextrose_ is a form of glucose.
– _Fructose_ is a concentrated fruit sugar. It is found naturally in fruits, vegetables and honey.
– _Glucose syrup_ is made from starch.
– _Invert syrup_ is made from sucrose and dextrose.
Most words on an ingredients list that end in 'ose' or include the word 'syrup' are a type of sugar.

Beware of manufacturers' sweeping claims. Close inspection of a new brand of 'sugar-free lollipops' revealed that they are made of hydrogenated glucose which, like sugar, is a concentrated sweetener containing no fibre, minerals or vitamins. A random bottle of orange squash picked up in a grocer's shop proclaimed in large letters 'no artificial colour' which is encouraging, but this does not automatically mean it is particularly healthy. The second and third largest ingredients were sugar and glucose syrup, pepped up by a boost of saccharin.

Sugar-free Shopping

As public concern has risen about sugar, a number of companies and supermarkets have begun to offer alternatives.

It is not easy to recommend individual products as the market is highly volatile, with new names constantly appearing and old names vanishing. I carried out a survey for _The Sunday Times_ two years ago and many of the products included in that survey have since disappeared from the shelves.

Soft drinks without sugar are appearing on health food shop shelves. They are based on juices and carbonated water. Whole Earth and Free produce a small range including lemonade and a cola drink using the cola nut from West Africa and the guarana seed from Brazil. A wider choice is available in concentrated juices. Exotic combinations offered by Meridian include apple and strawberry and apple and cherry.

Baby food manufacturers have been responsive to concern over the amount of sugar used in their products. Drinks have undergone the most dramatic change, with the syrupy liquids which comforted generations being exchanged for concentrated fruit juices. Delrosa have eliminated glucose and introduced apple-based flavours with a dash of rosehip. (These drinks should still be well diluted.)

Heinz has brought out a special No Added Sugar range of baby food which is sweetened with concentrated juice, ordinary strength juice and sometimes pure fruit. Ironically many Swiss and German baby foods imported by health food shops sweeten fruit meals and rusks with honey. Cow & Gate and Boots have both brought out special Low Sugar Rusks, which contain sugar and glucose; Boots is the lowest with a combined total of 19 per cent, but this is still a lot of sugar for a baby. The combination baby cereals contain a mixture of sucrose, dextrose and fructose, but Boots bring out plain cereals such as Porridge Oats and Protein Baby Cereal which can be sweetened at home with fruit.

Most *breakfast cereals* contain added sugars. Often the name tells you everything – Sugar Puffs or Sugar Smacks are apt descriptions of the product. Others have names that conjure up the healthy life, but still come drenched in sugar. However, those old standbys Puffed Wheat and Shredded Wheat, made from the whole grain, are widely and cheaply available. Sweeten them at home with dried or fresh fruit. Granola-type cereals of oat flakes and almonds sweetened with apple juice, dates and figs are made by Whole Earth: the texture is splendid, but they are not cheap. Muesli is widely available, but some manufacturers still sweeten with raw cane sugar and honey instead of dried fruit alone.

Packets of *fruit juice* are usually concentrated juice and water. Tinned varieties sometimes contain added sugar.

Tinned fruit in natural juice is made by many of the large supermarkets' 'own brands' and by the well-known tinned fruit manufacturers.

The typical carton of *fruit yogurt* has two to three teaspoons of sugar in it. Sweeteners range from raw cane sugar to aspartame. St Ivel and Holland and Barrett produce brands that contain only yogurt and fruit, but they might not be to everyone's taste. The best fruit yogurts are made in a couple of minutes at home with natural yogurt and fresh fruit.

A limited selection of manufactured *biscuits* can be found in the shops. Quality is very mixed, and as with all manufactured goods you have to shop around to find the right brand. Those that have a balanced use of dried fruit seem to get it right. A large Brighton-based co-operative, Infinity, imports Dutch biscuits which use organic wholemeal flour and are sweetened with dates, figs, raisins and carob – they are outstanding, but difficult to locate. Prewetts produce a cheaper and more readily obtainable range of biscuits sweetened with dried fruit.

Cakes are harder to find. Hampton, which distributes mostly in and around London, makes a very rich fruit cake which is successful as a Christmas cake. Health food shops sell unpackaged cakes without sugar, but close questioning often reveals that they are sweetened with brown sugar or honey. Blind faith is not enough when buying a product that does not include a list of ingredients.

Successful alternatives to *sweets* are hard to find – no one has yet worked out how to make bull's-eyes, barley sticks or lemon sherbet without sugar. A sugar-free sweet is a totally different product. Yogurt- or carob-coated raisins, dates and peanuts are the closest manufacturers have got so far. They are produced by a few firms and are most enjoyable.

Fruit bars can be a minefield for sugar avoiders. Scrutinize the wrappers and you will find that many contain both sugar and honey. Fruit leather strips made by Okanagan have a light and pleasant taste although they are pricey. Wilcox & Lomer's Fig Cakes use fruit, nuts and spices to attain exquisite delicacy, while Sunfoods' Carib-Bar with peach and apricot is chewy with just the right level of sweetness. The Shepherdboy fruit bars come in an endless number of combinations, but watch out for the Banana Fruit and Nut bar in this range because it contains honey.

The good news about *carob bars* and carob specialities is that this is a steadily expanding area. Earthlore, a small family firm, was set up after the owners discovered their son was allergic to milk products, and had the good sense to realize that many people would like to buy carob products without sugar. They perfected creamy recipes for Easter eggs, Christmas gifts and other novelties. Carriba bars come in orange or fruit and nut flavour, or plain carob, and are made in Cyprus for Holly Mill. Beenys, a favourite with children, are oval-shaped light-coloured carob drops also made in Cyprus and distributed by the Carob Confectionery Company. Dove Cottage sells packets of carob-coated dates and fruit nuggets made with raisins, dates and sesame seeds.

Carob spreads are produced by Meridian – their dark-coloured Caronut is a mixture of ground hazelnuts, peanuts and carob powder sweetened with apple juice; while Cirencester-based Clare's Kitchen produces a Hazelnut and Carob Spread which is what it says it is although the colour does not always appeal to younger consumers.

For *baked beans*, *ketchup*, *curries* and meals in a tin only Whole

Earth has a total commitment not to include sugar. Their labels declare, 'We do not use sugar, glucose, grape juice, saccharin or aspartame in any Whole Earth product.' Holland and Barrett's lentil dhal contains no sugar and has a 'no added sugar' sign emblazoned across the tin, but in the same range mild vegetable curry, vindaloo hot vegetable curry and Mexican-style red curry beans all contain sugar. Granose display a similar inconsistency.

Sugar-free *chutneys*, *relishes* and *mayonnaise* are found in health food shops. Whole Earth sells American-style Cucumber and Corn Relish, while Classic chutneys with evocative names such as Spicy Apricot and Date and Rich Pineapple and Ginger are made by Down to Earth. Clare's Kitchen offers Organic Tomato and Marrow Chutney, and Celebration bring out a general Curried Fruit Chutney.

Sugar-free *jams* proliferate. Following the health food firms some supermarket chains, such as Safeways and Waitrose, and established jam manufacturers, have moved comfortably into this field offering reasonably priced jams and marmalades. The quality of Robertson's and Whole Earth's sugar-free jams are noteworthy.

Crunchy and smooth *peanut butters* are made with sea salt and no sugar by a small number of food firms. You will need to experiment to discover the taste and texture that suits you best.

Pick of the Sugar-free Packaged Foods

Soft drinks
Whole Earth Real Lemonade
Whole Earth Orange Soda
Free Lemonade
Free Tropical Kiwi Fruit
Free Ginger and Ginseng
Meridian Apple and Strawberry Juice
Meridian Apple and Orange Juice

Biscuits
Infinity Carob Biscuits
Infinity Fruit and Nut Biscuits
Prewetts Raisin and Coconut Biscuits
Prewetts Carob Chip Biscuits

Fruit bars
Wilcox & Lomer Fig Cake with cinnamon and aniseed
Sunfoods Carib-Bar with peach and apricot
Okanagan Sunshine Kids Raspberry Fruit Snack

Carob confectionery
Earthlore Easter Eggs
Carob Confectionery Beenys
Carriba Orange Chunky Carob Bar

Sauces and relishes
Whole Earth Kensington Sauce
Whole Earth Tomato Ketchup
Whole Earth Cucumber Relish
Down to Earth Rich Pineapple and Ginger Chutney
Kite Wholefoods Mayonnaise

Cereals
Quaker Puffed Wheat
Nabisco Shredded Wheat
Whole Earth Almond Crunch

Jams and spreads
Robertson's Pure Fruit Strawberry Spread
Whole Earth Sweet 'n' Fruity Italian Peach Jam
Clare's Kitchen Blackcurrant Extra Jam
Whole Earth Crunchy Peanut Butter

Tinned foods
Waitrose Baked Beans
Whole Earth Organic Baked Beans

Baby food
Heinz no added sugar Muesli
Heinz no added sugar Pure Fruit

Sweeteners

Our taste-buds enable us to savour and enjoy a sweet taste and there seems no reason to deny this pleasure. Sugar should not be its source. The main sweeteners used in the recipes in this book are dried fruit and fresh fruit.

Dried fruit – prunes and dried apricots need some soaking before using, but dates, figs, raisins and sultanas, once washed and rinsed, can be chopped or boiled with water to make a mushy paste. If the recipe requires a smooth paste, blend after the dried fruit has absorbed all the cooking water.

Fresh fruit – banana and apples are the most commonly used. Either mash peeled bananas or if they are to be used in a swiss roll-type sponge put them through a food mill or a sieve to make a smooth thick liquid.

Use apples with the peel if possible, but always wash well first. Depending on the recipe apples can be grated, sliced or puréed with a little water in a blender.

Juice is only used in small amounts in the recipes. This is because when drunk by itself it can raise blood sugar levels rapidly because it is liquid and contains no fibre. Juice offers nutritional benefit by providing vitamins and minerals, and for the best flavour there is nothing better than fresh juice.

Minerals and dried fruit

Dried fruit is high in minerals. Compare the figures below for dried fruits with those for sugar, glucose and honey.

How to dry fruit

Fruit is traditionally dried out in the sun, but if you don't live in a hot country you can dry fruit by other methods. An ordinary oven, used in a slightly different way from usual, can dry small quantities of fruit, while specially designed food driers are sold in some kitchen shops, although they tend to be expensive.

Dried fruit is readily available from supermarkets or can be bought in bulk from specialist outlets or wholefood warehouses, so there is rarely any need to dry fruit unless you have a glut of fruit or your freezer has broken down. Apples, apricots, bananas, cherries, grapes, plums, pears, figs, pineapple and strawberries are all suitable for drying. Fruit used should be ripe, fresh and unblemished.

Drying is an effective method of preserving fruit because the food is

(tr = trace, − = unknown)	Sodium	Potassium	Calcium	Magnesium
Sugar	tr	2	2	tr
Glucose	150	3	8	2
Honey	11	51	5	2
Dried apricots	56	1880	92	65
Dried dates	5	750	68	59
Dried figs	87	1010	280	92
Prunes	12	860	38	27
Raisins	52	860	61	42
Sultanas	53	860	52	35

(McCance and Widdowson, *The Composition of Foods*, 1979)

made inhospitable to bacteria and moulds by removing much of the water. It is a slow process, and the fruit is reduced to 20–25 per cent of its original weight, darkening and taking on a wrinkled appearance.

The basic procedure is to wash the fruit and remove cores, stalks, stones and pips. When cutting the fruit, slice it into even-sized pieces so that each piece will require the same amount of drying. Fruit can be laid straight on to trays or first dipped into boiling water or steamed to crack the skins. Discoloration is avoided by painting the fruit with lemon juice or a solution of ascorbic acid (vitamin C) and water.

The trays used should be made of wood or stainless steel mesh with sufficient space for the air to circulate. The fruit is laid out evenly without any overlap. Halves of fruits such as peaches and pears are placed skin side down which prevents the fruit from sticking and speeds up the drying time by exposing more of the cut surface of the fruit.

The fruit is dried in a food drier at a very low temperature – gas mark ¼/70°C/200°F. The amount of drying time depends on the size of the fruit. Allow 6 hours for apple slices, 10–12 hours for halved apricots, 8 hours for halved bananas, 6–8 hours for sultana grapes and 10 hours for plums. Rotate the trays to allow even exposure to the heat.

An oven can also be used for drying small quantities of fruit. When using an oven make sure the bottom tray is at least 20cm (8in) away from the heat source. Do not crowd in too many trays of fruit because this will affect how well it all dries. Switch on to gas mark ¼/70°C/200°F, and keep the oven slightly propped open during most of the drying time.

Test a few pieces of fruit from each tray before removing from the heat. If the fruit is not dried thoroughly it will become mouldy. The aim is to produce dried fruit that is leathery but not stiff. If it is too dry, the

Phosphorus	Iron	Copper	Zinc
tr	tr	0.02	—
11	0.5	0.09	—
17	0.4	0.05	—
120	4.1	0.27	0.2
64	1.6	0.21	0.3
92	4.2	0.24	0.9
83	2.9	0.16	—
33	1.6	0.24	0.1
95	1.8	0.35	0.1

temperature of the oven was too high for too long and you will need to allow more time at a lower heat. If the fruit is too hard it means the initial temperature was too high.

Fruit leathers are made by puréeing fruit, spreading it thinly over a tray and leaving it to dry very slowly at an extremely low temperature, even switching off the oven for some of the time. After 24 hours it should be dry enough to peel off. A basic recipe is to combine apple with another fruit.

Food driers provide hot air from an electric fan with a close-fitting lid. In her book *Food Drying at Home* Naomi Nichols constructed her own food drier from a zig-zag wooden clothes horse. A 1200 watt heater was positioned at the bottom, trays were placed across the different levels of the clothes horse and a cloth covering was placed over the whole frame so that the air circulated within a restricted area. Temperature was regulated by opening and closing the cloth covering and trays were rotated during drying.

A freak summer with uninterrupted hot weather may encourage you to try drying fruit outside in the sun. Here are a few tips.

— Use trays which allow a free flow of air.
— Do not leave the trays outside when the weather is sticky and humid.
— Protect the drying fruit from the birds; a net of some kind is one solution.
— Move the fruit around to ensure even drying.

Inside or out, drying is an ancient method of preserving fruit and even if you do not intend to become an expert it is fun to experiment at least once and to observe how the water slowly dries off from the fruit, completely changing its texture and shape.

Storing dried fruits, nuts and grains

Buy dried fruit, nuts and grains in medium-sized quantities unless you intend to use them within two months. If stored for too long they can become stale and lose their flavour. Nuts tend to turn rancid because of their high oil content, so when buying them in a supermarket check the sell-by date. When sold loose, make sure they do not look as if they have spent a long time in the shop. If in doubt do not purchase too great a quantity at one time.

All of these foods can become infested by insects. Infestation is an unpleasant surprise, but it can happen to anyone and does not reflect on the cleanliness or tidiness of your kitchen. One way to prevent or at least contain an outbreak is to store food in glass or plastic containers with very tight-fitting lids. Resist monster-size bargain packets which may end up languishing on your shelves and create ideal conditions for a holiday home for maggots.

The flour moth is one of the most common villains. Its larvae can eat their way through whole grains, usually leaving a trail of silken threads. The thin white threads or webbing sometimes found around the outside and inside of packets of oats and flour indicate infestation.

Dried fruits are not too badly at risk. Raisins and prunes are usually insect free. Dates are prone to infestation, but as they are generally fumigated before export any insects or larvae tend to be killed off, but watch out for figs, dried bananas and dried apricots. Infestation experts consider that oil around the fruit can increase the chances of attracting insects because of the presence of extra moisture. Sun-dried fruit is available, but cross-infestation can take place at any stage of the fruit's journey to your kitchen.

Horror stories abound of maggots found in barley, dried apricots, spaghetti, crackers and shelled peanuts bought from health food shops and mass supermarket chains. If you are unfortunate enough to have purchased food in this condition, take it back to the shop and insist on a refund. If the infestation has spread contact the Environmental Health Department of your local council which will send pest control officers to spray your cupboard; or else purchase a suitable deterrent from a chemist's.

Be forewarned and store medium amounts of these foods in jars in cool dark cupboards.

Pesticides and their effects on food

If you are health-conscious enough to consider using whole grains and whole foods then pesticide residues in your food will be a matter for concern. Pesticides were originally used to help farmers make a reliable living from their crops, but they have proliferated enormously in the last forty years.

The London Food Commission, an independent consumer watchdog originally set up with the help of a GLC (Greater London Council) grant, claims certain pesticides are linked to cancer, reproductive problems, birth defects and allergic reactions. DDT is an insecticide banned in the UK in 1984 but the residues are so persistent that they enter the food cycle and are still found in milk and meat products. Banned pesticides are sold in third world countries and return to Britain via imported food. Derek Cooper of Radio 4's *Food Programme* writes in the *Listener* about 'Mediterranean countries where lettuces and courgettes destined for British shops are grown in polythene tunnels exposed to a constant mist spray of fertilizers, pesticides and fungicides.'

Organic food is not widely or cheaply enough available to provide a solution. As much of the food we buy has been treated with pesticides here are some ways of trying to keep levels low in your diet:

— Signs of insect damage or visiting slugs indicate that fresh food has not been too heavily sprayed. If it's good enough for the creepy crawlies then hopefully it will be good enough for you.
— Beware of shiny apples. They don't come off the trees looking like that but have been dipped in a wax solution.
— Cut the fat off meat not just to minimize saturated fats, but because this is where certain types of pesticide concentrate.
— Fruit with thick peels such as citrus fruit, bananas, pineapples, melons and pomegranates protect the flesh of the fruit and minimize the effect of pesticides. If organic ones are not available always scrub the outsides of fruit such as oranges with a brush before grating them for their zest. Thin-skinned fruits such as apples, pears, grapes and cherries are not protected in this way and should always be washed well before eating. The problem with removing peel from all fruit and vegetables is that you miss out on much nutritional goodness found under the surface of the fruit skin.

Organic Food

Organic food is grown without artificial fertilizers or pesticides. The result is a better taste and a healthy product, recommended not just by health faddists but also by famous chefs like the French brothers, Albert and George Roux. Organic food is not always easy to find and costs more because of the lower yield per acre. Organic fruit and vegetables are sold in specialist health food shops, and Safeways has trail-blazed the way for organic produce in supermarkets, its range even includes an organic lunch pack. Waitrose also sells organic fruit at selected branches. Organic butchers are few and far between and so are organic cheeses.

Many pulses and grains proclaim 'organic' on the label and your only check is the trustworthiness of the wholesaler or the appropriate supervisory body, of which there are a bewildering number:

— *The Soil Association* lays down the most stringent conditions about crop rotation and use of natural manure and employs inspectors to enforce them.
— *Organic Farmers and Growers* have similar basic standards, but allow the use of Chilean nitrate and are less strict about crop rotation.

– *International Federation of Organic Agriculture Movements* lays down international standards. This is necessary because the 700 organic farms in Britain do not supply enough to meet demand and 60 per cent of organic fruit and vegetables are imported from abroad.
– *The Farm Verified Organic Information Centre* is a private body funded by commercial interests which certifies imported organic food.

The Ministry of Agriculture is attempting to establish one set of standards instead of several and has set up a UK Registry for Organic Food Standards. This will benefit consumers and trading standard officers. Other European countries have similar problems; for example, France has four or five organizations issuing standards.

A tip for self-catering holidaymakers abroad is that variations on the words 'biologique' or 'biologisch' are used to mean organic produce.

Substitutes

Running out of ingredients is a nuisance, particularly if it happens half-way into making a cake or dessert. Special diets may require omitting a particular food, and certain ingredients are not always popular with everyone. Here is a list of alternatives:

Soya flour – if a pastry recipe contains both wholewheat flour and soya flour it is possible to substitute wholewheat flour for soya flour. The carbohydrate total will increase slightly. Provided the amount specified is very small it can be substituted in cakes as well.

Wholewheat flour – it is harder to find alternatives for wheat flour. Soya flour is not dense enough to substitute for it. Barley, rye and brown rice flour can be substituted, although the results will differ texturally from the original recipe. A number of recipes are included which do not use wheat flour.

Ground almonds are used for their texture-enhancing effect and because of their low carbohydrate count. However, they are expensive even when bought in bulk. An effective alternative in biscuit recipes is finely ground porridge oats. Substitute these for up to a third of the ground almonds and the taste will not be too radically changed, although the carbohydrate content will increase.

Skimmed milk – soya milk is an adequate substitute.

Raisins can replace dates and vice versa.

Eggs can be replaced with yogurt or milk in pastry or in a filling requiring one egg.

Butter or margarine – oil can be substituted in cake or crumble-type recipes, but it is not an effective substitute in a rough puff or choux pastry. Pastry recipes using only oil are included in this book.

Sugar-free jams – if you do not have the recommended flavour a similar jam will do.

The recipes included in this book have been made and tested using the listed ingredients so for the best results try and use these.

Freezing

A freezer is useful if you do most of your own cooking and baking. There is not always time or energy to quickly whip up a special cake or extra food for unexpected guests, and if something can be pulled out of the freezer it is very welcome. When you find recipes that you particularly like double the quantities so that half can be frozen.

The basic rules for freezing are:

1. Only freeze food when it is fresh.
2. Food should be cold before being wrapped for the freezer.
3. Always eliminate as much air as possible from the packaging or the food will become dehydrated and flavour, colour and texture will suffer.

Freezing has different effects on different foods; I find that it makes spices duller, for example, so you may need to add extra spices to main dishes. You may also need to add icing to cakes: if you intend to decorate a cake Carob Icing (see page 82) will freeze well, but for a fresher look decorate after thawing.

Wrap cakes, biscuits and bread in greaseproof-lined sheets of foil in freezer bags or put directly into a freezer container. If you want to keep a watch on carbohydrate and calorie content write a small label with the amount per slice together with the date of freezing.

Thawing

Cakes – keep them in the freezer wrapping while thawing otherwise the cake will lose moisture and the result will be a drier texture.
Biscuits that have a cake-like texture should be thawed in the same way.
Pastry – remove from wrapping or it will become soft.
Fruit tarts – for the best results freeze the pastry cases and only fill with fruit when you intend to use them, to avoid the pastry becoming soggy.
Bread – keep it in the freezer packaging and thaw at room temperature for a few hours or so, or leave in the fridge overnight.

Rolls – thaw in the freezer packaging at room temperature for a couple of hours.

Meat and chicken dishes – thaw completely before reheating. Eat as soon as they are properly cooked.

Store cakes, biscuits, scones and fruit rolls for up to 3 months. The smaller crisper biscuits are better left for only 2 months. Bread freezes for up to 1 month. Ices freeze for up to 2–4 weeks.

Measurements

Measurements are given throughout in both metric (grams) and imperial (ounces) weights. When the recipes were created metric measurements were used, so if very exact measurements are important to you then it is recommended that you follow the metric set of figures.

Note: the measurements given for bananas are without the peel and those for apple include the peel and core unless otherwise specified.

Basic Ingredients

These basic ingredients stored in your cupboards should enable you to attempt most of the recipes in this book.

Brown rice – rice which has not had the outer husk removed, either long grain, short grain or basmati. Available from supermarkets and health food shops.

Butter – butter gives a better taste to pastry, but the question of whether it is more or less healthy than margarine is still hotly disputed. If you choose to use butter spread it sparingly and make sure that polyunsaturated oils are also included in your diet.

Carob powder – a dark brown powder ground from the carob pod. Available from health food shops.

Dried fruits – mineral-rich sweeteners and a source of fibre. *Dates* are very sweet and grow in the Middle East and North Africa. *Dried apricots* have their own strong flavour. They are bright orange in colour if they have been preserved with sulphur and dark brown if not. *Prunes* are made from dried plums, and can be bought already stoned. Californian prunes are the best known. *Raisins* are small dried grapes mainly from California, South Africa and Afghanistan. *Sultanas* are made from a special variety of grape originally produced and named after Smyrna in Turkey. They are now grown in Turkey, Greece, Australia, America and South Africa. Sun-dried versions of the last two taste far superior to those preserved in mineral oil. Avoid dried fruit that has been treated with sulphur and mineral oil if you can.

Eggs — free-range eggs are produced by hens that are not housed in batteries. The taste is markedly improved.

Margarine — those high in polyunsaturates and unhydrogenated are recommended. The introduction of hydrogen helps oils solidify but creates new elements known as trans-fatty acids in the margarine, the effects of which are not sufficiently known. Unhydrogenated margarine is sold by a couple of firms, but it is expensive.

Nuts — almonds, walnuts, hazelnuts and peanuts contain polyunsatured oils as well as minerals and protein.

Oils — sunflower, safflower, soya bean and sesame seed oil are high in polyunsaturates. Olive oil is high in monounsaturates. Cold-pressed oils are recommended — this is when the oil is not subject to processing at very high temperatures. Avoid oils described as 'vegetable' or 'edible' — they are not necessarily high in polyunsaturates.

Oat bran and germ — these are extracted from the oat grain. Oat bran is high in soluble fibre and is available from health food shops.

Porridge oats — rolled oats, available from grocers, supermarkets and health food shops.

Sesame seeds — small light brown seeds used to decorate pies and biscuits. Available from health food shops.

Soya flour — a pale yellow flour which is high in protein and low in carbohydrates.

Spices — these are invaluable for both sweet and savoury cooking. *Cinnamon* is a dark brown aromatic spice. *Mixed spice* is a mixture of cinnamon, cloves, allspice and nutmeg. *Cayenne pepper* is a hot red peppery spice. *Coriander* is used in Asian and Mexican food.

Tofu — soya bean curd originating from China. It is low in calories and fat. Available from health food shops and Chinese grocers.

Vanilla — natural vanilla essence or vanilla pods are available from health food shops, grocers and supermarkets.

Wheatgerm — the nutritious germ of the wheat. Store in the fridge once it has been opened to avoid it turning rancid.

Wholewheat flour — used as the basic flour. It contains every part of the whole grain — the fibrous husk, germ and starchy endosperm. Available from health food shops, grocers and supermarkets. Finely milled or wholewheat pastry flour is available from specialist health food shops.

Fruit and vegetables

Apples – seasonal eating apples are a handy source of sweetening. Store in a cool dark cupboard or fridge.

Bananas – quite a concentrated sweet fruit. Store in a cool dark cupboard, but not in the fridge as this makes the skins turn black.

Carrots – a sweet vegetable available all year round. Store in a cool dark cupboard.

Oranges – use in season. The segments and juice add a tasty tang to foods. Store in a cool dark cupboard or fridge.

Pears – a very sweet fruit which ripens while stored. Store in a cool dark cupboard or fridge.

Note: All dried fruit, fresh fruit and vegetables should be washed and dried before using, unless, as with bananas, the outer skin is discarded.

Essential Equipment

3 glass or china mixing bowls – large, small and medium

wooden spoon
tablespoon
dessertspoon
teaspoon
slotted spoon
sharp cutting knife
spatula
ice cream scoop
pastry brush

lemon squeezer
grater
chopping board
pepper mill
sieve
scales with small metric and imperial measurements
wooden rolling pin
wooden rolling board
measuring jug for liquid
round cutters, 5cm (2in), 6.2cm (2½in), 7.5cm (3in)
icing bag and nozzles

foodmill
egg-beater, hand-held or electric
food processor
blender
electric coffee grinder

baking sheet, stainless steel
standard swiss roll tin
20cm (8in) cake tin, stainless steel, ceramic or glass
25cm (10in) cake tin, stainless steel, ceramic or glass
jam tart tin
cake rack

large cast-iron frying pan
griddle
stainless steel or enamelled cast-iron saucepans, large, medium and
    small, with lids.

glass jars for chutneys and spreads
biscuit or cake tin
freezer containers

1 Breakfast

Read o'er this;
And after, this: and then to breakfast with
What appetite you have.
                    The King in *King Henry VIII*, William Shakespeare

Breakfast is a serious business, setting the pattern for the whole day. In the USA it is the day's first meeting; on honeymoon it is eaten in bed. Some people roll out of bed to a drink and a hearty meal while others bath or exercise or even do a couple of hours' work before they eat or drink. Others leave it out altogether, making a day more difficult than it has to be.

The ideal breakfast differs all over the world. The Japanese start with a bowl of soup while the French get going with black coffee and crusty bread. When I was a student my large, kind landlady would produce massive breakfasts of cereal followed by fried eggs, sausages and potatoes. The other student lodging there would consume all this grease with great gusto urged on by the thought of not having to eat again until the evening. As an impecunious student I was attracted by the economic considerations, but was unable to stomach more than a roll and butter.

Forcing yourself to eat huge quantities of a particular food because a book or parent tells you to is not taking heed of your own needs. Either overdoing it or skimping can result in an unpleasant few hours surmounting the side effects. Individual needs vary tremendously and only you can know what your body requires. The key principle when contemplating breakfast is to decide what you want breakfast to do for you. Is it a brief mouthful, sufficient to give you a little energy until your mid-morning snack, or do you need a meal that will see you through till noon or later? Wholewheat bread or high-fibre cereals provide slow-burning energy, while fruit and juice give an immediate burst. A combination of cereal and fruit will provide a balance of both.

People who simply cannot face food in the morning may manage a bite of toast or a mouthful or two of yogurt or a piece of fruit. For them breakfast is a mid-morning snack or brunch. All the recipes given here can be eaten mid-morning as well as first thing. But do avoid fried food in the morning: it is greasy and heavy on the stomach and represents an assault on a vulnerable digestive system.

A range of manufactured sugar-free breakfast cereals is available, either sweetened with juice or sold as a wholegrain product that you sweeten yourself. Read muesli ingredients carefully – some products confidently declare themselves natural and additive-free but include honey or sugar. If you want to sweeten your porridge try adding a spoon of sultanas or raisins. It means that every flake won't be sugar-coated, but as you are already used to a more natural sweet taste from using the recipes in this book you will discover that porridge has its own enjoyable flavour.

Breads made with wholewheat flour are slow-burning foods, but when combined with a fruit spread (see pages 78–80) or a commercial jam they will provide a quick energy boost. Recipes for plain breads, fruit loaf and scones are also included (see pages 54–74). One of the yeast cake recipes with a fruit filling, such as Apple Slice (see page 227), also provides a combination start to the day.

This section includes a few suggestions that might be new to you, but why not experiment and try something different?

MUESLI

A walk round the local health food shop will provide a host of ideas for suitable ingredients for home-made muesli. This recipe provides a basic guideline, but preferred grains can be substituted. The grains, particularly the oat bran and germ, will provide a slow-burning meal that will keep you going for a few hours. The dried fruit provides concentrated energy.

75g (3oz) porridge oats
25g (1oz) oat bran and germ
75g (3oz) barley flakes
50g (2oz) wheat flakes
25g (1oz) raisins
25g (1oz) dried apricots
25g (1oz) brazil nuts

Makes 6 servings.

Combine all the ingredients and store in an airtight tin or glass jar.

When serving leave to stand in the milk, soya milk or yogurt for at least 15 minutes before eating. A little grated apple added to the muesli gives a pleasing flavour.

Each serving without milk is 30g CHO. 175 kcals.

FRUIT YOGURT

Dr Douglas Latto, one of the early proponents of the high-fibre diet, has treated serious conditions such as cancer with high-fibre diets. He recommends yogurt and fruit sprinkled with wheatgerm as a healthy start to the day. The fruit provides an energy burst while the live bacteria in non-pasteurized yogurt help to maintain the balance of bacteria in the intestine.

200g (7oz) banana, peeled
150g (5oz) grapes
2 eating apples
300ml (10 fl oz) low-fat
   natural yogurt
2 tbs wheatgerm

Makes 2 servings.

Slice the fruit and mix with the yogurt. Sprinkle 1 tbs wheatgerm on top of each bowl of yogurt and fruit.

Each serving is 45g CHO. 250 kcals.

APPLE AND WHEATGERM

A gentle way to eat fruit in the morning is to serve it stewed (see pages 214–15 for instructions for stewing different fruits).

½ recipe stewed apple
2 tbs wheatgerm

Makes 2 servings.

Stew the apple according to the instructions (see page 215). Divide it between two bowls. Spoon the wheatgerm evenly over the surface of the apple and either serve as it is or place the bowls under the grill for a few seconds to brown the wheatgerm before serving.

Each serving is 20g CHO. 105 kcals.

ORANGE AND CARROT SOUP

Fruit soups are usually eaten at the end of a meal, but they also provide an invigorating start to the day. This soup should be prepared in the morning. A night in the fridge spoils the taste and excessive exposure to oxygen reduces the vitamin C content of the fruit.

500g (1lb 2oz) oranges with peel
175g (6oz) carrots
½–1 tsp cinnamon
100ml (4 fl oz) apple juice
100g (4oz) strawberries

Makes 4 large servings.

Peel the oranges and remove the pith. Break into segments and put in a food processor or blender together with the carrots, cinnamon and apple juice to make a thick liquid. If using a blender, first cut the carrots into thin slices. Pour the soup into bowls and garnish with sliced strawberries. If the texture is too thick for your liking add a little spring water to thin.

Each serving is 15g CHO. 60 kcals.

SUMMER PUDDING

This combination of bread and berries provides a light nourishing start to the day.

My daughters, seeing a photograph of this classic English dish in a children's cookery book, were drawn to the violet-purple and red colours and asked me to make it sometime. Towards the end of July, near the finish of the raspberry season, I remembered their request and made this pudding one afternoon as a surprise for the next morning's breakfast.

Redcurrants contain 40mg of vitamin C, and the minerals they contain include calcium, magnesium and iron.

175g (6oz) wholemeal bread,
   without crusts
250g (9oz) eating apple
100ml (4 fl oz) apple juice
100ml (4 fl oz) water
250g (9oz) redcurrants
50g (2oz) ripe banana, peeled
350g (12oz) raspberries

Makes 6 servings.

Cut the bread thinly and put about five slices of bread around the base and sides of a pudding basin.

Slice the apple into a medium-sized saucepan with the apple juice and water. Bring to the boil and simmer until half the liquid has evaporated. Add the redcurrants, having removed their stems, and cook for a few minutes until the juice begins to run and the liquid turns red. Remove from the heat. Strain the fruit so that the juice is separated. Blend the apples, redcurrants and banana in a liquidizer or mouli. Allow to cool a little.

Pour most of the juice over the bread around the sides of the dish, colouring it purple-red. Spoon in half the raspberries. Then spoon half the fruit purée over the raspberries. Repeat this process once more so that there are two layers of raspberries and two layers of purée. Place the remaining slices of bread on the top and cover with the leftover juice. Cover the top of the pudding basin with a plate and put it in the fridge with a weight on top to press it down – a full jar of jam is about right. Leave overnight. Just before serving the pudding, turn out of the dish by loosening the sides with a knife and then inverting it on to a plate.

Each serving is 20g CHO. 85 kcals.

2 BREADS AND SCONES

The smell of freshly baked bread is irresistible. Whether it wafts down the street from the bakery or through your home it is an aroma that goes straight to the senses.

The thought of baking one's own bread is both exciting and daunting. Yeast can be intimidating for many people. If you have grown up with yeast cookery then you are probably free of inhibitions, but if it is a new element in your repertoire any setback can distract you from ever trying again. I first used yeast at school and remember it as a very unpredictable substance surrounded by instructions about heating equipment and ingredients and fixed temperatures and on and on through a succession of hurdles which grew higher at each jump. The whole business was so daunting that I did not venture to work with yeast again for a number of years.

What changed my attitude was discovering a method of using yeast with no sugar. The mystique dissolved and my anxieties with it, and I became confident enough to handle yeast. The idea of preparing a tray of wholemeal rolls no longer held any fear for me, and a spicy fruit loaf did not daunt me.

Yeast has been used for thousands of years. The ancient Israelites left Egypt taking dough with them before it was leavened, indicating that they knew how to make raised bread. The Egyptians, who distilled wine and beer, used the fermenting liquor as a raising agent. Yeast was something of a mystery. People would carefully set aside a piece of yesterday's dough to use as tomorrow's yeast starter.

Yeast is a living organism whose activity causes fermentation – a definition only arrived at in 1857 when Louis Pasteur isolated it as a single-celled plant that is only visible under a microscope. The yeast breaks down starch and sugar into alcohol and carbon dioxide. Put in warm, moist surroundings such as damp flour, the yeast responds by setting off the process of fermentation. A natural sugar develops in the dough as it ferments, providing nourishment for the yeast. Although most breadmakers add sugar to their fresh yeast, this is unnecessary, and too much sugar in a recipe at an early stage hinders the yeast fermenting.

The main point to remember when using yeast is not to overheat it before it is baked. Any liquids used should be at body temperature; and when leaving the dough to rise do not put it in contact with direct heat as excess heat will kill the yeast and ruin your recipe.

However, I have found that yeast is resilient enough to non-perfectionists. I do not use a thermometer, for example, to measure the heat of the liquid, but either combine half boiling water with half cold milk from the fridge or dip a finger in to make sure it is no more than body temperature. If the rising stage needs speeding up, put the dough in an oven that has been heated for a few minutes and then switched off, or if you have a spin drier, switch it on for a couple of minutes, switch it off and put the bowl containing the dough inside and close the door. Enclosing warmth is always very effective.

If the yeast cells are kept cold they will remain dormant until placed in a warm damp environment. Fresh yeast can be stored in the coldest part of the fridge for up to 2 weeks loosely wrapped in a polythene bag. It can also be frozen and will keep for 2 months if properly wrapped.

Flour Wheat is the only grain whose proteins when mixed with water form a gluten strong enough to produce raised bread. The elastic quality of gluten enables the dough to change its shape under pressure and return to its original shape when pressure is removed. If gluten were removed from flour dough and examined it would have a stretchy texture similar to chewing gum. The gluten allows the wheatflour loaf to expand to include the carbon dioxide produced by yeast.

The flour used in all the recipes is wholewheat, containing all the fibre and nutrients of the original grain. A wheat grain is made up of three parts: the outer part is the husk or fibre, which covers the vitamin- and mineral-rich wheatgerm and the starchy endosperm. Plain white flour has had 30 per cent of the grain removed or extracted. It consists largely of the endosperm and contains only 3.4 per cent fibre and greatly reduced amounts of vitamins and minerals.

Flour used to be ground by large stones which crushed the grain, but the development of steel roller milling in the 1880s made it possible to separate most of the starch in the wheat from the bran and germ. Extra bleaching is necessary to produce a pure white flour.

White bread has always been desired by the rich and cherished as a symbol of purity. The upper classes of Ancient Greece and Rome ate off-white bread which had some of the bran sifted out, and the use of increasingly finer sieves continued into the 18th century. The advent of the steel roller mills in the late 19th century completely changed the methods of production and resulted in flour with a much higher extraction rate.

The industrial separation of wheat alarmed a number of doctors. In America, Sylvester Graham published a *Treatise on Bread Making*. He condemned the separation of bran as 'put[ting] asunder what God had joined together' and urged the use of 'coarse wheaten bread' to end constipation. His ideas influenced John Harvey Kellogg, the American breakfast cereal manufacturer, and Thomas Richard Allinson, an English doctor. In *The Advantages of Wholemeal Bread* Allinson wrote, 'If a law could be passed forbidding the separation of the bran from the fine flour, it would add very greatly to the health and wealth of the nations, and lessen considerably the receipts of the publican, tobacconist, chemist, dentist, doctor and undertaker.' He devised a recipe for wholemeal bread and offered to give a certificate to bakers to hang in their windows if they made this bread and sold it cheaply. The numbers grew too great for him to supervise and he began producing his own bread, the forerunner of the Allinson bread that is widely sold today.

White bread is still more popular than brown. The British Federation of Bakers estimates that 70 per cent of its present sales are white bread and 30 per cent wholemeal bread. In 1986 there was a sudden 50 per cent increase in the sales of wholemeal bread, but this has steadied as new types of white sliced bread have hit the market. These breads pay lip service to the public demand for fibre by including added bran or a mixture of refined grains, but these are no substitute for the original wholewheat flour.

After baking your own wholemeal bread you will look at shop bread with new eyes. The deep brown hues and light speckled shades of some loaves will suggest the use of caramel or white flour mixed with wheatgerm. Always buy your wholemeal bread from a reliable baker, and if it is wrapped, carefully read the ingredients before purchasing.

Vitamin C and yeast Fresh yeast combined with vitamin C or, as it is also known, ascorbic acid, speeds up the process of preparing the dough. If you have ever felt intimidated by yeast then this method is liberating because the results are so quick. There are no long anxious hours waiting to see if the bread has risen. When I have taught this method in my cookery classes there is tremendous pleasure and relief at being able to bake a batch of rolls in an evening, and people become receptive to experimenting with new recipes. This is the method used by the commercial bakeries, but tastes and smells rather better when made at home.

A dried yeast already mixed with vitamin C is available from health food shops and instructions for its use are given on the packet. This is worth having in your cupboard for an emergency, but I have found results are best when using fresh yeast.

Basic method of making bread

1. Prepare flour and other ingredients in a large bowl.
2. Pour body temperature (38°C/100°F) liquid over the crumbled yeast and crushed vitamin C tablet and mix into a cream.
3. Pour the liquid and yeast into the flour and bind to make a soft dough.
4. Knead for 10 minutes. This is a very important stage.
5. Cover with cling film and leave to rest for 10 minutes – considerably less than the usual 1½–2 hours.
6. Shape the dough and place in a greased baking tin.
7. Cover the tin with cling film and leave to rise for about 40 minutes until the dough has virtually doubled in bulk.
8. Bake in a hot oven.

These are guidelines for the basic approach. Read the instructions for Bread Rolls (see page 55) for a fuller and more detailed account.

BREAD ROLLS

Rolls are even quicker to make than bread because they need less time to rise. With experience you should be able to make and bake these rolls in one hour and ten minutes, and for much of that time the rolls need little attention for they are either rising or baking.

Vitamin C, also known as ascorbic acid, can be obtained from the chemist's. You need ordinary vitamin C tablets, not the fizzy kind. Often it is only possible to buy 50mg tablets, in which case use half.

600g (1lb 5oz) wholewheat
  flour
1 heaped tsp sea salt
25g (1oz) margarine
425–450ml (15–16 fl oz)
  skimmed milk and water
25g (1oz) fresh yeast
25mg tablet of vitamin C
a little milk for glazing

Makes 20 rolls.

Pour the flour and salt into a large bowl. Cut up the margarine into the flour and rub it in with your fingertips. (For those who are reluctant to rub margarine into flour an alternative method is to melt it and add it to the flour when it has cooled together with the other liquids.)

Heat the milk and water to body temperature (38°C/100°F). This feels tepid. I find that by combining equal combinations of cold milk with boiling water the temperature is about right.

Crumble the yeast and crush the vitamin C tablet into a medium-sized bowl. Pour some of the warm liquid on top and mix into a cream. Add this liquid to the flour and stir in together with enough of the remaining warm liquid to make a soft dough. Because you may use less liquid than the amount recommended, or maybe more, depending on the flour that you use, always add the non-yeast liquid gradually.

Remove the soft dough from the bowl and place on to a wooden board or clean work top. Knead it for 10 minutes. There is no one fixed way of kneading bread, but an effective method is to use the heel of your hand to push down on the dough as you fold over the top part. Give the dough a quarter turn and repeat this process. The aim is to achieve a dough that is elastic and supple. If you prefer to use a food processor which has a dough hook attachment for the kneading, look in the instructions for the equivalent machine time of 10 minutes' hand kneading. It is probably about 3 minutes, but check carefully because although it is hard to overwork dough when you are kneading by hand, it can be overworked by a machine.

Return the dough to the mixing bowl and cover the top of the bowl with cling film and a clean tea towel and leave for 10 minutes.

Remove the dough from the bowl and divide it in half. Pat each piece into a long oblong and mark off 10 sections on each one. Break these off and shape them into 20 round rolls. Work them lightly in your hands so that the top side is smooth and any joins are tucked underneath. Place the rolls on a large, greased, warmed baking tray and cover loosely with cling film.

Leave the baking tray in a warm place for the rolls to rise: near but not on the cooker is usually a warm spot. The rolls need a warm environment but not direct heat. After 20 minutes they should have increased in bulk and be ready for baking. Glaze the tops with a little milk.

Bake in a preheated oven gas mark 8/230°C/450°F for 15 minutes until the rolls are browned on top and slightly brown underneath.

Each roll is 20g CHO. 110 kcals.

This recipe can also be used to make a loaf of bread. Instead of a baking tray grease two 1-pound loaf tins. Divide the dough in half and make each half into an oblong shape, smooth on top with any joins underneath. Cover with cling film and leave to rise in a warm place for about 40 minutes until the dough increases in bulk or reaches the top of the tin. Bake in a preheated oven gas mark 8/230°C/450°F for 30 minutes until well browned. The way to test if it is ready is to tap the underside of the loaf with your knuckle. If the bread has cooked through it will have a hollow sound. If the inside is not set it will sound and feel heavy and dense. Remove the finished loaf from the tin and leave to cool.

Bread Rolls without Vitamin C

The recipe for bread rolls can be made using yeast alone. The disadvantage to this method is that the dough has to be left longer to rise and a little more preparation is required, but it does not have to be kneaded for so long and many bread bakers maintain that it produces a better-tasting roll. The only other difference in ingredients is that slightly less yeast is used – it is reduced from 25g to 20g. This approach is based on the method used by Elizabeth David in English Bread and Yeast, Cookery.

Weigh out the flour and salt and put it in a large bowl in the oven with a casserole lid on top. Preheat the oven to gas mark ¼–½/110–130°C/225–250°F. Leave it in for about 5 minutes until the flour is warmed.

While the flour is warming crumble the yeast into a medium-sized bowl and pour half the lukewarm milk and water on top and leave for about 5 minutes.

Remove the bowl with the flour from the oven, but leave the casserole lid inside to continue heating. Rub in the margarine.

The yeast will now be soft and easily mixed to a cream. Pour this into the warm flour together with enough of the warm milk and water to make a soft dough. Work it into a ball. Cover the top of the bowl with a thin, clean tea towel, and place the heated lid from the oven on top. The lid should not touch the dough. This is a useful way of keeping a warm environment for the yeast.

Leave the dough to stand for 1½–2 hours. At the end of that time it will have doubled its size, and will look spongy. Give a firm punch to the middle of the dough to knock it back. Then pick it up in a ball and knead it on a wooden board or work top for 4 minutes. The punching and kneading redistributes gas bubbles produced by the yeast.

Continue as in the vitamin C version (see page 56) by dividing the dough into 20 rolls. Place them on a warmed, greased baking tin and cover with cling film. Leave to rise for 20 minutes. Glaze with milk and bake in a preheated oven gas mark 8/230°C/450°F for 15 minutes.

Each roll is 20g CHO. 110 kcals.

RYE BREAD

Rye bread is popular in Scandinavia and eastern Europe. Rye flour is low in gluten so when it is used for bread it is mixed with wheat flour which has a higher gluten content, resulting in a loaf with a dense texture. The advantage of a rye loaf is that it stays moist longer than wholewheat bread, and it is quite filling because it takes a long time to digest. This is because its carbohydrates include long chains of sugar units – five per unit. Compare this to glucose which is made up of one sugar unit and is quickly absorbed by the body, or sucrose which is made up of two sugar units.

The caraway seeds used in this recipe give the rye bread a very distinctive flavour, although if you have an aversion to them you can leave them out. Caraway seeds are meant to be good for the digestion and to prevent flatulence.

300g (11oz) wheat flour
300g (11oz) rye flour
1 tsp salt
25g (1oz) margarine
2 tsp caraway seeds plus some extra seeds for decoration (optional)
350ml (12 fl oz) milk and water
25g (1oz) fresh yeast
25mg tablet vitamin C
50g (2oz) banana, peeled
a little milk or egg for glazing

Combine the flours and salt together in a large bowl. Rub in the margarine. Stir in the caraway seeds.

Crumble the yeast and crush the vitamin C tablet into a medium-sized bowl. Heat the milk and water to body temperature (38°C/100°F) by combining cold milk with boiling water. Pour this over the yeast and vitamin C and mix in well so that no yeast sticks to the bottom of the bowl. Pour into the flour mixture, stirring the liquid into the flour, together with the mashed banana, and bind to make a soft dough.

Remove the dough from the bowl and place on to a wooden board or clean work top. Knead it by hand for 10 minutes or use the dough hook attachment of a food processor or mixer. Check the machine equivalent of 10 minutes' hand kneading: it is probably about 3 minutes. (See pages 55–6 for advice on kneading.)

Return the dough to the mixing bowl, cover the top of the bowl with cling film and a clean tea towel and leave for 10 minutes.

Remove the dough from the bowl and form it into a long narrow rectangle, folding the ends underneath so that it has a smooth top, and place in a warmed greased loaf tin. Cover loosely with cling film and leave to rise in a warm place for 45 minutes until it has doubled in bulk.

Brush the top lightly with milk or egg and sprinkle over some caraway seeds. Bake in a preheated oven gas mark 8/230°C/450°F for 30 minutes until well browned.

Each 25g slice is 10g CHO. 55 kcals.

CHALLAH

The traditional Jewish plaited loaf baked specially for the sabbath and festivals is often sweetened and always white. Working out a wholewheat alternative is difficult because it must taste richer than everyday wholewheat bread. This recipe uses eggs for a richer taste and a ripe pear to enhance the texture. If you want a really sweet challah add 50g (2oz) raisins to the flour mixture before the liquids are added. The quantity in this recipe is enough for two loaves.

600g (1lb 5oz) wholewheat flour
1 heaped tsp sea salt
3 tbs oil
1 ripe pear weighing about 150–175 g (5–6 oz), grated
2 eggs
200–250ml (7–9 fl oz) skimmed milk and water
25g (1oz) fresh yeast
25mg tablet of vitamin C
a little beaten egg mixed with water for glazing
poppy seeds for decoration

Makes two challahs.

Combine the flour and salt in a large bowl. Stir in the oil and grated pear with a wooden spoon. Whisk the eggs well and stir them into the flour.

Heat the milk and water to body temperature (38°C/100°F). I always add an equal amount of cold milk to the boiling water and this gives a temperature that feels right. Crumble the yeast and crush the vitamin C tablet into a medium-sized bowl. Pour half the liquid over them and mix to a cream. Stir this into the flour mixture together with as much of the remaining warm liquid as is necessary to make a soft dough. If it is on the sticky side just sprinkle a little more flour over the dough, but avoid a dough that is too dry and stiff.

Remove the dough from the bowl and place on to a wooden board or clean work top. Knead it by hand for 10 minutes, sprinkling with flour if necessary.

This recipe makes a soft pliable dough that is very pleasurable to work. The dough hook attachment of a food processor or mixer can be used, but check the machine equivalent of 10 minutes' hand kneading: it is probably about 3 minutes. (See pages 55–6 for advice on kneading.)

Return the dough to the mixing bowl, cover the top of the bowl with cling film and a thick, clean tea towel, and leave for 10 minutes.

Remove the dough from the bowl and divide it into two halves. Divide each of these into three pieces of roughly equal size. Roll them into long sausages. Join three of these together at one end and plait them, joining them together again at the other end. Repeat this with the remaining three long sausage shapes to make the second challah.

Place the two loaves on a warmed, greased baking tin and cover loosely with cling film. Leave to rise for about 45 minutes. They take slightly longer to rise than an ordinary wholewheat loaf because the ingredients are richer, but if they are left for too long, say over 60 minutes, they will lose their plaited shapes. If you have to go out it is possible to leave them covered with the cling film in the fridge for up to 3 hours, as the cold atmosphere slows

down the action of the yeast and the
vitamin C.

Glaze the tops of the loaves with a little
beaten egg mixed with a spot of water
and then scatter poppy seeds over the
top. Bake in a preheated oven gas mark
7/220°C/425°F for 15 minutes and
then reduce the heat to gas mark
5/190°C/375°F for a further 15–20
minutes. The breads are cooked when
tapping the underneath produces a
hollow sound.

*Each 25g slice of bread is 10g CHO.
55 kcals.*

BAGELS

*These rolls with a hole in the middle are unusual not just because of
their shape, but also because they are boiled before they are baked.
The result is a very particular taste that is quite delicious so don't be
put off by this additional step. In New York bagels are traditionally
sandwiched with smoked salmon and cream cheese, while in the
Middle East street vendors sell them decorated with hyssop, sesame
seeds and salt and they are eaten without any other additions. The
wholemeal bagels go very well with any chosen filling; my favourite is
avocado.*

450g (1lb) wholewheat flour
2 tbs wheatgerm
1 tsp sea salt
1 egg, separated
250ml (9 fl oz) skimmed milk
40g (1½oz) butter
25g (1oz) fresh yeast
25mg tablet of vitamin C

Makes 16 bagels.

Combine the flour, wheatgerm and salt
in a large bowl. Whisk the egg yolk
lightly and add to the flour.

Heat the milk and butter in a small pan
until the butter has melted and the milk
is at body temperature (38°C/100°F).
Crumble the yeast and crush the
vitamin C tablet into a medium-sized
bowl. Pour half the liquid over them
and mix to a cream. Add the rest of the
liquid. Whisk the egg white stiffly and
add to the liquid. Combine with the
flours to make a soft dough.

Remove the dough from the bowl and place on to a wooden board or clean work top. Knead it by hand for 10 minutes or use the dough hook attachment of a food processor or mixer. Check the machine equivalent of 10 minutes' hand kneading: it is probably about 3 minutes. (See pages 55–6 for advice on kneading.)

Return the dough to the mixing bowl, cover the top of the bowl with cling film and a clean tea towel and leave for 7 minutes. Remove the dough from the bowl, pat it into a long oblong shape and mark off 16 equal slices. Break or slice these off and roll each piece into a long sausage about the thickness of your finger. Shape each piece into a ring, carefully sealing the ends by slightly overlapping and working them together to make an even thickness. Leave them to stand on the wooden board or work top for 20 minutes, loosely covered with cling film.

While the rolls are rising fill a wide-based saucepan with about 6cm (2½in) water and bring it gently to the boil. After the bagels have finished rising drop three or four at a time into the water. When they have cooked on one side they will rise to the surface of the water. Let them cook for about one minute on each side and use a slotted spoon to turn them over. Remove them from the pan and leave them to drain on a board. Repeat this process with the remaining bagels.

Place the boiled bagels on a greased baking tray. Brush the tops with the beaten egg yolk mixed with a spoonful of water, to give a shiny effect when baked, and sprinkle with sesame seeds.

Bake in a preheated oven gas mark 8/230°C/450°F for 15 minutes until they are browned.

Each bagel is 20g CHO. 120 kcals.

FRUIT LOAF

This lightly spiced yeast fruit loaf is baked in a ring mould and tastes delicious spread with creamy butter for tea. A fruit loaf is richer than an ordinary loaf and has a higher natural sugar content. This extra sugar slows down the yeast fermentation so the loaf takes longer to rise.

50g (2oz) prunes, stoned
50g (2oz) dried apricots
25g (1oz) dried dates
300g (11oz) wholewheat flour
50g (2oz) porridge oats
50g (2oz) oat germ and bran
1 tsp cinnamon
1 tsp mixed spice
¼ tsp ground cloves
50g (2oz) margarine
150g (5oz) banana, peeled and
    mashed
1 egg, lightly beaten
25g (1oz) yeast
25mg tablet of vitamin C
125–150ml (4½–5 fl oz)
    skimmed milk

Makes 16 large slices.

Chop the washed fruit finely. Combine the flour, oats, oat germ and bran and spices in a large bowl. Rub the margarine lightly into the flour. Stir in the chopped dried fruit together with the mashed banana. Mix the egg into the flour and fruit mixture.

Crumble the yeast and crush the vitamin C tablet into a medium-sized bowl. Heat the milk to body temperature (38°C/100°F). Add most of the milk to the yeast and stir well so that no yeast sticks to the bottom of the bowl. Pour into the other ingredients and stir in, adding as much of the remaining warm milk as is necessary to make a soft dough.

Remove the dough from the bowl and place on to a lightly floured wooden board or clean work top. Knead it by hand for 10 minutes, sprinkling more flour on the board if the dough is very sticky, or use the dough hook attachment of a food processor or mixer. Check the machine equivalent of 10 minutes' hand kneading: it is probably about 3 minutes. (See pages 55–6 for advice on kneading.)

Return the dough to the mixing bowl, cover the top of the bowl with cling film and a clean tea towel and leave for 10 minutes.

Remove the dough from the bowl and press into a greased 20cm (8in) diameter plain ring mould. Cover loosely with cling film and leave to rise in a warm place for 55–60 minutes until it has doubled in bulk or has reached the top of the tin.

Bake in a preheated oven gas mark 7/220°C/425°F for 15 minutes. Reduce to gas mark 5/190°C/375°F and cook for a further 15 minutes.

Each slice is 20g CHO. 135 kcals.

DOUGHNUTS

It may seem odd to find doughnuts in the bread section, but doughnuts are basically a rich bread dough filled with something sweet and fried instead of baked. In this recipe they are filled with a stoned prune which bulks them up nicely and means that they cook quickly because the innermost part is not dough. It is also possible to fill them with a jam spread (see Chapter 3) or a commercially made sugar-free jam. Either put the jam in the middle of the dough before frying or cut the doughnut in half afterwards and spread with jam.

24 prunes, stoned, weighing about 200g (7oz)
450g (1lb) wholewheat flour
pinch of salt
25g (1oz) fresh yeast
25mg tablet of vitamin C
300ml (10 fl oz) skimmed milk
50g (2oz) margarine
2 eggs, size 3, lightly beaten
oil for frying

Soak the prunes for at least an hour in a little cold water before using.

Combine the flour and salt. Crumble the yeast and crush the vitamin C tablet into a medium-sized bowl. Heat the milk to body temperature (38°C/100°F) and pour half of it over the yeast and vitamin C. Cut up the margarine and leave it to melt in the remaining half of a little desiccated coconut for decoration

Makes 24 doughnuts.

the milk. Mix the milk and yeast well so that no yeast sticks to the bottom of the bowl and pour into the flour. Stir in with a wooden spoon. Add the melted margarine and milk and stir well. Fold the eggs into the flour mixture to make a dough. If it is a little moist sprinkle with flour.

Remove the dough from the bowl and place on to a wooden board or clean work top. Knead it by hand for 10 minutes or use the dough hook attachment of a food processor or mixer. Check the machine equivalent of 10 minutes' hand kneading; it is probably about 3 minutes. (See pages 55–6 for advice on kneading.)

Return the dough to the mixing bowl, cover the top of the bowl with cling film and a clean tea towel and leave for 5 minutes.

Remove the dough from the bowl and break it into quarters. Divide each of these into six pieces. Take each piece of dough and roll it into a ball. Slightly flatten the ball, place a soaked prune in the middle and wrap the dough round it into a ball again. Leave the doughnuts on a board covered with cling film for 20–25 minutes until they have doubled in bulk.

Fill a frying pan with about 2.5cm (1in) oil and heat until it is sufficiently hot to brown a small piece of bread dropped into the oil. Place a few doughnuts in at a time. Fry for a few minutes until browned and then turn them over to brown the other side.

Remove the doughnuts from the pan with a slotted spoon and leave to drain on absorbent paper. Sprinkle with desiccated coconut before serving.

Each doughnut is 15g CHO. 100 kcals.

SCONES

Scones are quick to make, but there are a few general points to remember:

— Work quickly so that you avoid overworking the dough
— Rub the margarine in lightly so that you get as much air into the mixture as possible
— The dough should be softer than pastry which means adding more liquid than you would to pastry
— Roll out the dough lightly and pat any leftover pieces out with the palm of your hand rather than rerolling
— Scones need a hot oven so always remember to switch the oven on when you start preparing the scone dough
— One advantage of scones for fat-watchers is that they do not need to be baked on a greased baking tray.

Scones achieve their lightness by a combination of bicarbonate of soda with cream of tartar. The bicarbonate of soda is alkaline and the cream of tartar is acid. When mixed with water or milk the alkaline and acid elements enter into a chemical reaction and form a carbon dioxide gas. This gas starts working on the dough straight away. In order to get the full benefit of its raising powers the dough should be put in the oven as soon as it has been cut or shaped.

Mix the bicarbonate of soda and cream of tartar well before adding them to the flour. Baking powder contains the same ingredients already mixed together plus extra ingredients such as wheat flour which prevents the two substances acting on each other before they are needed.

This is a basic scone recipe which combines wheatgerm and soya flour with wholewheat flour to provide extra proteins and vitamins. Wheatgerm is a good source of vitamin E and the B vitamins, and when eaten raw it is said to be beneficial for the digestive and nervous systems. Because of its high oil content it can turn rancid and once a packet is opened it should be stored in the fridge.

125g (4½oz) wholewheat flour
25g (1oz) soya flour

Combine the flours and wheatgerm, bicarbonate of soda and cream of

50g (2oz) wheatgerm
½ tsp bicarbonate of soda
1 tsp cream of tartar
25g (1oz) margarine
150ml (5 fl oz) skimmed milk

Makes 10 scones.

tartar in a medium-sized bowl. Rub in the margarine to make fine crumbs. Bind with the milk to make thick moist crumbs and work these together to form a soft dough.

Remove the dough from the bowl and roll out on a barely floured wooden board or clean work top to a 1.2cm (½in) thickness. Cut into 10 scones using a 6cm (2½in) cutter. Place on an ungreased baking tray and bake in a preheated oven gas mark 7/450°F/220°C for 10 minutes until browned. Serve hot, cut in half and spread with butter.

Each scone is 10g CHO. 90 kcals.

PEANUT SCONES

Despite their name peanuts are not nuts at all, but legumes or pulses. They grow on a bush and the nuts mature below ground. They originate from South America and have been found in Peruvian tombs dating around 950 B.C. Peanuts contain 24g of protein per 100g which makes them very nutritious: 100g of peanuts has the same amount of protein as a grilled lamb chop.

150g (5oz) wholewheat flour
15g (½oz) wheatgerm
100g (4oz) ground peanuts
½ tsp bicarbonate of soda
1 tsp cream of tartar
½ tsp mixed spice
25g (1oz) margarine
100g (4oz) ripe banana, peeled
75–100ml (3–4 fl oz) low-fat
  natural yogurt

Makes 12 scones.

Combine the wholewheat flour, wheatgerm, ground peanuts, bicarbonate of soda, cream of tartar and mixed spice in a large bowl. Rub the margarine into the flour mixture. Mash the banana with a fork and stir in. Add enough yogurt to form a soft malleable dough.

Remove the dough from the bowl and roll or pat out on a lightly floured wooden board or clean work top to a thickness of 1.2cm (½in). Use a 6cm (2½in) cutter to make 12 scones. Place on an ungreased baking tray and bake

in a preheated oven gas mark
7/220°C/425°F for 15–20 minutes
until they are well browned on top and
underneath. Serve hot, cut in half and
spread with butter.

Each scone is 10g CHO. 115 kcals.

LEMON SCONES

'The doctor is sure that my health is poor,
He says that I waste away;
So bring me a can of the shredded bran,
And a baleful of the toasted hay.'

(Walt Mason, late 19th century American humorist
and poet, in *Health Food*)

At last, a scone recipe with bran!

150g (5oz) wholewheat flour
50g (2oz) bran
½ tsp bicarbonate of soda
1 tsp cream of tartar
pinch of cinnamon, ground
    cloves and nutmeg
    (optional)
25g (1oz) margarine
100g (4oz) ripe pear, grated
1–2 tsp lemon zest
150ml (5 fl oz) skimmed milk

Makes 12 scones.

Combine the flour, bran, bicarbonate
of soda, cream of tartar and spices in a
medium-sized bowl. Rub the
margarine into the flour mixture. Stir
in the grated pear and lemon zest,
making sure they are spread evenly
through the flour mixture. Use enough
of the milk to bind the ingredients
together to a soft dough.

Remove the dough from the bowl and
roll out to a thickness of 0.5–1cm
(¼–⅜in). Cut into 6cm (2½in) circles.
The mixture makes 12 good-sized
scones. Place them on an ungreased
baking tray and bake in a preheated
oven gas mark 8/230°C/450°F for
about 10 minutes until evenly
browned. Serve plain or with butter.

Each scone is 10g CHO. 70 kcals.

BARLEY LOAF

This loaf is quick to make as it is raised with bicarbonate of soda instead of yeast. The texture is more crumbly than a loaf of bread. If it is baked the evening before it will keep well for the whole of the next day.

In ancient Rome barley was the special food of the gladiators and they were known in Latin as 'the barley-eaters'. By the Middle Ages in Europe barley bread was the staple of the peasants while the upper classes ate wheat. Bread made of barley flour and wheat flour could still be found in the mid-19th century in certain parts of the British Isles such as Wales and Cornwall, but today it has become a rarity.

Make sure that the barley you use is milled from the whole grain. It can be obtained from health food shops. This loaf can be made as a plain bread or with raisins.

Buttermilk, as its name suggests, is what is leftover in the churns from making butter. It works very well with a soda bread like this recipe because the lactic acid acts on the bicarbonate of soda and helps to lighten the dough.

300g (11oz) barley flour
100g (4oz) wholewheat flour
25g (1oz) bran
2 tsp baking powder
1 tsp bicarbonate of soda
¼ tsp salt
50g (2oz) margarine
4oz (100g) raisins, washed and dried (optional)
375–400ml (13–14 fl oz) buttermilk and skimmed milk mixed together

Makes 20 slices.

Combine the flours and bran together in a large bowl. Mix the baking powder, bicarbonate of soda and salt and stir into the flours. Rub the margarine into the mixture lightly. If you are sweetening the loaf with raisins stir them in at this point. Slowly add the buttermilk and skimmed milk to the mixture to make a soft dough. Only add as much as is necessary to achieve this.

Divide the dough into two halves and place on a lightly floured wooden board or clean work top. Gently work them into two round loaves about 2.5cm (1in) thick all the way round. Slash the tops with a knife and place them on a greased baking tin. Bake in a preheated oven gas mark 5/190°C/375°F for 35–40 minutes until they are browned all over. If you are leaving them overnight wrap them up in a clean tea towel to keep the moisture in.

Each slice without raisins is 15g CHO. 100 kcals.
Each slice with raisins is 20g CHO. 110 kcals.

DROP SCONES

Using a griddle is a quicker way to cook a scone than in the oven because the heat is more direct. Griddles, or bake stones as they were traditionally known in some parts of England, are not always easy to come by and a suitable substitute is a heavy frying pan. I use a simple low-cost cast-iron one which is sold in a couple of the national household chain stores. To season one of these pans heat it gently and rub well with oil. Leave it to stand for a while and then wipe off the oil.

When cooking drop scones, heat the pan and oil it very lightly. Do not overheat or the outside of the scone will burn before the heat has penetrated to the inside. Scones cooked on a griddle are rolled out more thinly than those baked in the oven. After using, wipe the inside of the pan with some kitchen paper and a little salt, rather than washing it up. Soaking a frying pan in water makes food more likely to stick next time it is used and to counteract this you would have to use extra oil.

The batter for the drop scones can be whizzed up in a few minutes.

90g (3½oz) wholewheat flour
15g (½oz) wheatgerm
½ tsp bicarbonate of soda
½ tsp cream of tartar
1 egg, lightly beaten
100ml (4 fl oz) buttermilk
100ml (4 fl oz) skimmed milk
a little oil for cooking

Makes 15 drop scones.

Combine the flour and wheatgerm in a medium-sized bowl. Mix together the bicarbonate of soda and cream of tartar and add to the flour. Pour the egg into a well in the middle of the flour. Continue to beat until the egg gradually absorbs some of the flour. Add enough of the buttermilk and skimmed milk to make a smooth thick batter.

Heat the griddle or heavy frying pan and grease it very slightly with a little oil. Use a tablespoon to drop even quantities of the mixture on to the griddle. It should make 15 scones. When bubbles appear on the surface of the scones turn them over until browned on the other side. Serve hot with butter or jam.

2 drop scones are 10g CHO. 65 kcals.

SINGIN' HINNY

This recipe is based on the traditional griddle cake made in the north of England.

200g (7oz) wholewheat flour
25g (1oz) soya flour
2 tsp baking powder
25g (1oz) butter
40g (1½oz) currants
175–200ml (6–7 fl oz) low-fat natural yogurt

Combine the flours and baking powder together in a large bowl. Rub the butter into the mixture. Stir in the washed and dried currants and use as much yogurt as necessary to bind it into a soft dough.

Remove the dough from the bowl and roll out on a lightly floured board or work top to the same size as your griddle or large frying pan; prick the surface all over with a fork.

Heat and slightly grease the griddle. Cook the rolled-out dough on both sides until evenly browned. Traditionally this is cooked in one large piece, but you will probably find it easier to handle if you cut it into quarters. Eat hot spread with butter.

Each quarter is 45g CHO. 275 kcals.

OATCAKES

These taste good hot or cold. This recipe uses a mixture of oats and oat bran and germ as this increases the fibre content of the oatcakes. Bran from oats is one of the best sources of fibre. Soluble fibre dissolves in water and swells in the stomach to give a feeling of fullness which can reduce hunger. According to studies made by Dr James Anderson of Kentucky University soluble fibre from oats also slows down the rate at which food is absorbed, which is beneficial for people with diabetes because it results in a stable blood sugar level. It was also found to reduce cholesterol levels.

If buying oatcakes do read the list of ingredients carefully, because most brands I have come across include a sweetening agent. The traditional flavouring is just a pinch of salt, and you can spread something savoury or sweet on top.

50g (2oz) oatmeal
50g (2oz) oat germ and bran (if not available use oatmeal)
pinch of sea salt
1 tbs oil
about 50ml (2 fl oz) boiling water

Makes 16 triangular oatcakes.

Combine the oatmeal, oat germ and bran and salt in a medium-sized bowl. Stir in the oil. Work in as much hot water as necessary to make a soft pastry.

Remove from the bowl and roll out thinly on a wooden board or work top. If the pastry is too moist dust the board with oatmeal. Cut into 11cm (4½in) circles and cut each one into four triangles. Cook on a greased griddle, making sure it is not smoking hot, for about 4 minutes on each side. The oatcakes should be firm, but not brown when cooked. Alternatively they can be baked on an ungreased tray in a preheated oven gas mark 3/170°C/325°F for 20–25 minutes.

3 oatcakes are 10g CHO. 95 kcals.

MUFFINS

There are two types of muffins: American and British. Both kinds include an egg, but the American variety is made without yeast and baked in the oven while the British kind is a rich yeast dough that is cooked on the griddle. I find the American muffins quicker to make and tastier to eat.

175g flour (6oz) wholewheat flour

Combine the flour, wheatgerm and baking powder in a medium-sized

25g (1oz) wheatgerm
3 tsp baking powder
25ml (1 fl oz) oil
1 egg, well beaten
175ml (6 fl oz) skimmed milk

Makes 12 muffins.

bowl. Stir in the oil together with the egg and milk. Divide into 12 greased muffin tins and bake in a preheated oven gas mark 6/200°C/400°F for 15–20 minutes until brown on top.

Each muffin is 10g CHO. 85 kcals.

APPLE MUFFINS

Oats are a nutritive grain with a high mineral content, including potassium, phosphorus and magnesium. They are rich in vitamin B and also contain vitamin E. Herbalists consider them a useful nerve tonic and good for building bones. One need look no further than the hardy Scottish Highlanders with their traditional breakfast of porridge oats to realize there is a solid basis for these observations.

50g (2oz) porridge oats
50ml (2 fl oz) apple juice,
    unsweetened
50g (2oz) oat germ and bran
75g (3oz) wholewheat flour
2 tsp baking powder
½ tsp cinnamon
1 egg, well beaten
75g (3oz) firm tofu
100ml (4 fl oz) skimmed milk
2 medium apples weighing
    about 225g (8oz), finely
    chopped

Makes 12 muffins.

Mix the oats and apple juice together and leave to stand for 5 minutes. Combine the oat germ and bran, flour, baking powder and cinnamon. Add the moist oats which have absorbed the juice. Fold in the egg together with the minced or moulied tofu, milk and finely chopped apples.

Spoon into 12 greased muffin tins and bake in a preheated oven gas mark 5/190°C/375°F for 25–30 minutes until well browned.

Each muffin is 10g CHO. 70 kcals.

3 SPREADS AND TOPPINGS

The alternative food industry has had its greatest successes with sugar-free substitutes for sticky jams and nut spreads. Varieties that range from strawberry to Italian peach and lemon shred can now be found in many supermarkets, and traditional jam-makers like Robertson have joined the sugar-free jamwagon.

The jams are made from fruit, pectin and fruit juice rather than sugar and fruit. Because of the easy access to manufactured jam it is not essential for sugar-free cooks to invest a lot of time making spreads. However, it is worth knowing the basic methods.

Nut spreads are often sweetened. In the USA up to 10 per cent sugar can legally be added to manufactured peanut butter. Some sugar-free versions are available, although the end product differs greatly – to such an extent that one firm's crunchy peanut butter can be the answer to your dreams while their smooth version can seal your jaws in a cement-like vice.

The spreads in this section can be used on bread or double up as fillings in cakes. The fruit fillings can be stored in the fridge for up to a week. If they are made with a soft white cheese such as quark they should be consumed the same day.

Basic icing recipes are also given. Some cake and biscuit recipes refer specifically to a filling or topping while Children's Parties (see pages 295–301) gives ideas on how to use them to decorate birthday cakes.

PEANUT BUTTER

Peanuts, asserts the American food authority Dr Caroline Shreeve, are mildly aphrodisiac. They contain three amino acids which she claims improve sexual performance. She does not specify the amount of peanuts needed to achieve the desired effect – whether it is ounces, pounds or tonnes.

200g (7oz) peanuts
2 tsp oil

Spread the peanuts out on a shallow baking dish and put in a preheated oven gas mark 4/180°C/350°F for 20–30 minutes until they are browned, but not burnt. Grind the cooled roasted peanuts and oil in an electric coffee grinder until a paste is formed. Store in a glass jar in the fridge.

Peanut Butter is 17.5g CHO. 1230 kcals.

APRICOT-ALMOND SPREAD

This spread requires no cooking. The main benefits are protein from the almonds, vitamin A from the dried apricots and vitamin C from the apple.

75g (3oz) dried apricots
75g (3oz) whole almonds
spring water
1 medium apple weighing about 150g (5oz), chopped

Place the dried apricots and almonds in a small bowl. Pour on as much spring water as is necessary to cover them and leave overnight. In the morning blend or process the apricots, nuts and water together with the chopped apple. (There is no need to peel the apple before chopping; simply wash and pat dry.) Blend until all the fruit and nuts have been broken down to a creamy paste. Pour into a glass jar and store in the fridge.

Apricot-Almond Spread is 50g CHO. 610 kcals.

PINEAPPLE CONSERVE

Pineapple conserve is first boiled and then combined with apple pectin to create a more jam-like consistency. Pectin can be made from other fruits such as lime. It can also be purchased from the chemist's.

Apple pectin
450g (1lb) apples, including cores and peel
600ml (20 fl oz) water

Save apple cores and peel for when you make this because they are high in pectin.

Combine the ingredients in a heavy saucepan and boil for 30 minutes. Pour the liquid through a colander to separate it from the fruit. Boil it down to about 125ml (4½ fl oz). It can be stored in the fridge in a sealed jar.

Conserve
400g (14oz) pineapple without skin, chopped
150g (5oz) eating apple, grated
100ml (4 fl oz) apple juice, unsweetened
125ml (4½ fl oz) apple pectin

This conserve is blended before cooking, for speed. Liquidize the chopped pineapple, grated apple and apple juice, pour into a heavy stainless steel saucepan and boil for 10–12 minutes. Add the pectin and boil for a further 3–5 minutes. Most of the juice will be absorbed during the cooking. Remove from the heat. Pour into a prepared glass jar and store in the fridge.

Pineapple Conserve is 75g CHO. 300 kcals.

TAHINI-BANANA SPREAD

Tahini is made from sesame seeds and is a source of calcium.

Use a good quality tahini for this recipe – Greek brands are usually very suitable. The tahini in the jar should have quite a liquid texture.

50g (2oz) banana, peeled
50g (2oz) tahini
4 tbs orange juice, freshly squeezed

Mash the banana with a fork and combine with the tahini and orange juice to make a smooth paste. It can be used as a spread for bread or as a cream to put between two halves of a cake. It is best eaten the same day so only mix up as much as you need.

Tahini-Banana Spread is 20g CHO. 370 kcals.

MINCEMEAT

This recipe for mincemeat substitutes tofu for suet and uses a mixture of fresh fruit, dried fruit and vegetable to achieve that distinctive mincemeat flavour. This recipe makes enough to fill two rolls of Rough Puff Pastry (see page 160).
The mincemeat keeps in the fridge for about a week.

300g (11oz) eating apples, chopped
100g (4oz) raisins, soaked in a little water for 30 minutes and chopped
100g (4oz) sultanas, soaked in a little water for 30 minutes and chopped
75g (3oz) grapes, chopped
1 medium orange weighing about 150 g (5 oz), juice and grated zest
½ lemon, grated zest and juice (about 3 tbs)
50ml (2 fl oz) apple juice (unsweetened)
125g (4½oz) carrot, grated finely
225g (8oz) firm tofu
50g (2oz) ground almonds
2 tsp miso melted in 1 tbs boiling water
¼ tsp cinnamon
¼ tsp allspice
pinch cloves
1 tbs brandy (optional)

Combine the chopped apples, raisins, sultanas and grapes, orange and lemon zests, orange, lemon and apple juice and grated carrot in a heavy saucepan. Simmer for 30 minutes. Put the tofu through a food mill then stir it into the pan together with the ground almonds and simmer for a few more minutes.

Mix the miso with 1 tbsp of boiling water so that it becomes liquid. You can also add a little juice from the fruit mixture to the miso paste to make it more runny. (If you add miso without mixing it with liquid it will not dissolve evenly into the fruit mixture.) Stir in the miso liquid together with the cinnamon, allspice, cloves and brandy and remove from the heat.

Leave to cool in the pan, then place in a container. Cover and leave in the fridge overnight before using.

Mincemeat is 210g CHO. 1230 kcals.

CHERRY CREAM

This sweet-tasting cream can be used to sandwich two cakes together or spread on top of a cake.

75g (3oz) cherries
1 tbs apple juice
75g (3oz) skimmed milk quark

Destone the cherries. Blend with the apple juice to make a thick purée. Fold in the quark to make a deep pinkish-red cream.

Cherry Cream is 15g CHO. 100 kcals.

HAZELNUT-CAROB CREAM FILLING

75g (3oz) hazelnuts, ground
25g (1oz) carob powder
2 tbs orange juice, freshly squeezed
115g (4¼oz) skimmed milk quark
75g (3oz) banana, peeled

Combine the ground hazelnuts and carob powder in a medium bowl. Stir in the orange juice, quark and mashed banana to make a thick cream that is ready to spread. Use the same day.

Total value is 40g CHO. 500 kcals.

CHESTNUT-SATSUMA CREAM FILLING

This rich creamy filling is ideal for filling a Swiss roll or a baked tart case. This gives enough to fill a 20cm (8in) diameter pastry case. Use half the quantity for a Swiss roll.

4 satsumas
1 quantity Crème aux Marrons (see page 275)

Peel the satsumas and remove the white pith. Chop into small pieces with a sharp knife and add, together with any juice, to the Crème aux marrons. Stir together and it is ready to use.

Total value is 125g CHO. 660 kcals.

CAROB ICING

This creamy sweet icing quickly becomes firm. It is ideal for decorating cakes and biscuits and also freezes well.

25g (1oz) butter or margarine
25g (1oz) carob powder
75ml (3 fl oz) skimmed milk
15g (½oz) ground almonds
1 tsp brandy or brandy essence
 (optional)

Prepare the icing by putting the margarine, carob powder and milk in a small saucepan. Slowly heat, stirring the ingredients all the time until a smooth liquid is formed. It should hardly boil. Take off the heat and add the ground almonds and brandy.

An alternative to ground almonds in this recipe is to use 15g (½oz) finely ground porridge oats.

Carob Icing is 15g CHO. 365 kcals.

COCONUT ICING

This thin white icing absorbs any colour. The carbohydrate content is negligible, but it is high in saturated fat so use in small quantities.

50g (2oz) coconut cream
150ml (5fl oz) water
colouring (optional)

Heat the cut-up coconut cream and water in a medium-sized saucepan until the lumps of coconut cream have dissolved, forming a thickish white paste. Use plain or add colouring.

Coconut Icing is neg CHO. 165 kcals.

4 Biscuits, Bars and Sweet Nothings

'To take the biscuit' means to deserve a prize for excellence. It is a phrase so old and obscure that its origin is assumed to be Latin. In 1610, at an international innkeepers' congress at a hostelry in Rothenburg-am-Tauber (now in West Germany), the daughter of mine host was deemed to be so attractive that the Secretary wrote beside her name: '*Ista capit biscottum*' – 'That one takes the biscuit'.

Biscuits have different functions at different times. In the morning they are required to be substantial snacks and provide an extra supply of energy, while in the afternoon they are only required to keep you going till the evening meal.

Biscuits come in all shapes and textures. Crescents, squares, circles and small balls can all be found piled up in the biscuit tin. Some are crunchy, others soft or hard. Everyone has their own idea of what their favourite biscuit should be. The ones given in this section are made from a dough and rolled into shapes, dropped by the spoonful on to trays, poured into flat tins and sliced into bars, or crisp pastries sandwiched together with creams.

MEDITERRANEAN HALF-MOONS

These half-moon-shaped biscuits with a firm cake-like texture are perfumed with the pungent aniseed.

25ml (1fl oz) boiling water
25g (1oz) prunes, stoned
100g (4oz) wholewheat flour
50g (2oz) carob powder
3/4–1 tbs aniseed
25g (1 fl oz) oil
1 egg, lightly beaten
50g (2oz) cottage cheese

Makes 20 biscuits.

Pour the boiling water over the prunes and leave to stand for 15 minutes. Combine the flour, carob powder and aniseed in a medium bowl. Add the oil, egg and cottage cheese that has been sieved or put through a food mill to remove the lumps.

Put the prunes and small amount of liquid in an electric coffee grinder and blend. Fold into the flour mixture and work to form a moist dough.

To make the dough into equal-sized crescents divide it into half and roll each piece into a long sausage about 50cm (20in) long. Cut each one into ten 5cm (2in) lengths. This will give a total of 20. Gently bend each piece into a half-moon or crescent, making the ends slightly pointed, so that the crescent is a little thicker in the middle. Place them on a greased baking tray and bake in a preheated oven gas mark 3/170°C/325°F for 15–20 minutes until firm.

1 biscuit is 5g CHO. 45 kcals.

SESAME SQUARES

The sesame seeds used in the recipes in this book are very small, brown and are unhulled, which means they still have their mineral-rich outer covering. Sesame seeds are rich in linoleic unsaturated fatty acids. These are known as essential fatty acids because the body cannot make them itself and is dependent for its supply on foods containing them.

50g (2oz) dried dates, chopped
100ml (4fl oz) water
100g (4oz) sesame seeds
50g (2oz) wholewheat flour
50g (2oz) ground almonds
zest of 1 small lemon
juice of half a lemon (about
    1½ tbs)
1 egg, lightly beaten

Makes 18 squares.

Put the dates and water in a small saucepan on a low heat and cook till the water is absorbed and the dates have become mushy. Leave to cool. Combine the sesame seeds, flour and ground almonds in a medium bowl. Stir in the lemon zest, juice and date paste. Fold the egg into the sesame, flour and date mixture. This will give a thick paste-like texture.

Oil a 22.5cm (9in) square baking dish and spread the mixture evenly over the base of the dish using the back of a spoon to flatten the surface.

Bake in a preheated oven gas mark 4/180°C/350°F for 15–20 minutes until evenly browned. Cut into 18 squares when cool.

Each Sesame Square is 5g CHO. 70 kcals.

CHESTNUT FUDGE FINGERS

Chestnuts are a welcome winter treat. This is the time of year when you see chestnut sellers in the streets of Central London warming themselves by their hot furnaces in between urging bags of roasted nuts into your gloved hands.

Unlike many other nuts chestnuts are high in carbohydrates, but low in oils. They contain 500mg of potassium per 100g and include small amounts of calcium and magnesium and some of the B vitamins.

Chestnut purée can be bought in tins or you can make it yourself. If using fresh chestnuts peel them then boil until soft and all the cooking water is absorbed. Then sieve or put through a food mill. Out of season it is possible to obtain dried chestnuts, but these have to be boiled for a considerable length of time.

100g (4oz) dried dates,
    chopped
100ml (4 fl oz) water

Put the dates and water in a small saucepan and cook over a low heat until the water is absorbed and the

100g (4oz) wholewheat flour
50g (2oz) soya flour
25g (1oz) wheatgerm
1 tsp bicarbonate of soda
2 tsp cream of tartar
200 ml (7 fl oz) low-fat natural
     yogurt
1 tbs rum or 1 tsp rum essence
25g (1oz) soya flakes soaked in
     1 dessertspoon orange juice
100g (4oz) chestnut purée,
     unsweetened

Makes 16 biscuits.

dates have become mushy. Combine
the wholewheat flour, soya flour,
wheatgerm, bicarbonate of soda and
cream of tartar in a medium bowl. Fold
in the date mixture and yogurt. Add
the rum, soya flakes and chestnut
purée. This makes a creamy texture.

Pour into a greased and floured 20cm
(8in) square baking tin and bake
in a preheated oven gas mark
4/190°C/350°F for 30–40 minutes
until evenly browned. Cut into 16
fingers.

Each biscuit is 15g CHO. 75 kcals.

GINGERBREAD MEN

*Use the special cutters for these figures and decorate them with raisin
eyes and buttons. For parties and those who prefer a sweeter taste
lightly spread sugar-free jam over the surface, sprinkle them with
desiccated coconut and place raisins on top.*

250g (9oz) wholewheat flour
50g (2oz) bran
2 tsp bicarbonate of soda
1–2 tsp ground ginger
1 tsp cinnamon
½ tsp cloves
50g (2oz) margarine
100g (4oz) ground almonds
100g (4oz) bananas, peeled
1 tbs lemon juice
1 egg, lightly beaten
100–125 ml (4–4½ fl oz) low
     fat natural yogurt
50g (2oz) raisins for
     decoration

Makes 20 Gingerbread Men.

Combine the flour, bran, bicarbonate
of soda and spices in a medium bowl.
Rub in the margarine. Stir in the
ground almonds. Add the mashed
banana, lemon juice, the egg and the
yogurt to make a soft dough. Chill in
the fridge for 30 minutes before using.

Roll out the pastry on a lightly floured
board or work top to 1cm (½in)
thickness. Use a gingerbread man
cutter to make 20 figures. Place them
on a baking tray and decorate with
chopped raisins for eyes and buttons.
Bake in a preheated oven gas mark
5/190°C/375°F for 15–20 minutes
until lightly browned.

Each one is 10g CHO. 110 kcals.

BANANA DROPS

50g (2oz) dried dates
100ml (4 fl oz) water
350g (12oz) bananas, peeled
75g (3oz) millet flakes
75g (3oz) porridge oats
a few drops of vanilla essence
1 egg, lightly beaten

Makes 20 biscuits.

Heat the dates in a small saucepan with the water. Cook gently until the water is absorbed and the dates have become mushy. Mash the banana in a bowl with a fork. Mix in the millet flakes, porridge oats and vanilla essence. Add the date purée, and fold in the egg.

Using a dessertspoon measure out 20 heaped spoonfuls on a greased baking tray. Bake in a preheated oven gas mark 5/190°C/375°F for 20–25 minutes until the biscuits are evenly browned.

Each biscuit is 10g CHO. 50 kcals.

OAT SNACKS

This is a filling biscuit for a mid-morning snack. It should provide enough even energy to keep you going until lunch as the oats are high in soluble fibre which aids slow absorption of food in the body. The tofu provides protein and the carob gives sweetness and more fibre.

100g (4oz) porridge oats
100g (4oz) oat bran and germ
50g (2oz) carob powder
100g (4oz) banana, peeled
200g (7oz) firm tofu
50ml (2 fl oz) skimmed milk or
 soya milk

Makes 15 biscuits.

Combine the oats, oat bran and germ and carob powder in a medium bowl. Put the banana and tofu through a hand mill or blend in a liquidizer and combine with the dry ingredients. Add as much of the milk as necessary to make a pastry dough.

Pat or roll out on a floured board or work top to a thickness of about 1cm (½in). Use a 5cm (2in) cutter to make 15 thick rounds. Place on an ungreased baking tray and bake in a preheated oven gas mark 3/170°C/325°F for 30–40 minutes until lightly browned and firm.

Each biscuit is 15g CHO. 70 kcals.

MUESLI SLICES

30g (1oz, generous) sultanas, chopped
50g (2oz) prunes, stoned and chopped
a little water
50g (2oz) porridge oats
50g (2oz) millet flakes
50g (2oz) rye flakes
50g (2oz) soya bean flakes
50g (2oz) bran
50g (2oz) barley flakes
200ml (7 fl oz) skimmed milk
25g (1oz) sunflower seeds
50g (2oz) flaked almonds
2 pears, grated
½–1 tsp cinnamon
pinch of ground cloves

Makes 24 slices.

Cover the sultanas and prunes with a little water and leave to soak for 15 minutes.

Combine the oats, millet flakes, rye flakes, soya bean flakes, bran and barley flakes in a medium bowl. Pour the milk over them and leave to stand for 15 minutes.

Combine the chopped dried fruit with the different flakes and milk. Add sunflower seeds, flaked almonds, grated pears and spices to make a thick mixture.

Spoon the muesli mixture into a 20–22.5cm (8–9in) square greased baking tin, smoothing the surface down with a spoon. Bake in a preheated oven gas mark 3/170°C/325°F until evenly browned. Cut into 24 slices when cool.

Each slice is 10g CHO. 70 kcals.

SESAME OAT BARS

Either allergies are becoming more common or people's awareness of them has radically increased – I am forever being asked for recipes that exclude one sensitive foodstuff or another. These bars are suitable for a number of exclusion diets because they contain no egg, flour or milk.

Sesame seeds are rich in calcium, with 815mg per 100g. It is difficult to eat many in cakes, but savoury foods such as tahini, which is made of ground sesame seeds, or gomasio, a Japanese condiment of toasted ground sesame seeds mixed with a little salt, are a more concentrated source.

50g (2oz) prunes, stoned and chopped

Heat the prunes and dates in a small saucepan with the water over a low

25g (1oz) dried dates, chopped
100ml (4 fl oz) water
100g (4oz) porridge oats
100g (4oz) sesame seeds
100g (4oz) soya bean flakes
25g (1oz) sultanas, chopped
100ml (4 fl oz) orange juice,
   unsweetened
100ml (4 fl oz) soya milk

Makes 20 bars.

heat until all the water is absorbed and a mushy paste is formed.

Combine the oats, sesame seeds and soya bean flakes. Add the sultanas, date and prune paste, orange juice and soya milk to make a moist mixture. Spread the mixture evenly over the base of a 22.5cm (9in) square greased baking tin. Bake in a preheated oven gas mark 4/180°C/350°F for 25–30 minutes until browned all over. Cut into 20 slices.

Each bar is 10g CHO. 85 kcals.

CAROB FUDGE SQUARES

Carob is widely used in health food circles as an alternative to chocolate, but it does have its own unique taste. The reasons that a sugar-free cook prefers carob to chocolate are that it contains fibre, is high in natural sugar and remarkably low in fat, with only 1/34 of the fat content in chocolate. In addition carob is free of the two stimulants caffeine and theobromine which are found in chocolate. (Theobromine has been linked with migraine and allergic responses; caffeine stimulates the central nervous system and taken in excess can become addictive.) Carob is also bursting with such minerals as calcium, magnesium, potassium and phosphorus.

These creamy squares are messy to eat, but worth getting sticky fingers for.

100g (4oz) wholewheat flour
100g (4oz) porridge oats
½ tsp mixed spice (optional)
50ml (2 fl oz) oil
½ tsp almond essence
1 medium ripe pear, grated

Filling
4 eating apples weighing about
   500g (1lb 4oz)

Combine the flour, oats and mixed spice. Stir in the oil and almond essence. Add the pear and work into a moist dough. Divide the dough in half. Pat one piece with the flat of your fingers over the base of a 20cm (8in) square greased baking tin. Pat the second piece out on a similar-sized tin, but as it will eventually be broken into

25g (1oz) dried dates, chopped
100ml (4 fl oz) water
15g (½oz) carob powder
2 egg yolks

Makes 20 small squares.

large crumbs you do not have to work it so carefully.

Bake in a preheated oven gas mark 5/190°C/375°F for 25 minutes until the pieces of pastry are evenly browned.

While the pastry base is cooking slice the apples into a saucepan together with the dates and water. Bring to the boil and simmer until the fruit is softened. Stir in the carob powder about a minute before you remove the apples from the heat. Pour all these ingredients into a blender to make a thick purée. Return the carob, apple and date purée to the pan and add the broken-up pieces of the second sheet of baked pastry. Heat the fruit purée and crumbs for about a minute so that it is hot, but not boiling.

Lightly beat the two egg yolks with a fork. Pour the fruit mixture over the egg yolks, stirring as you add it to the eggs. (If the fruit mixture is too hot you will have fried eggs and that should be avoided.) The filling takes on a lovely creamy texture. Pour it evenly over the first pastry base and when cold chill in the fridge.

Each square is 10g CHO. 80 kcals.

CAROB OAT BISCUITS

These are popular with children. The soya flour and egg ensure a high source of protein and the brewer's yeast provides a vitamin B booster.

Brewer's yeast can be added to all the baked recipes in this book whenever you want to provide extra B vitamins. A number of nutritionists in this century have emphasized the importance of B vitamins. Robert McCarrison, famous for his research work into diets in the 1920s, reiterated the point that 'a large part of the food eaten by civilized [sic Western] people has been deprived of vitamin B by "improvements" in manufacture.' Adelle Davis, the American nutritionist, was an avid fan of brewer's yeast and claimed that 'the use of [brewers'] yeast alone could correct the majority of the world's nutritional problems.'

Brewer's yeast contains some protein, almost all the B vitamins and chromium. B vitamins are important for growth, nerves and general well-being while chromium affects how glucose is dealt with by the body.

25g (1oz) sultanas
225g (8oz) bananas, peeled
25ml (1 fl oz) oil
½ tsp vanilla essence
100g (4oz) porridge oats
25g (1oz) carob powder
50g (2oz) soya flour
1 tsp brewers' yeast
1 egg, lightly beaten

Makes 16 biscuits.

Cover the sultanas with a little water so that they will be nicely plumped up by the time they are needed.

Mash the bananas with a fork in a bowl so that they become a fine paste. Add the oil and vanilla essence. Combine the oats, carob powder, soya flour, brewer's yeast and gradually mix in. Fold in the egg.

Measure out 16 heaped dessertspoons on to a large greased baking tray. Bake in a preheated oven gas mark 4/180°C/350°F for 15 minutes until the biscuits have become firm and only very slightly browned at the edges.

Each biscuit is 10g CHO. 75 kcals.

CAROB HAZELNUT SLICE

Hazelnuts grow mostly in Turkey and Europe. They contain some of the important minerals – including potassium and zinc – with a sizeable 21mg of vitamin E in every 100g. Culpeper, the 17th century herbalist, recommended using the pounded nuts or nut milk for treating a persistent cough. When mixed with a little pepper, this was thought to 'draw rheum from the head'.

1 quantity Sweet Seed Pastry
(see page 163)

Filling
150g (5oz) finely chopped
hazelnuts

Use your fingers to press the pastry over the base of a 20 × 25cm (8 × 10in) baking dish. Bake in a preheated oven gas mark 4/180°C/350°F for 10 minutes until

50g (2oz) carob powder
75g (3oz) dried apricots, finely chopped
150ml (5 fl oz) water
2 egg whites

Makes 20 fingers.

lightly browned around the edges.

Combine the hazelnuts and carob powder. Put the dried apricots and water in a small saucepan and heat until the water is absorbed and the apricots have become paste-like. Cool. Mix the apricot paste with the nuts and carob. Whisk the egg whites to stiff snowy peaks and fold in to make a moist paste.

Spread this mixture evenly over the half-baked pastry, return to the oven and bake for a further 10 minutes. It only needs to be baked enough so that it sets. If it cooks for too long the hazelnut will become hard and not chewy.

Cut into fingers for serving when cool.

2 fingers are 10g CHO. 150 kcals.

CAROB ALMOND BALLS

These small soft carob balls coated in white coconut are a pleasant introduction to carob. Carob powder is made from a crescent-shaped pod that is found growing in the Near East and southern Mediterranean lands. It has been used for thousands of years. References to it have been found in ancient Sumerian texts and the Romans called it 'carobi'. It is also known as St John's Bread after the time John the Baptist wandered in the wilderness and used this mineral-rich pod as a means of survival. The carob that we buy in the shops has been roasted and ground a couple of times.

75g (3oz) dried dates, chopped
25g (1oz) dried prunes, stoned and chopped
150ml (5 fl oz) water
250g (9oz) ground almonds
50g (2oz) carob powder
3 egg whites, stiffly beaten

Heat the dates, prunes and water in a small saucepan over a low heat until the water is absorbed. Be careful that the mixture does not burn. The dried fruit should become very mushy. If the texture does not become paste-like blend the dried fruit. Mix the ground

25g (1oz) desiccated coconut, unsweetened, for decoration

Makes 27 Carob Almond Balls.

almonds and carob powder together. Add the date and prune mixture. Fold in the egg whites to make a moist but stiff consistency.

Divide the mixture into three equal portions and use a teaspoon to measure out 9 equal pieces from each portion. Roll these between the palms of your hands into small balls. Place on a greased tray and bake in a preheated oven gas mark 3/170°C/325°F for 20–25 minutes until lightly browned. While still warm remove from the tray and roll them in a plate of coconut. Only a little of the coconut will stick to the balls so sprinkle some over the top as well.

3 balls are 10g CHO. 215 kcals.

CAROB SECRETS

These crunchy carob treats taste very like chocolate and are always a pleasant surprise to guests bravely trying carob for the first time. Carob contains 46 per cent natural sugar which makes this a very sweet treat.

75g (3oz) flaked almonds
75g (3oz) sultanas
scant 25g (scant 1oz) carob powder
50ml (2 fl oz) water
½ tsp vanilla essence
18 sweet cases

Makes 18 Carob Secrets.

Chop the flaked almonds into halves. Wash, drain and chop the sultanas into thirds or very briefly chop in an electric grinder – the danger with an electric machine is that it can quickly reduce the sultanas to a pulp.

Put the carob powder, water and vanilla essence in a small saucepan and heat on a low light until the carob powder has dissolved. Add the sultanas and flaked almonds to the carob mixture. Stir with a small wooden spoon, crushing the flakes a little more.

When the sultanas and almond flakes are mixed together and well coated with the carob sauce put a heaped teaspoon in each of the 18 miniature paper cases. Leave to chill in the fridge for one hour before serving.

They are delicious after a meal or as a special sweet treat.

3 carob secrets are 10g CHO. 110 kcals.

CAROB NUT CLUSTERS

This is a crunchy combo of four different kinds of nuts sweetened with a few sultanas. Eating the nuts together gives the benefit of the different nutritional properties of each one. They are topped with a sweet, shiny carob icing.

50g (2oz) sultanas
25ml (1 fl oz) boiling water
50g (2oz) peanuts, chopped
50g (2oz) hazelnuts, chopped
50g (2oz) flaked almonds
50g (2oz) walnuts, chopped
2 egg whites, stiffly beaten
1 quantity Carob Icing (see page 82)

Makes 18 Carob Nut Clusters.

Leave the sultanas to soak in the boiling water for about 10 minutes then roughly chop them up in a grinder. Combine the four different types of nuts in a mixing bowl with the chopped sultanas. Use the egg whites to bind the nuts and sultanas together.

Using a dessertspoon place 18 heaps of the mixture on a greased baking tray. Bake in a preheated oven gas mark 3/170°C/325°F for 10–15 minutes until they are lightly browned. Cool on a wire tray.

Put teaspoonfuls of the icing on top of the baked nut clusters. An alternative icing can be made by gently melting a carob bar and using it as a rich carob coating.

3 nut clusters are 10g CHO. 255 kcals.

CINNAMON DROPS

'And lucent syrops, tinct with cinnamon', wrote Keats in The Eve of St Agnes, *evoking the exotic imagery conjured up by this fragrant Eastern spice to hint at the beauty of his sleeping love. The origins of cinnamon are decidedly unromantic. It is the dried inner bark of a small tree from the East Indies and was among the first commodities traded from the East to the Mediterranean, mentioned repeatedly in the Bible and an indispensable adjunct to worship in Solomon's temple.*

125g (4½oz) dried dates, chopped
100ml (4 fl oz) water
225g (8oz) ground almonds
4 tsp cinnamon
2 egg whites, stiffly beaten

Makes 27 drops.

Heat the dates and water in a small saucepan until all the water is absorbed and a paste is formed. Blend in an electric coffee grinder to a smooth consistency. Leave to cool.

Combine the ground almonds and cinnamon in a mixing bowl then fold in the date mixture. Bind with the egg whites. To shape the drops moisten the palms of your hands with cold water and roll the mixture into 27 small balls. Place them on a lightly greased baking tray.

Bake in a preheated oven gas mark 3/170°C/325°F for 20–25 minutes, so that they are slightly brown on the outside and underneath. The drops should be firm outside, but with a chewy texture inside.

3 drops are 10g CHO. 180 kcals.

COCONUT MACAROONS

50g (2oz) dried dates, finely chopped
100ml (4 fl oz) water
75g (3oz) unsweetened desiccated coconut

Heat the dates with the water in a small saucepan until the water is absorbed. Mash with a fork. Leave to cool.

Combine the coconut, ground almonds

75g (3oz) ground almonds
25g (1oz) wheatgerm
juice and zest of half a lemon
  (makes about 2 tbs lemon
  juice)
1 large egg, lightly beaten

Makes 20 macaroons.

and wheatgerm in a mixing bowl. Add the date paste, lemon juice and zest and mix together. Use the egg to bind the whole mixture to a thick paste.

To shape the macaroons moisten the palms of your hands with cold water and roll generous teaspoons of the mixture into 20 small balls. Place them on a greased baking tray. Bake in a preheated oven gas mark 3/170°C/325°F for 15–20 minutes until very lightly browned.

4 macaroons are 10g CHO. 235 kcals.

CAROB COCONUT MACAROONS

Makes 20 macaroons.

Add 15g (½oz) carob powder to the Coconut Macaroons recipe (see page 97) when combining the coconut, ground almonds and wheatgerm. The addition of the carob gives these biscuits a rather mellow taste. The lemon rind and juice taste less dominant in this version and give a fuller flavour to the biscuit. Some of my biscuit tasters prefer the carob version to the plain coconut one.

4 macaroons are 10g CHO. 240 kcals.

PINE AND ALMOND CRESCENTS

Pine nuts, said Culpeper, are 'excellent restoratives in consumption and after long illness'. They are also a light and delicious nut which makes a welcome addition to sweet and savoury dishes. It is worth comparing prices in a few shops before purchasing because there is usually quite a disparity.

The almond dough is quick to make, but rolling the crescents in a plate of pine nuts and ensuring that the nuts become embedded on the outside of the crescents can take at least 15 minutes so it is worth sitting down comfortably with an interesting radio programme to listen to.

This recipe uses very few dates, but still tastes quite sweet. The reason for this is that the nuts themselves are naturally sweet.

50g (2oz) dried dates
50ml (2 fl oz) water
150g (5oz) ground almonds
juice and zest of half a lemon
1 egg white, stiffly beaten
100g (4oz) pine nuts

Makes 15 biscuits.

Put the dates and water in a small saucepan and simmer on a low heat until the water is absorbed. Allow to cool then purée to a smooth paste.

Combine the date purée with the ground almonds and lemon juice and zest in a mixing bowl. Add the egg white to the almond mixture to make a sticky paste.

Spread out the pine nuts on a large plate. Take a generous teaspoonful of the mixture and roll it into a sausage in the palm of your hand. Roll it in a plate of pine nuts so that it becomes encrusted with them. As you lay the sausage shape on a greased baking tray curve it into a crescent shape making the ends slightly narrower than the middle. Coating with the pine nuts makes the crescents larger than the original piece of almond dough.

Bake in a preheated oven gas mark 3/170°C/325°F for 10–15 minutes until very lightly browned.

3 crescents are 10g CHO. 315 kcals.

PRUNE AND PEAR DROPS

These are very moist titbits.

50g (2oz) dried prunes, stoned
   and finely chopped
50ml (2 fl oz) water

Put the prunes and water in a small saucepan and simmer on a low heat until the water is absorbed. Combine

75g (3oz) ground almonds
¼ tsp mixed spice
1 egg white, stiffly beaten
200g (7oz) pear

**Makes 16 Prune and
Pear Drops.**

the softened prunes with the ground
almonds and mixed spice in a mixing
bowl. Grate the pear into the almond
mixture and stir; fold in the egg white
to make a thick paste.

Place 16 dessertspoons of the mixture
on a greased baking tray. Bake
in a preheated oven gas mark
3/170°C/325°F for 20 minutes until
browned.

4 drops are 10g CHO. 150 kcals.

CINNAMON HAZELNUT STICKS

*These are an all-time favourite. They look like they have come out of a
patisserie, but are quite simple to make.*

50g (2oz) dried dates, finely
   chopped
75ml (3 fl oz) water
75g (3oz) ground hazelnuts
75g (3oz) ground almonds
½ tsp cinnamon
2 egg whites, stiffly beaten
1 quantity Carob Icing (see
page 82)

Makes 20 small sticks.

Put the dates and water in a small
saucepan and simmer on a low heat
until the water has been absorbed.
Mash with a fork to make a paste.
Combine the hazelnuts, almonds and
cinnamon in a mixing bowl. Add the
date paste to the nuts, working it in
with a spoon. Use the egg whites to
bind the nut dough.

Either roll the mixture in your hands to
make the sticks or for a more
professional finish pipe them on a
lightly greased baking tray. I use an
icing bag without any of the nozzles at
the end, but only the plastic holder
which is about 1.3cm (⅝in) diameter.
Pipe out the sticks to about 7.5cm (3in)
in length. The mixture makes 20 sticks.
Bake in a preheated oven gas mark
3/170°C/325°F for 15–20 minutes
until lightly browned.

When cool, dip each end of the sticks in Carob Icing as it begins to thicken. They look very tempting.

4 cinnamon hazelnut sticks are 10g CHO. 245 kcals.

PRUNE AND CAROB CRESCENTS

The fun in eating these is the different textures you meet with each bite: through the hard pastry shell to the inner layer of soft prune and then the hard almond in the middle. They are a very dainty dish to serve at the end of a meal.

1 quantity Carob Pastry (see page 162)

Filling
30 plump prunes
30 whole almonds

Makes 30 crescents.

Cover the pastry and leave it to stand for half an hour before using.

The prunes need to be soft so that you can easily remove their stones. Either leave them to soak overnight or soak for at least 5 hours before using. Remove the stones and replace them with an almond.

To prepare the crescents roll the pastry out thinly and cut 30 circles with a 7.5cm (3in) diameter cutter. Place a prune filled with an almond in the centre of each circle. Bring the outer edges of the circle together in the middle and pinch them close to make a crescent.

Place the crescents on an ungreased baking tray and bake in a preheated oven gas mark 4/180°C/350°F for 15–20 minutes until very lightly browned at the top.

Each crescent is 10g CHO. 45 kcals.

SUNFLOWER CHEWS

50g (2oz) dried dates, chopped
25g (1oz) prunes, stoned and
  chopped
100ml (4 fl oz) water
75g (3oz) sunflower seeds
15g (½oz) unsweetened
  desiccated coconut
25g (1oz) peanut butter

Makes 12 Sunflower Chews.

Put the dates and prunes in a small saucepan with the water and cook over a low heat until the water has been absorbed. Mash with a fork to make a thick paste.

Grind the sunflower seeds in an electric coffee grinder. Put them in a bowl and mix with the coconut, date and prune paste and peanut butter.

Roll the mixture into 12 balls, moistening the palms of your hands with cold water. Chill in the fridge for a couple of hours before serving.

2 chews are 10g CHO. 140 kcals.

PECAN FUDGE

50g (2oz) dried dates
100ml (4 fl oz) water
75g (3oz) pecan nuts, coarsely
  chopped
1 dessertspoon tahini

Makes 8 portions.

Put the dates in a small saucepan with the water and cook over a low heat until the water has been absorbed. Mash with a fork to make a thick paste.

Remove the pan from the heat. Stir in the nuts and tahini and mix well. Press into an 18cm (7in) diameter baking tin. Leave in the fridge for one hour to chill. Cut into 8 chunks and serve.

Each portion is 5g CHO. 85 kcals.

CAROB APRICOT TREATS

Making your own carob-coated fruit is quick and simple. Be sure to use a good quality carob bar for a ravishing result (see pages 28–9 for recommendations).

All carob chocolates are high in fat and contain as many or more calories than milk chocolate, so keep them for special occasions.

Make sure that you use dried apricots that are soft and plump and not wizened and hard.

50g (2oz) carob bar
100g (4oz) whole dried
   apricots

Makes about 16–18 treats.

Cut the carob bar into small pieces and place in a bowl in a pan filled with boiling water. Leave until it has melted. Be very careful that no water gets into the bowl. As soon as the carob has melted dip the individual apricots into the bowl and coat them all the way round. Leave to harden on a sheet of greaseproof paper or a marble slab. Store in the fridge until needed.

About 3 Treats are 10g CHO. 80 kcals.

CAROB DATE TREATS

Using the foregoing recipe, substitute dried dates to make a deliciously sweet treat. As dates are smaller than dried apricots 100g (4oz) will make about 22 Carob Date Treats.

About 2 Carob Date Treats are 10g CHO. 45 kcals.

(The carbohydrate and calorie contents in these recipes are based on Carob obtainable from Earthlore of Ross-on-Wye.)

MARZIPAN

This recipe uses ground almonds and a fig paste, but if this becomes too expensive it is possible to substitute fine oatmeal for 25g (1oz) of the ground almonds. The quantities would then be 50g (2oz) ground almonds and 25g (1oz) fine oatmeal. Everything else remains the same.

The taste of this marzipan is close to that of the sugar variety. The texture is not fine enough for modelling detailed shapes, but does work well with larger forms (see Marzipan Mice and Marzipan Fruit, below).

50g (2oz) dried figs
50ml (2 fl oz) water
½ tsp almond essence
colouring (optional)
75g (3oz) ground almonds

Heat the dried figs and water in a pan until all the water is absorbed. Blend to a smooth paste.

When the mixture has cooled add the almond essence and any colouring if used. Work in the ground almonds until a paste is formed. Wrap with greaseproof paper and chill in the fridge for 30 minutes before using.

This recipe is 30g CHO. 530 kcals.

MARZIPAN FRUIT AND MARZIPAN MICE

The marzipan can be coloured although generous amounts of colouring will have to be used because the colour of the fig paste is brown. For the best effect add the colouring to the ground almonds before mixing them into the fig paste. A natural colouring is available from health food shops, or an alternative is to use juices such as beetroot and carrot for red and yellow. If you do use these then aim for subtle colours because a lot of juice will affect the taste of the marzipan.

Fruit

Strawberries – use red marzipan. Work the pieces of marzipan into the conical shape typical of strawberries and stick green pumpkin seeds into the sides for strawberry seeds.
Apples – use green marzipan. Work it into round shapes and use a clove as a pungent stalk.
Stuffed dates – roll the green marzipan into oval shapes. Cut fresh dates in half and remove the stones. Place a green

oval in each date half. This dish is worthy of Scheherazade and the tales of a thousand and one nights!

Mice

double quantity of marzipan

Prepare the marzipan paste. Use the natural colour or make it slightly pink. Divide it into 8 equal pieces for 8 mice. From each one take a small piece of the marzipan and roll it into a ball for the head. Squeeze two little ears from the top of the head. Insert a couple of small raisins for eyes. Roll the rest of the marzipan into a sausage shape and attach to the head. Flatten the underneath of this shape so that it will sit on a flat surface. Cut a piece of coloured string for the tail and push it into the end of the body.

Repeat this process with the other 7 pieces of marzipan.

These are very popular with children and are something they can help to make. Decorative cardboard boxes such as those from herb tea make a suitable 'home' for the mice.

Each mouse is 7.5g CHO. 135 kcals.

The soft drinks sector is the second heaviest industrial user of sugar and the most imaginative at marketing its wares. To compete in your own kitchen with cosmetically enhanced attractions of cola drinks is virtually impossible. All you can do is invent new drinks that distract your children from the products they see advertised on TV.

One of the leading health food manufacturers, Whole Earth, has produced a harmless cola drink and a lemonade, based on apple juice and carbonated water, but they cost twice as much as branded cola and are available only in health food shops.

Cold fruit-based drinks are easily whizzed up in a liquidizer. They should be drunk promptly to get the most vitamin C, much of which is destroyed on exposure to oxygen.

The main problem for the aspiring sugar-free person is to become accustomed to drinking tea and coffee without sugar. Very determined people can give it up straight away; others find it is the last thing to go.

PINEAPPLE DRINK

400g (14oz) fresh pineapple
  without skin
350g (12 fl oz) low fat natural
  yogurt
rosewater
ice cubes
desiccated coconut,
  unsweetened, for decoration

Makes 4 drinks.

Blend the pineapple and yogurt in a
liquidizer. Add a little rosewater
according to taste. Pour into 4 glasses
and add ice cubes to each glass.
Garnish with a little coconut.

Each glass is 15g CHO. 105 kcals.

ORANGE AND LEMON FIZZ

200ml (7 fl oz) orange juice,
  freshly squeezed
4 tbs lemon juice, freshly
  squeezed
2 tbs apple juice
carbonated mineral water
4 thinly cut slices of orange, for
  decoration

Makes 4 drinks.

Combine the juices and stir well.
Divide between 4 glasses. Dilute with
fizzy mineral water, but make sure the
taste is still sweet enough. Garnish with
a thinly cut slice of orange.

Each glass is 5g CHO. 25 kcals.

MELON FIZZ

A very refreshing drink.

600g (1lb 5oz) sweet
  honeydew or galia melon,
  weighed without the seeds
carbonated mineral water
ice cubes
2 strawberries, sliced, for
  decoration

Makes 4 drinks.

Cut the melon off the rind and blend in
a liquidizer or food mill. Divide the
melon purée between 4 large glasses.
Add fizzy mineral water to each glass.
Dilute enough to make it fizzy. Stir
well. Add an ice cube on hot days and
garnish with a couple of slices of
strawberry.

Each glass is 7.5g CHO. 30 kcals.

MELON COOL

This is sweeter than Melon Fizz, but without the sparkle.

900g (2lb) ripe honeydew or galia melon, weighed without the seeds
8 tbs orange juice, freshly squeezed
ice cubes

Makes 4 drinks.

Cut the melon off the rind and blend in a liquidizer or food mill. Mix with the orange juice. Pour into 4 glasses and add ice cubes to each glass.

Each glass is 15g CHO. 60 kcals.

PEAR DRINK

This is a sweet thirst-quenching drink.

4 ripe pears, weighing about 600g (1lb 5oz), chopped
4 tbs lemon juice, freshly squeezed
12 ice cubes

Makes 4 drinks.

Put the pears in a blender with the lemon juice and ice cubes. Pour the liquid into 4 glasses and serve.

Each glass is 10g CHO. 45 kcals.

PAPAYALATA

Papaya is one of the tropical fruits that has become a more familiar sight on greengrocers' shelves in recent years. Unripe papaya contains the protein-digesting enzyme papain which in tablet form is used as an aid to digestion. The ripe papaya contains only small amounts of papain, but it is still regarded as a digestive aid. It is also rich in vitamins and minerals and contains large amounts of carotene.

1 large papaya, weighing about 450g (1lb)
300g (11oz) strawberries, hulled
4 tbs Banana Velvet Ice Cream (see page 283)

Makes 4 drinks.

Peel the papaya and remove the pips. Place in a blender together with the strawberries for a few seconds until the fruit makes a thick juice. Pour into four glasses. Serve topped with a tablespoon of ice cream.

Each glass is 17.5g CHO. 70 kcals.

STRAWBERRY MILKSHAKE

This is a thick fruity drink.

450g (1lb) strawberries
600ml (20 fl oz) skimmed milk
 or soya milk

Makes 4 drinks.

Blend the strawberries and milk in a liquidizer to make a thick pink drink. Alternatively use either a sieve or food mill to purée the strawberries. Half-fill a screw-top jar with the fruit purée and milk and shake well until the liquid becomes frothy.

Each glass is 15g CHO. 80 kcals.

HOT CAROB

Powdered hot chocolate drinks, with their images of evenings beside cosy firesides, contain 50–75 per cent sugar. An alternative, which requires some taste-bud adjustment, is to use carob.

400ml (14 fl oz) skimmed milk
1 dessertspoon carob powder
¼ tsp cinnamon

Makes 2 drinks.

Heat the milk in a pan with the carob powder and cinnamon and slowly bring to the boil, stirring all the time. Serve immediately.

Each cup is 10g CHO. 75 kcals.

RAISIN WINE

Hannah Glasse, an 18th century cookery writer, initiated her readers into the secret of making a sugar-free wine. Her special tips will still interest wine makers, although you might want to reduce the quantities as a hogshead contains about 50 gallons.

'First get a good white-wine cask, and in every hogshead put two hundred weight of raisins with their stalks on; fill it up with water, let it stand till it has done working, and put to it two quarts of French or raisin brandy; when it has quite done working, stop it up, and let it stand six months; then peg it, and if it proves fine, bottle it; then take the lees, distil them, and they will produce you a fine brandy; or you may make fine vinegar of the lees. Mallaga raisins make a sweet wine; raisins of the sun a dry wine; Belvedera raisins make fine cape wine; and each having a different flavour.

'*To give your Raisin Wine different flavours:*
Put into your cask a few walnut leaves; into your sweet wine a few bay leaves, just to give a flavour; and to another a few elder flowers.

'*To make them like red port:*
Take twelve gallons of black wine, two gallons of French brandy, the rest raisin wine; this will serve for a hogshead.'

6 SWEET AND SOUR MAIN-COURSE DISHES

He may live without books, – what is knowledge but grieving?
He may live without hope, – what is hope but deceiving?
He may live without love, – what is passion but pining?
But where is the man that can live without dining?

Owen Meredith, Earl of Lytton (1831–1891) in *Lucile*

The recipes in this section demonstrate how to adapt your favourite sweet and sour dish to a sugar-free one. Unlike cakes, which need to maintain a delicate balance, main courses can withstand a fair amount of manipulation. The point to remember is to add only a little of the alternative sweetener at a time so that you have a chance to taste the food and decide whether to add more. Even if you do overdo it and pour in too many raisins or apple slices, they do not dissolve in water the way sugar does and can be scooped out with a slotted spoon.

When you use a recipe from your standard cookery book and find sugar in it:
– If it is a teaspoon or less, ignore it and leave out the sugar: all it does is enhance flavours and you can do this by adding more flavouring.
– If it specifies 1–2 tbs (1–2oz) then it is needed for sweetening and you should use a dried or fresh fruit substitute, or juice.

The following recipes are a complex combination of tastes and should be served with rice, pasta, potatoes or vegetables that are cooked simply.

TOMATO SAUCE

Tomato sauce is a basic tool for all cooks whether you pour it over spaghetti, or simmer fish, meat or vegetables in it. Many recipes include a teaspoon of sugar with the pepper and herbs, but I do not find it necessary. If you want to add a subtle sweetness try dissolving a little miso, Japanese fermented soy beans mixed with a grain, at the end of the cooking.

1 tbs oil
1 onion
2 cloves of garlic
450g (1lb) ripe tomatoes
freshly ground black pepper
sea salt (optional)
bay leaf
½–1 tsp miso

Heat the oil on a low heat in a medium-sized saucepan until hot. Add the finely chopped onion and garlic and cook for a couple of minutes. Add the peeled and chopped tomatoes and stir in well. Add the pepper, salt and bay leaf. Reduce the heat to a low light and simmer for 20–30 minutes. At the end of the cooking time remove 2 tbsp of the sauce and dissolve the miso in it. Return to the sauce in the pan and heat for 2 minutes before serving.

Tomato sauce is 20g CHO. 230 kcals.

STUFFED ROLLS OF LAMB

This delicious main course is quite quick to prepare. Ask your butcher to cut some lamb into thin fillets if he does not usually sell this cut.

125g (4½oz) dried apricots
1 dessertspoon oil
125g (4½oz) brown rice
50g (2oz) parsley
6 spring onions
sea salt (optional)
freshly ground black pepper
4 fillets of lamb
450g (1lb) tomatoes
2 cloves garlic
1 tbs freshly squeezed lemon
    juice

Makes 4 portions.

Cover the dried apricots with a little boiling water and leave to soak.

Heat the oil in a medium-sized heavy saucepan and add the washed and drained rice. Leave to cook for about one minute, stirring the rice a little, then add enough hot water so that there is an extra 2.5cm (1in) above the rice. Bring to the boil, then place the lid on the pan and simmer on a low heat. When all the water has been absorbed and the rice is soft small holes will appear on the surface. Never stir the rice while it is simmering or it will turn into a sticky porridge.

Chop the parsley finely with the spring onions. Combine with the cooked rice. Chop the apricots into small pieces. Stir into the rice mixture together with the salt and pepper.

Lay out the washed fillets of lamb and put an equal amount of rice stuffing in each one. Roll each fillet up into a tight roll. Secure with a piece of white cotton (remember to remove this just before serving). If there is any leftover stuffing pat it into a ball with a tablespoon and wrap round with a lettuce leaf or cabbage leaf.

Wash and chop the tomatoes, slice the garlic and place with the lemon juice in the bottom of a shallow baking dish. Place the lamb rolls on top. Bake in a moderate oven gas mark 4/180°C/350°F for 1–1¼ hours until browned on the outside.

Each Lamb Roll is 45g CHO. 350 kcals.

Serving suggestion: serve with Jerusalem artichokes baked whole in the oven, and carrot salad.

POLISH SWEET AND SOUR STEAK

The meat in this recipe is cooked on top of the cooker until it is very tender. Only a little liquid is added at the beginning, as the onion and meat gradually produce more juice during cooking. This gentle increase in liquid prevents the meat from becoming tough and tasteless.

1kg 100g (2lb 7oz) chuck steak
1 tbs oil
550g (1lb 4oz) onions
50g (2oz) dried dates (use
　according to taste)
100ml (4 fl oz) cider vinegar
75–100ml (3–4 fl oz) water
freshly ground black pepper
pinch of sea salt

Serves 6.

Wash the meat and pat dry on paper towels. Heat the oil in a heavy saucepan large enough to contain the meat. Fry the meat on both sides until it is browned. Add the thinly sliced onions to the pan. Simmer them together with the meat on a low light for 10 minutes.

Wash and chop the dates finely and mix with the vinegar and water. Pour this into the pan together with a little pepper and salt. Bring to the boil then cover the pan with the lid and simmer on a low light for about 2½–3 hours until the meat is tender. It may be necessary to add a little extra water if the gravy begins to dry up.

Each serving is 10g CHO. 390 kcals.

Serving suggestion: serve with mashed potatoes and lightly cooked cabbage.

FRUIT CHICKEN WITH YELLOW SPLIT PEAS

Yellow split peas cook quickly and do not require soaking beforehand. They add fibre to this dish.

100g (4oz) yellow split peas
3 rounded tbs wholemeal flour
1½–2kg (3–4lb) roasting
　chicken, cut into portions
oil
1 large onion
1 clove garlic
2 eating apples, weighing
　about 225g (8oz)
juice of one lemon
2 tbs orange juice, freshly
　squeezed
freshly ground black pepper
grated nutmeg
sea salt (optional)

Wash the split peas and cook in a medium-sized saucepan with about 300ml (11 fl oz) of water. Bring to the boil then simmer on a low light until most of the water is absorbed and the split peas are softened.

While the split peas are cooking prepare the chicken. Place the flour on a plate and toss the chicken in the flour so that the portions are lightly coated. Cover the base of a frying pan with a thin layer of oil and heat it well before frying the chicken portions. Brown

Makes 6 servings.

them on both sides and remove with a slotted spoon to drain on kitchen paper until needed. Frying the outside of the chicken before cooking in the casserole seals the juices and gives it a rich taste.

When the split peas are ready stir in the chopped onion, sliced garlic, chopped apple, lemon and orange juice. Pour this mixture into a medium-sized casserole. Lay the fried chicken portions on top. Flavour with a little black pepper, grated nutmeg and salt. Add enough water to enable the split peas to become a thick gravy during the rest of the cooking time. If it seems to be drying up add more water.

Place the lid on the casserole and cook slowly in a preheated oven gas mark 3/170°C/325°F oven for 1–1½ hours.

Each serving is 20g CHO. 310 kcals.

Serving suggestion: serve with plain rice and green runner beans.

SWEET AND SOUR CHICKEN

Authentic Chinese five spice powder does not include sugar or salt. It is a combination of aniseed-flavoured spices mixed with cinnamon, cloves and sometimes sharpened with black or Szechuan pepper.

Ginger root once cut can be stored by peeling and slicing into thin 0.3cm (⅛in) slices. Place the ginger slices in a solution of half water and half wine vinegar and store in a jar in the fridge for up to a year.

350g (12oz) chicken breast
pinch of Chinese five spice
  powder
1 large green pepper
2 tbs flaked almonds

Use a sharp knife to slice the chicken into small thin slices. Sprinkle with five spice powder. Cut the green pepper into 5cm (2in) long strips about 0.3cm (⅛in) wide and put on a plate ready for

100g (4oz) and 200g (7oz)
  fresh pineapple, without
  skin
50ml (2 fl oz) wine vinegar
1 tbs shoyu soy sauce
1 tsp arrowroot
4 spring onions
1 clove garlic
1 dessertspoon ginger root
3 tbs oil

Makes 4 portions.

cooking. Toast the flaked almonds under the grill until they are lightly browned.

Blend the 100g (4 oz) quantity of pineapple with the wine vinegar, soy sauce and arrowroot. Cut the 200g (7 oz) quantity of pineapple into 2.5cm (1in) chunks and put on a plate.

Cut the spring onions, garlic and ginger root into thin slices. Heat 1 tbs of oil in the wok or frying pan and stir these three ingredients in it for about a minute. Remove to a plate.

Pour 2 tbs oil into the wok, heat and toss the chicken slivers in it until they are just browned – about 3–5 minutes. Add the sliced green pepper and stir for about a minute. Add the cooked spring onion, garlic and ginger root, pineapple chunks and toasted almond flakes. Pour the pineapple and vinegar liquid over the top of the ingredients in the wok and stir for a few more minutes until it has thickened and then serve.

Each portion is 10g CHO. 275 kcals.

Serving suggestion: serve with rice and lightly boiled Chinese leaves.

FISH WITH SULTANAS AND PINE NUTS

When buying fish always make sure that it is really fresh. This is the most important contribution to the success of this recipe. The cod should be white and firm and should not have an unpleasant smell. The sauce ingredients are quickly put together. Try and obtain fresh dill, if it is not ridiculously expensive, because it adds a delicate complementary flavour.

For a spicier southern Mediterranean taste omit the nuts and add 1

*generous teaspoon of coarsely ground coriander seeds and as much
cayenne pepper as you like.*

4 portions cod fillet weighing
   about 675g (1lb 8oz)
freshly ground black pepper
sea salt (optional)
300g (11oz) onion
2 tbs oil
2 cloves garlic
500g (1lb 2oz) tomatoes
50g (2oz) sultanas
200ml (7 fl oz) white wine
25g (1oz) fresh dill
50g (2oz) pine nuts (if
   unavailable use flaked
   almonds)

Makes 4 servings.

Wash the fish and place in a wide
shallow baking dish. Sprinkle with a
little black pepper and salt.

Slice the onion and cook in the oil on a
low heat for 10 minutes until it is well
softened. Add the chopped garlic and
fry for a few more minutes. Peel the
tomatoes by pouring boiling water
over them and leaving them to stand
for 30 seconds; pierce the skin with a
sharp knife and peel. Chop the
tomatoes and add to the onions.
Simmer for a further 5 minutes. Add
the sultanas and wine and bring to the
boil.

Take off the heat and stir in the
chopped dill. Pour this sauce over the
fish. Sprinkle the pine nuts on top.
Bake in a preheated oven gas mark
4/180°C/350°F for 30—40 minutes.

Each serving is 20g CHO. 370 kcals.

Serving suggestion: serve with mashed
potatoes and lightly cooked
mange-tout.

PASSION FRUIT SALMON

*Salmon is highly recommended by nutritionists because it is high in
polyunsaturated oils. Fish oils have been shown to help fight heart
disease by lowering the cholesterol level in blood and preventing blood
clotting. Farmed salmon have become widely available in fish shops at
quite a reasonable price, but ideally try and find wild salmon. In their
natural state they swim thousands of miles before being caught and
this activity affects the taste of the fish.*

*The passion fruit available in this country are small and round and, for
the moment, expensive. The skin is blackish and when ripe becomes*

crinkled. Passion fruit are a good source of potassium and contain small quantities of other minerals.

4 salmon fillets
freshly ground black pepper
sea salt (optional)
juice of ½ lemon
12 ripe passion fruits
4 tbs apple juice, unsweetened

Makes 4 servings.

Wash the salmon fillets. Sprinkle a little pepper, salt and lemon juice over the fish and leave to stand for half an hour at least.

Grill or charcoal the salmon until the red flesh turns pink and it is lightly browned on both sides.

While the fish is grilling prepare the sauce. Scoop out the flesh and seeds of the passion fruits and put in a small pan together with the apple juice. Heat to just below boiling point and pour the sauce on the plates. Lay the salmon fillets on top.

Each serving is 5g CHO. 250 kcals.

Serving suggestion: serve with new boiled potatoes and a lettuce salad or chopped endive with a vinaigrette dressing.

SWEET AND SOUR TOFU

Tofu, or soya bean curd, has come to play an ever larger role in my cooking. Initially I used it for making cakes. When creamed in a liquidizer, food processor or food mill it has the texture of a very stiff cream, and is ideal for cheesecakes or any recipe that needs a creamy filling. It does not have an intrusive taste, but absorbs the flavours of whatever food it is mixed with. This led me to experiments with savoury dishes such as spinach pie. From that point I slowly began to use tofu by itself.

The basic texture is soft and fleshy, but by removing water from the tofu it can become firmer and is very satisfactory stir-fried or deep-fried in a crispy batter. The transition to using tofu should be gradual because it is an unusual food for the Western palate. It is very well known, however, in Japan, Indonesia, Korea, the Philippines,

Thailand, Vietnam, Taiwan and China; Indonesia has more than 11,000 tofu shops for a population of 130 million.

Tofu was discovered in about 164 B.C. by Lord Liu of Huai-nan, a Chinese scholar, philosopher, ruler and politician. As he was interested in Taoist meditation and friendly with Taoist students it is thought he undertook experiments with tofu to introduce variety into their simple meatless diet. Tofu is amazingly versatile and the way it is prepared differs not only between countries but also between regions. Tofu pouches, thin fermented slices of tofu, sun-dried salted strips of tofu, silken tofu and firm tofu all taste very different from each other.

Tofu is made by soaking soya beans and puréeing them with water. The purée is brought to the boil and strained through a cloth. This liquid is called soya milk. It is boiled and simmered again for some minutes, then removed from the heat and a small amount of solidifier is added. A popular solidifier is nigari which consists mainly of magnesium chloride and causes the milk to separate into curds and whey. The curds are ladled into tofu moulds lined with cheesecloth. They are covered with the cloth, a lid and weights are placed on top and the tofu is left to set quickly.

Purchasing a good quality brand is important. Firm tofu, vacuum-packed in a little water, is the most readily available version in health food shops, and it can be stored in the fridge for a couple of weeks. The firm consistency allows it to keep its form during cooking and makes it ideal for use in frying, stir-frying, sautéeing and crumbling. The brands sold in health food shops have a sell-by date as a guide to how long they can be stored in the fridge. Once opened any leftover tofu should be kept in a bowl of water in the fridge; the water should be changed every day.

Tofu is a low-fat, low-carbohydrate food containing almost as much protein as wheat. The fat content of firm tofu is about 5 grams per 100 grams and 80 per cent of these are unsaturated fats. The carbohydrate content is very low at 3g per 100g. Important minerals found in it are calcium, phosphorus, and iron — there is the same amount of iron in 100g tofu as in the equivalent weight of roast beef — plus small amounts of some of the B vitamins.

This is a very tasty dish which uses the stir-fry method of cooking. The actual cooking takes very little time, but all the vegetables have to be chopped beforehand. Use either a wok or a large cast-iron frying pan with 5–7.5cm (2–3in) high sides.

Nori is a seaweed and can be bought in flakes ready for use. Seaweeds are beneficial because they contain trace minerals and iodine.

Shoyu is the Japanese word for soy sauce. It is aged in wooden casks for two or three years before being used, and the long fermentation produces B vitamins and amino acids. It is usually made of soy beans, wholewheat, water and salt, although non-wheat-flour versions are available. Watch out for brands of soy sauce which use caramel colouring and have not been fermented. Read the ingredients label when purchasing. The well known health food manufacturers produce a shoyu soy sauce and it can also be purchased in specialist Japanese shops.

400g (9oz) firm tofu

Tofu dressing
2 level tsp arrowroot
3 tbs shoyu soy sauce
6 tbs lemon juice
2 tsp nori flakes

Vegetables
1 clove garlic
1 tsp chopped ginger root
1 green pepper
1 red pepper
150g (5oz) carrots
125g (4½oz) courgettes
100g (4oz) runner beans

Sauce
1 rounded tsp arrowroot
1½ tbs shoyu soy sauce
3 tbs lemon juice
150ml (5 fl oz) orange juice

4 tbs oil

Makes 4 servings.

Wrap the tofu in a clean tea towel with a heavy weight, such as a saucepan, placed on top and leave it to stand for 20–30 minutes. This will remove excess water without affecting the firmness of the tofu. Slice the tofu into pieces about 2.5 × 1cm (1 × ½in) and about 0.6cm (¼in) wide.

Prepare the dressing by combining the arrowroot with a little of the shoyu soy sauce, then add the remainder of the soy sauce, the lemon juice and the nori flakes. Toss the sliced tofu strips in this mixture and leave to stand while preparing the vegetables.

Prepare the vegetables: chop the peeled garlic into thin slices. Peel the ginger root and chop into very small pieces. Halve the green and red peppers and remove the bitter seeds from the inside. Cut into thin slices about 5cm (2in) long. Cut the carrots into thin strips. Cut across the courgettes with a sharp knife to make thin circles. Cut off the ends of the runner beans and cut in half.

Prepare the sauce by mixing the arrowroot with a little of the soy sauce and then add the remainder, the lemon and orange juice.

Heat a wok or heavy frying pan ready for cooking. Put 2 tbs oil in the bottom of the pan and when it is very hot but not smoking add the tofu coated with the dressing. Let it fry for 1 minute on each side, turning it over with a wooden spoon as it becomes browned on one side. Remove from the pan and put aside on a plate. Scrape the surface of the pan clean and put in 1 tbs oil. Heat the oil and add the chopped garlic and ginger root. Cook for about 1 minute until browned and then add to the plate containing the tofu.

Again spoon 1 tbs oil into the pan. Heat and stir fry the carrots and courgettes for 2–3 minutes. Stir in the green beans and red and green peppers and cook for a further 2 minutes.

Add the cooked tofu, garlic and ginger to the vegetables and pour the sauce over them. Toss all the ingredients in the sauce so that they are well covered. Serve immediately.

Each serving is 15g CHO. 260 kcals.

Serving suggestion: serve with long grain or the more delicate basmati brown rice and oriental pickles.

TOFU DUMPLINGS WITH CARROTS AND PRUNES

Grandmothers used to urge us to eat lots of carrots; they were meant to help us see in the dark. Carrots are certainly high in vitamin A, minerals and fibre and during the Second World War people were advised to eat them to improve their vision in the blackout. Herbalists prescribe large amounts of carrot juice in cancer treatment.

The addition of fennel adds a delicate aniseed flavour to this dish. Fennel is good for the digestion and is very enjoyable eaten raw and dipped in a little olive oil. The foliage is said to improve the memory and act as a tonic for the brain.

1 dessertspoon sesame oil
1 small onion
250–350ml (9–12 fl oz)
    vegetable stock or water plus
    vegetable stock cube
400g (14oz) carrots
1 medium fennel
50g (2oz) prunes, stoned

Dumplings
175g (6oz) firm tofu
1 egg
1 tbs oil
freshly ground black pepper
sea salt (optional)
100g (4oz) wholewheat flour

Makes 4 portions.

Heat the oil in a medium-sized casserole that can be used on top of the cooker as well as in the oven. Add the finely chopped onion and fry slowly until it is slightly browned. Pour in the vegetable stock.

Prepare the vegetables: chop the carrots so they are about 1.8cm (¾in) wide. Cut the fennel in half down the middle and slice across the bottom to give half-moon shapes. Chop the prunes. Add these three ingredients to the onions and water. Bring to the boil and then put, covered, in a preheated oven gas mark 3/170°C/325°F for about 1½ hours.

While the vegetables are slowly cooking prepare the dumplings. Blend or process the tofu, egg, oil, pepper and salt and add the flour to make a stiff dough. (If doing this by hand whisk the egg and add the tofu (which has been put through a food mill), oil, pepper, salt and flour.)

Fill a medium-sized saucepan with water and bring to the boil. Divide the dumpling mixture into 8 portions and roll into balls. Drop the balls into the boiling water. Leave to cook for about 5 minutes. In a few moments the dumplings will swell up and rise to the surface of the water. Remove with a slotted spoon.

Add the dumplings to the casserole after it has been in the oven for about ½ hour. Spoon the mixture over the dumplings so that they absorb the juices of the vegetables and fruit.

Each portion is 30g CHO. 220 kcals.

Serving suggestion: serve with wholewheat pasta and grated celeriac salad.

PEANUT AND SPROUTS STIR-FRY

The orange and red colours in this dish catch the eye instantly and it provides an interesting combination of textures. Like all stir-fry dishes this one requires the vegetables to be prepared before the cooking begins. The actual cooking takes only a matter of minutes then the dish is ready to be served straight away.

Sprouting beans and legumes are ideal vegetables to eat during the winter when the choice of fresh vegetables is limited. When the seeds sprout they have a high vitamin C content because they are in the process of germinating. You can sprout your own at home or buy packets of mixed sprouting beans at a health food shop.

75g (3oz) raw peanuts
1 medium orange weighing about 175–200g (6–7oz)
1 red pepper
150g (5oz) mixed sprouting beans and legumes (combination of aduki, brown lentils, green lentils or mung beans)
2 thick spring onions
1 clove garlic
pinch of cayenne pepper
½ tsp cumin seeds
2 tbs shoyu soy sauce

Makes 4 small servings for a starter or 2 servings for a main course.

Place the peanuts on a baking dish in a preheated oven gas mark 5/180°C/375°F until they are roasted but not burnt.

Peel the orange, removing all the pith, and cut into segments. Use a sharp knife to slice the segements crossways into triangles. Put on a plate ready for use.

Cut the red pepper in half and remove the seeds. Slice it into thin strips.

Rinse the sprouts with cold water so that they are ready for use.

Trim the end leaves of the spring onions and cut across the stem to make thin circles. Slice the garlic thinly and put on a plate together with the spring onions.

To stir-fry use either a wok or a heavy cast-iron frying pan. Heat the oil, then add the cayenne pepper, pounded cumin seeds (use ground cumin if the seeds are not available), sliced spring onion and garlic. Toss in the oil for 1 minute. Add the roasted peanuts. Stir in the red pepper strips and mixed sprouts. Lastly add the orange triangles and soy sauce. Stir for 1 minute until all the vegetables are coated with the sauce and the oranges are very slightly softened. Serve immediately.

1 small portion is 10g CHO. 170 kcals.

Serving suggestion: serve with pasta.

STUFFED PEPPERS

These can be eaten as an appetizing starter or as a main course. The stuffing contains no meat, but tastes satisfying enough to serve as a main dish. Every cook has their own particular way of cooking stuffed vegetables. I prefer mine cooked quickly in a medium oven so that the vegetable is still firm rather than sodden. When picking a pepper choose one that is firm and green all the way round.

This recipe is high in vitamin C. Raw green peppers have 100mg of vitamin C per 100g, which is two and a half times more vitamin C than oranges. Even when cooked they still contain 60mg of vitamin C.

Parsley, surprisingly for the many who regard it as only a decorative vegetable, is rather like a mini-multi-vitamin pill. Raw parsley is very high in vitamin C, containing 150mg per 100g. It is also high in potassium, calcium and iron with nearly as much carotene or vitamin A as carrots. It contains small amounts of the B vitamins and almost as much vitamin E as butter, but, of course, without the fat.

In parts of Iran the custom is to start a meal with a huge plate of fresh green herbs – far more beneficial than a synthetic vitamin pill. An English friend, who used to suffer from ulcerative colitis, found it 'mysteriously' disappeared during the years she lived and ate in Iran.

175g (6oz) brown rice
1 dessertspoon oil
30g (1oz generous) fresh parsley
30g (1 oz generous) fresh dill

Heat the oil in a medium-sized heavy saucepan and add the washed and drained rice. Leave to cook for about 1 minute, stirring the rice a little, then add enough hot water so that there is

60g (2½oz) dried apricots
50g (2oz) pine nuts (optional)
freshly ground black pepper
sea salt (optional)
6 green peppers, weighing
   about 700g (1lb 9oz)
500g (1lb 2oz) tomatoes
pinch of cayenne pepper
parsley for garnishing

Makes 6 Stuffed Peppers.

an extra inch (2.5cm) above the rice.
Bring to the boil, then place the lid on
the pan and simmer on a low heat.
When all the water has been absorbed
and the rice is soft small holes will
appear on the surface. Never stir the
rice while it is simmering or it will turn
into a sticky porridge.

Chop the parsley, dill and apricots with
a sharp knife, or put the ingredients in
an electric coffee grinder. (Grind the
herbs separately from the dried fruit.)
Combine well with the cooled rice,
together with the pine nuts and salt and
pepper to taste.

Wash the peppers. Cut the tops off and
scoop out the seeds. Fill them with the
rice mixture and then pack the peppers
into a flameproof casserole, standing
upright if possible.

To prepare the sauce, pour boiling
water over the tomatoes and leave
them to stand for 30 seconds. Pierce
the skin with a sharp knife and peel.
Either mash the tomatoes with a fork
or blend for just a second or two so
that not all the tomato is reduced to
liquid. Add the cayenne to the
tomatoes for a piquant peppery flavour
and pour them over the peppers.

Bring the contents of the casserole to
the boil on top of the cooker, then
cover with the lid and bake in a
preheated oven gas mark
4/170°C/350°F for 30–35 minutes.
Sprinkle with a little finely chopped
parsley before serving.

Each pepper is 35g CHO. 215 kcals.

Serving suggestion: serve with cooked chickpeas sprinkled with salt, black pepper and crushed garlic and a mixed vegetable salad.

LEEKS IN TOMATO AND LEMON SAUCE

Leeks, the national symbol of Wales, grow well in most parts of Britain. The Welsh, fighting under King Cadwallader, wore them in their hats to distinguish themselves from the invading Saxons when they defeated them in 640 A.D.

Leeks contain fair amounts of iron, calcium and potassium. The green outer leaves are rich in carotene – the vegetable precursor of vitamin A.

Brown lentils are small and cook quickly. They have a more delicate taste than red or green lentils and are used extensively in Middle Eastern cooking.

The sweet and sour combination of tomato and lemon juice sets off the leeks very well.

150g (5oz) brown rice
75g (3oz) brown lentils
1 dessertspoon olive oil
1 small onion weighing about
     125g (4½oz)
¼ tsp turmeric
½ tsp cumin
Freshly ground black pepper
sea salt
25g (1oz) parsley, chopped
     finely
550g (1lb 4oz) leeks
1 dessertspoon olive oil
275g (10oz) tomatoes

Sauce
juice of 1 lemon
1 dessertspoon apple juice
2 generous tsp of tomato purée
about 250ml (9 fl oz) water

Makes 6 portions.

Wash the rice and lentils separately, picking out any stones and rinsing well. Heat the oil in a heavy saucepan, add the chopped onions and cook until they are softened. Add the spices and cook for 1 minute. Add the lentils and coat them in the onions and spices. Cover with enough water so that there is 2.5cm (1in) above the lentils. Bring to the boil and simmer for 20 minutes. Add the rice and a little more water and cook for a further 15–20 minutes until all the water is absorbed. The rice and lentils do not need to be completely cooked at this stage. Stir in pepper and salt according to taste, and parsley.

Wash the leeks. Trim off the tops and outer leaves and cut off the bases. To separate the leaves, cut the leeks lengthways with a sharp knife and pull each individual leaf away. Open them out and wash well.

Put the olive oil on the base of a large heavy saucepan. Lay the chopped tomatoes on top. Cover these with a layer of leeks. Spoon half the rice and lentil filling over them. Cover with another layer of leeks. Spoon the remaining rice and lentils over the leeks. Cover finally with all the remaining leeks.

To make the sauce, mix the lemon juice and apple juice with the tomato purée and water and pour it over the leeks and rice. The liquid should almost cover the leeks. Add more water if the sauce seems to be disappearing too soon. Bring to the boil and simmer on a low heat for 45 minutes until the leeks are very soft and most of the liquid is absorbed.

Each portion is 35g CHO. 215 kcals.

Stuffed Leeks

This variation is for those with patience and dexterity: the leeks are stuffed rather than layered.

Cut the leeks as directed above so that the leaves are as complete as possible, and plunge them into a pan with a little boiling water. Cover with a lid and boil for a few minutes until the leaves are soft enough to fold. Remove and fill each one with 1–2 dessertspoons of filling and roll up lengthways. Do not place the filling too near the ends or it will spill out. Prepare the tomatoes and the sauce. Put a layer of broken leek leaves over the tomatoes before placing the stuffed leeks on top.

RICE PILAV

This harmonious combination of rice, vegetables and dried fruit can be eaten as a main course or served as a complement to fish, meat or egg.

300g (11oz) long grain or
  basmati brown rice
1 small onion
1 tbs oil
1 red pepper
1 green pepper
225g (8oz) tomatoes
25g (1oz) dried apricots, finely
  chopped
25g (1oz) raisins, finely
  chopped
400ml (14 fl oz) vegetable
  stock or water plus vegetable
  stock cube
flaked almonds for decoration

Makes 6 servings.

Wash the rice well and leave to soak in cold water until it is needed.

Chop the onion into small pieces and fry in the oil. Add the red and green peppers chopped into small squares. Pour boiling water over the tomatoes and leave them to stand for 30 seconds. Pierce the skins with a sharp knife and peel. Chop into small pieces and add to the peppers and onion. Simmer for 10 minutes.

Drain the water off the rice and add to the vegetables. Stir the rice around and leave to cook without a lid until much of the liquid is absorbed by the rice. Add the dried apricots, raisins and the hot vegetable stock and bring to the boil. Simmer until all the liquid has disappeared and the rice is very soft.

Toast the flaked almonds and when serving the rice sprinkle a few over each portion.

Each serving is 50g CHO. 260 kcals.

SPINACH SPECIAL

The spinach is flavoured with lemon juice, apple and garlic, making a delicious vegetable dish. Lemon juice is widely used in southern Mediterranean countries and the Middle East, and is a vital ingredient of such well-known dishes as hummus, tahini and avgolemono, the Greek egg and lemon soup. Herbalists use it for treating many ailments, including fevers.

More commonly known are the healing powers of garlic: macrobiotic nutritionists say garlic is a natural antibiotic. The last time I had serious flu with a fever I ate two crushed cloves with a cracker and cottage cheese to make it more palatable. The next morning the flu had improved, but I had to eat several sprigs of parsley to counteract the lingering garlic smell.

Spinach contains a sizeable 4mg iron per 100g and is the fabled source of Popeye's strength. However, a slipped decimal point in a nutritional chart misled the makers of the cartoon and sent Popeye's iron count soaring up to 40mg. What did Olive Oyl make of that?

450g (1lb) spinach
1 eating apple, grated
1 tbs lemon juice
1 crushed clove of garlic
sea salt (optional)
½ tsp hyssop (optional)

Wash the spinach leaves well. If the stems are not bruised cut off the ends and place them with the coarsely chopped leaves and the apple in a heavy saucepan. Cover with a lid and cook over a low heat. There is no need to add water: the slow cooking will draw out the liquid in the spinach. Simmer for 5 minutes until the leaves and stalks are softened.

Remove from the heat and add lemon juice, garlic, salt and hyssop.

Spinach is 30g CHO. 175 kcals.

Serving suggestion: serve with mushroom pie or roast lamb.

Sugar is not the first ingredient that comes to mind when you think of salads. But a surprisingly large number of dressings contain sweetener of some kind – and it is up to you to keep your salads as healthy as they look.

Salads are multi-purpose dishes. They can serve as a complete meal eaten with bread, as a side dish with a main course, or as an appetizer. One of their attractions is that they take little time to make – vegetables are washed, chopped, sliced or grated, and are eaten either as they are or with a dressing.

Commercial brands of mayonnaise and salad dressing include sugar, but there is no need to include it when you make your own. It does not appreciably benefit the taste nor do dressings require sugar to emulsify. Emulsions are the combining of one liquid with another which cannot evenly mix, such as oil with water.

The other type of sweetness associated with salads is when fresh fruit or dried fruit are combined with vegetables to give a sweet and savoury taste. This is a combination that I enjoy occasionally, but not every day.

Salads provide great opportunities for experimentation. By judiciously adding grated or chopped apple, a handful of raisins, chopped dried apricots, chunks of pineapple or mango you can achieve very unusual effects. If you have to watch your calorie or carbohydrate intake, remember to use fruit sparingly.

Salad dressings

The NACNE (National Advisory Committee on Nutrition Education) report recommended fat consumption to be reduced to 34 per cent of total intake for everyone over the age of five. Dressings made with oil provide a useful source of fat for young children, particularly if the family follows a low-fat regime. My own under-five-year-old has a saucer of dressing every day made from olive oil with a splash of vinegar, in which she dips raw carrots, cucumber and green beans plus various parts of herself.

Oils used in dressings

Olive oil, which is high in mono-unsaturated fats, has been used for thousands of years in Mediterranean countries and is credited with relieving constipation and, in some cases, dissolving gallstones. The latest research suggests that it also helps in combating heart disease.

Sesame seed oil is high in polyunsaturated fats and contains 41g per 100ml linoleic acid, an essential fatty acid. The human body cannot manufacture it itself and it is important that it is included in the diet. Severe lack of linoleic acid leads to skin conditions, poor wound healing and anaemia.

Sesame seed oil is recommended by macrobiotics, while ayurvedics advocate rubbing it into your scalp. I prefer mine in salads.

Sunflower seed oil contains over half its oil in the form of poly-unsaturates and a liberal dose of linoleic acid (58g per 100ml); the amount depends upon whether it is grown in a hot or cold climate.

Safflower oil contains three quarters of its oil in polyunsaturated form and contains 73g linoleic acid per 100ml.

Check the label to see if the oil has been cold pressed rather than produced at a high temperature; heat affects the composition of the oil. Cold-pressed oils have to be stored carefully in a cool, dark place or in the fridge. They are rich in nutrients and react with light and heat, oxydize with the air, and can become rancid if stored too long. Oils pressed under great heat remain more stable, but at the expense of their nutritional benefit.

No dressing will compensate for old, tired vegetables so always use the freshest available.

MAYONNAISE

The French invented mayonnaise and ought to know how to make it. Why then do English, American, German and other cookery writers insist on polluting this condiment with sugar? It may be that early cookery writers were subtly or unsubtly influenced by the sugar industry and the low price of sugar in the UK and the US; this dependence on sugar may also have something to do with the general tastelessness of the Anglo-American cuisine.

Eggs, the all-important ingredient in mayonnaise, contain such emulsifiers as lecithin and cholesterol which help to stabilize the mayonnaise emulsion. Use eggs that are at room temperature rather than straight from the fridge as this will make it easier for the mayonnaise to emulsify.

2 egg yolks
1 tsp mustard
freshly ground black pepper
sea salt (optional)
150ml (5 fl oz) olive oil
150ml (5 fl oz) sunflower oil
1 tbs white wine vinegar or 1
   tbs lemon juice

Put the egg yolks, mustard, pepper and salt in a bowl. Using either a whisk, hand held or electric, or even a fork, whisk the egg yolks lightly then add the oil drop by drop to begin with, whisking all the time. Gradually the mayonnaise will thicken. At this point you can start adding a little more oil each time, but keep on beating. The amount of oil you use may differ slightly each time you make this recipe so when the mayonnaise has the desired thickness add the vinegar or lemon juice to give a sharp taste. Finally add a few more drops of oil.

The mayonnaise can be stored in a glass jar in the fridge.

Mayonnaise is neg CHO. 2920 kcals.

VINAIGRETTE OR FRENCH DRESSING

freshly ground black pepper
sea salt (optional)
6 tbs oil
1½–2 tbs wine or cider
  vinegar

Season the oil then whisk in the vinegar until the texture thickens. If you are making a large quantity shake the dressing in a half-filled closed jar until it is ready. Store in the jar in the fridge.

Dressing is neg CHO. 825 kcals.

Variations:
– Add ½–1 tsp mustard.
– Add fresh or dried herbs to the dressing.

MEDITERRANEAN DRESSING

6 tbs oil
3 tbs lemon juice, freshly
  squeezed
freshly ground black pepper
sea salt (optional)

Combine all the ingredients and whisk well. Chopped parsley goes well mixed with this dressing.

Dressing is neg CHO. 810 kcals.

PEANUT-CARROT SALAD

75g (3oz) raw peanuts
1 tbs sesame seeds, toasted
300g (11oz) carrots, grated
25g (1oz) sultanas
1 quantity Mediterranean
  Dressing (see above)

Makes 4 servings.

Roast the peanuts on a shallow dish in a preheated oven gas mark 4/180°C/350°F. Leave to cool. Toast the sesame seeds for a minute or two under the grill so that they are lightly browned.

Combine the carrots, roasted peanuts, sultanas and toasted sesame seeds. Pour the Mediterranean Dressing over the salad and leave to stand for an hour before serving.

Each serving is 10g CHO. 255 kcals.

CHICORY SALAD

One sunny weekend in February I visited a friend and her daughter in Paris. She made this superb salad using green tarragon mustard in the dressing. The French call chicory endive *and* endive *chicory. It took us some time to agree on what we were eating.*

4 chicory heads
1 medium eating apple
75–100g (3–4oz) walnuts
2 sticks of celery
Vinaigrette Dressing (see p. 142)
½–1 tsp mustard (use tarragon mustard if available)

Makes 4 servings.

Wash the chicory heads. Chop them into slices and place in a salad bowl. Wash and chop the apple. Chop the walnuts into halves or quarters and add to the bowl, together with the chopped celery.

Add the mustard to the Vinaigrette Dressing. Quickly toss the salad in this before the chicory and apples turn brown.

Each serving is 5g CHO. 345 kcals.

ORANGE AND CHINESE CABBAGE SALAD

The sesame seed oil gives a very distinctive nutty flavour to this salad.

1 small Chinese cabbage weighing about 500g (1lb 2oz)
1 small orange weighing about 150g (5oz)
grated peel of half an orange

Dressing
6 tbs sesame seed oil
3 tbs orange juice
2 tbs lemon juice
freshly ground black pepper
sea salt (optional)

Makes 4 servings.

Wash the Chinese cabbage and slice into shreds. Peel the orange carefully. Put half the rind to one side for grating. Remove all the pith from the outside of the orange and cut the flesh into thin slices. Add to the cabbage.

Combine the dressing ingredients and pour over the salad. Toss, and garnish with the grated orange rind.

Each serving is 10g CHO. 245 kcals.

Chutneys, relishes, spiced fruit and vegetables are a piquant and colourful accompaniment to plain dishes such as meat, fish or pies. Chutneys are an English version of the Indian *catni* brought over in the days of the Empire. The Indians do not invariably sweeten their chutney although sugar was available to them 1000 years before it came to Europe. Why then have British cookery writers from the 19th century to the present day found it impossible to make chutney without sugar? Even in the Middle East, famous for its syrupy cakes and early use of sugar, fruit and vegetables are pickled in vinegar and salt without added sweetener. I have a wonderful recipe for fenugreek chutney (see page 151) given to me by a friend from India, who would be amazed at the suggestion of adding sugar.

Because Western palates have become accustomed to sweetened condiments, most of the recipes in this section are sweetened despite the logical and ethnic indication to the contrary. One, however, is made with no sweetener at all and uses lemon juice instead of vinegar.

The fruit and vegetables in pickles and chutneys are not preserved by the sugar, but by the acid in the vinegar which discourages the growth of bacteria. Another method of preservation is to use a brine solution of salt and water strong enough to prevent the growth of unwanted bacteria, but weak enough to allow the growth of bacteria that produce lactic acid. This method is used in many Chinese and Japanese fermented pickles.

A few tips for making chutneys and pickles:

– Use a stainless steel saucepan because the vinegar can interact in a harmful way with metals such as iron or copper.
– Choose fresh unblemished fruit that is not overripe.
– Jars should be air-tight.
– Lids should not be made of uncovered metal.

Commercially produced sugar-free chutneys and ketchups are available in health food shops and specialist Indian grocers. Some of the firms which make these, however, are still small and do not have nationwide distribution.

PINEAPPLE DATE CHUTNEY

Pickling spice is a mixture of spices such as coriander, mustard seeds, peppercorns, allspice, bay leaves, ginger and chillies. It can be bought ready mixed.

When removing the skin from the pineapple make sure that no sharp spiky bits are left on the fruit.

600g (1lb 5oz) fresh pineapple, without skin
175g (6oz) onions, peeled
350g (12oz) eating apples
40g (1½oz) dried dates
75g (3oz) raisins
225ml (8 fl oz) cider vinegar
1 tsp pickling spice

Slice the pineapple into small chunky pieces and put on one side.

Put the finely chopped onions, apples, dates and raisins in a saucepan and cover with the vinegar. Tie the pickling spice in a muslin bag and add to the saucepan. Simmer on a low heat for half an hour. You might need to add a little water from time to time so that there is enough moisture for the fruit and onion to cook in.

Add the chopped pineapple and continue simmering for a further 45 minutes, always making sure there is enough liquid in the pan. Remove the pickling spice. Pour the chutney into a glass jar and seal. Store in the fridge.

Chutney is 180g CHO. 740 kcals.

FRENCH-CANADIAN CHUTNEY

The gracious mother of an old friend of mine who looks as if she has spent her entire life sipping tea out of bone china cups has actually spent most of her life in exotic locations from the Caribbean to the Seychelles. After the Second World War she lived for a couple of years on a chicken farm near the French-Canadian town of Cherbourg. The local radio station used to announce each morning the names of the inhabitants who had died the night before, then proceed to give traditional French-Canadian recipes. This is one that she saved for me.

700g (1lb 9oz) tomatoes
125g (4½oz) ripe plums, chopped

Pour boiling water over the tomatoes and leave them to stand for 30 seconds.

275g (10oz) peaches, chopped
300g (11oz) pears, chopped
225g (8oz) onions, chopped
  very small
1 large green pepper
75ml (3 fl oz) cider vinegar
75ml (3 fl oz) apple juice,
  unsweetened
50g (2oz) raisins
½ tsp sea salt
1 tsp pickling spice

Pierce the skins with a sharp knife and peel. Chop into small pieces and put in a medium-sized stainless steel saucepan. Unless the skins of the plums, peaches and pears seem to be particularly thick they do not need removing as they become soft during cooking. Chop the onion into very small pieces. Cut the pepper open and remove all the seeds. Chop into small slices. Add all these ingredients to the pan.

Add the vinegar, apple juice, raisins and salt. Tie the pickling spice in a muslin bag and add to the pan.

Bring quickly to the boil and then simmer on a low heat for 1½–2 hours. Stir frequently as this chutney can catch easily. If there appears to be too much liquid at the end of the cooking time remove most of the fruit and vegetables and boil the liquid quickly so that it is reduced.

The chutney can be bottled directly in glass jars or it can be puréed if you prefer a smoother texture. Store in the fridge.

Chutney is 130g CHO. 565 kcals.

MANGO CHUTNEY

1 small clove garlic
pinch of cayenne
¼ tsp coriander seeds
¼ tsp ginger
¼ tsp cumin seeds
¼ tsp turmeric
150ml (5 fl oz) cider vinegar

Squeeze the garlic through a garlic press. If the spices are in seed form pound them with a pestle and mortar or grind them in a small electric coffee grinder. Combine all the ingredients except the mangoes in a heavy stainless steel saucepan. Bring to the boil and

150ml (5 fl oz) unsweetened
   apple juice
50g (2oz) raisins
2 ripe mangoes weighing about
   550–600g (1lb 4oz–1lb
   5oz)

then cook on a low heat for 15
minutes.

Peel the mangoes and cut them into
small chunks. Add to the simmering
spiced and sweetened vinegar and cook
on a low heat for a further 15 minutes
until the mango is cooked but still firm.
Pour into glass jars. Store in the fridge.

Chutney is 110g CHO. 440 kcals.

FENUGREEK CHUTNEY

*This Indian chutney is different from the sweet condiment we are used
to. The small yellow crushed fenugreek seeds enhance vegetable and
meat dishes. They can also be made into a calming drink by simmering
in water – the liquid is said to strengthen and soothe the intestines and
stomach.*

1 tbs fenugreek seeds
1 large clove garlic
1 tsp root ginger
100g (4oz) fresh coriander
   leaves (roughly half a large
   bunch)
juice of 2 lemons
sea salt
cayenne pepper (optional)

Leave the fenugreek seeds to soak in a
little water overnight. They will swell
up.

Peel the garlic clove and crush. Chop
the ginger root. Remove the coriander
leaves from the stalks. Combine these
ingredients with the lemon juice and
fenugreek seeds in the liquidizer or
food processor and blend to make a
paste. Add salt according to taste. If
you like a hot chutney add a little of the
cayenne pepper.

Chutney is 10g CHO. 95 kcals.

SPICED MELON AND PEARS

*Make this chutney when melons are in season towards the end of the
summer. The ones that are sold in the winter do not have such a full
sweet taste and will not contribute much in the way of flavour.*

Although melons are over 90 per cent water they still contain a number of minerals and vitamins such as potassium, magnesium and vitamin C, a trace of E and a few of the B vitamins.

450g (1lb) ripe pears, finely chopped
50g (2oz) dried dates, finely chopped
150ml (5fl oz) white wine vinegar
1 tsp pickling spice
1 large honeydew or galia melon weighing about 1kg (2lb 7oz)

Put the pears and dates in a stainless steel saucepan with the vinegar. Add pickling spice wrapped in a muslin bag. Simmer on a low light until the pears and dates are very soft. This takes about an hour and you may need to add a little extra water while they are simmering. When most of the liquid is absorbed remove the pickling spice and add the melon cut into chunks and cook for 15–20 minutes. Pour into a glass jar. Store in the fridge when cold.

Spiced melon is 100g CHO. 390 kcals.

9 PASTRY, PIES AND TARTS

Pastry is an important starting-point for many kinds of dish. It can serve as a container for a sweet filling or a savoury one, for a main course or a dessert. When pastry is made with wholewheat grains it provides a source of high fibre which contains all the original nutrients. This section includes ten different types of recipe for pastry. You will probably find a favourite variety which suits you and use it again and again. Pastry can be made from many different combinations: wheat flour and margarine, wheat flour and yeast, barley flour and oil, ground nuts and flour, ground nuts and seeds, wheat flour and egg, wheat flour and yogurt. Some types of pastry are thin and crisp, others thick and spongy. Choose the one that is most useful for your purpose.

Fillings abound in infinite variety and I have given no more than a taste in the pages that follow. Different countries across the world have their own special fillings and pastries. The Greeks and the Arabs use the paper thin filo (phyllo) pastry sheets made with flour and water which have oil or melted butter painted on between them. Chopped nuts are set between the multiple sheets and drenched in a scented syrup. The French *mille feuilles* is a supreme example of puff pastry sandwiched with cream; the Austrians are well-known for their yeast pastries filled with cinnamon and cheese; while the Americans talk about blueberry pie and apple pie in an almost mystical way.

In this book, fresh fruit, dried fruit, beans, vegetables, nuts and spices are all called upon to work their different magic. Any of your favourite fillings can easily be matched with a high-fibre pastry. Carbohydrate and calorie values are given after each pastry recipe and can be simply calculated for each slice. If, for example, you wanted to combine the rough puff pastry which has 100g CHO with your filling of say 60g CHO, the total carbohydrate count would be 160g CHO. If you mark off 16 slices on the pastry each individual slice will equal 10g CHO.

Pastry presents many opportunities for making superb dishes from limited ingredients, but some cooks are unable to exploit this potential because of a pastry phobia. The condition may sound bizarre, but my experience with cookery students has shown there exists a definite psychological block in many minds about making pastry. People are terrified at the thought of it and approach it convinced that it will not work out right. I have even met some home economics teachers and one or two cookery writers who began their careers with pastry anxiety. The main step on the path to successful pastry is to shake off crippling thoughts about not succeeding and to believe that anyone can do it. After that, all that remains is to make the pastry.

The main skills involved are lightness of touch both in binding the dough together and in rolling it out. The important thing to avoid is overworking the pastry. Nervously fiddling with the ingredients makes matters worse instead of better. When you pull the flour, fat and water together into a dough with your hands use large decisive movements, cup your hand so that it is like a massive spoon. Some of my students found this stage physically hard, but we discovered that this can be the result of a lack of flexibility at the wrist. Tilting the bowl to an angle brings the ingredients closer to hand.

Using a food processor or a food mixer does not solve the problem of pastry phobia. It merely puts a wall between yourself and the ingredients. If you use your hands when necessary and allow yourself to respond to the feel and touch of what you are handling, and use your eye to gauge the consistency, you will find that pastry making is a pleasurable experience. And once you are confident about what you are doing it will become a very quick process. It takes no more than a couple of minutes after the ingredients have been weighed.

Anything that goes wrong can be rectified. If you add too much liquid and a soggy dough results, add a little extra flour. If the dough feels too dry, you may need a little extra water or fat. Making pastry can be influenced by a number of factors such as how finely the flour is milled, the amount of water in the margarine, the size of the eggs, remembering to use cold water for mixing and bowls that are not hot from washing up. If it does not go exactly as it should there is no need to throw your hands up in despair, but work out for yourself what the problem is and solve it. If the situation is irredeemable you can always start again.

Making pastry is rather like learning to swim. At first you are very aware of every movement your legs are making until, with experience, the movements become automatic. Like swimming it is probably best to learn young and so avoid having to think about whether you can or cannot do it. The more you practise the better you become. When I teach my students pastry making I literally throw them in at the deep end with something really difficult like Rough Puff Pastry. Once they have mastered this they feel confident about all pastry.

Pastry keeps for 2–3 days. If the filling is a moist one it will keep longer than the drier fillings. One of the attractions of using pastry is that it is possible to prepare it for the next day if it is wrapped in greaseproof paper and foil and left overnight in the fridge. Remove half an hour before rolling out.

All pastry freezes well. It can be frozen prior to cooking or when baked. Raw pastry keeps for up to one month, cooked pastry for up to three months. Before freezing write a label with details of what the pastry is and if necessary the carbohydrate and calorie content.

Baking tins do not need to be greased unless the recipe specifies this. All the pastry recipes contain some fat or oil and this usually eliminates the need for greasing.

HASTY PASTRY

This is a very quick method of making a crisp wholewheat pastry which is very suitable for tarts or pie crusts. It has a very low fat content.

175g (6oz) wholewheat flour
2 tbs oil
1 tbs lemon juice
100–125ml (4–4½ fl oz)
  cold water

Put the flour in a mixing bowl. Stir in the oil and lemon juice with a knife or wooden spoon. Add just enough water to make thick crumbs which you can work into a soft pastry dough with your hands. This pastry should not be overworked, so do not knead it more than you have to.

Chill in the fridge for half an hour. When rolling it out, sprinkle the board or work top lightly with flour.

Total pastry is 115g CHO. 825 kcals.

YOGURT PASTRY

This is a crisp light pastry which uses very little oil. It has a cakier texture than the other pastries in this section. It should not be baked too long as it can burn easily.

A small 150ml pot of yogurt contains 270mg of calcium, 360mg of potassium, 1mg of zinc and traces of iron and copper. Apart from a high nutritive value live yogurt contains two bacteria, Streptococcus thermophilus and Lactobacillus bulgarius, both of which are beneficial for digestion of food in the intestine and in consequence for general well-being. These bacteria are only active in live yogurt, so read yogurt labels carefully when shopping: unless specified most are pasteurized. Bulgarian peasants used to consume large amounts of yogurt and their longevity has been linked to this.

150g (5oz) wholemeal flour
50g (2oz) soya flour
¼ tsp bicarbonate of soda
2 tbs oil
150ml (5 fl oz) low-fat natural
  yogurt

Combine the flours and bicarbonate of soda in a mixing bowl. Stir in the oil and bind with the yogurt. Work the pastry a little with your hands so that it becomes a light spongy dough. Chill in the fridge for half an hour before use if it has to be rolled thin. Otherwise it can be used immediately.

Total pastry is 120g CHO. 1000 kcals.

SHORT CUT STRUDEL

Crispy thin layers of strudel are a delight to eat and an art to make. It is fascinating to watch experienced pastry cooks working on a strudel pastry using the knuckles of their hands to stretch the dough to a tissue paper consistency. These are skills that most of us working away in our kitchens hoping to achieve maximum results with minimum effort cannot hope to emulate. Nevertheless, we can still make a delicious strudel-type pastry.

Using wholewheat flour in a strudel recipe affects the texture of the pastry and if not worked in the right way it turns out like cardboard. This recipe will not give a pastry as thin as the shop-made kind, but is a speedy route for the average cook to get a strudel-like result. It is fairly quick as the pastry is left to stand for only a short time. Adding oil while rolling it out increases elasticity in the pastry. A delectable strudel can be made without requiring you to learn the skills of generations of Viennese strudel makers!

1 egg, lightly beaten
100g (4oz) wholewheat flour
3 dessertspoons oil

Combine the egg with the flour and 1 dessertspoon oil in a mixing bowl to make a soft dough. Cover with a thick cloth and leave to stand for 15 minutes.

Roll out the pastry on a clean tablecloth. This stops the pastry sticking and removes any restrictions imposed by the size of the pastry board. Sprinkle the tablecloth with a little flour and roll out the pastry in an oblong shape until it will roll no further. Sprinkle 1 dessertspoon of oil evenly over the surface — rub it lightly across with a pastry brush or your fingers. Now roll out the pastry again, sprinkling a little flour on top so that it does not stick to the rolling pin. (Use a rolling pin without ornate end pieces because they make a ridge on thinly rolled pastry.) The pastry will become thinner.

Lightly sprinkle the remaining dessertspoon of oil over the pastry, again spreading it across the surface. Sprinkle with a little flour and roll out thinly. The pastry should be roughly about 41cm (16in) square and almost paper thin.

Before filling the pastry lift it on to the baking tray either with your hand or by lifting the tablecloth.

Total strudel pastry is 65g CHO. 480 kcals.

ROUGH PUFF PASTRY

This is a low fat high-fibre version of classic rough puff pastry. The wholewheat flour inhibits the creation of multiple layers of pastry which puff up, but the basic method of layers of fat separating the folds of pastry remains and this creates a supple, easy-to-handle pastry that can be rolled very thin and gives a light crisp result. I find it an invaluable part of my pastry repertoire.

150g (5oz) wholewheat flour
50g (2oz) margarine or butter
50–75ml (2–3 fl oz) cold
   water

Put the flour in a mixing bowl with the margarine. Cut the margarine into chunks while it is in the flour. Add enough water to bind the flour and margarine into a soft dough.

Place the dough on a lightly floured board or work top and roll it out in a long narrow rectangle about 25 × 10cm (10 × 4in). At this stage lumps of the fat will be visible in the dough. Mark the dough off lightly into three equal sections. Turn the top section over the middle one and fold the third over them both (see diagram opposite).

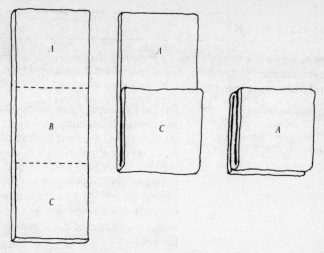

1. Roll out a long narrow rectangle and mark off three equal sections.
2. Fold C over B.
3. Fold A over B and C.

Give the pastry a quarter-turn and repeat this process of rolling out, folding into three and giving a quarter-turn three more times. After completing this the margarine will have been rolled into the flour and the pastry will have an even texture.

Wrap in greaseproof paper and chill in the fridge for 30 minutes. Roll out once more into a rectangle and fold into three before using.

Total pastry is 100g CHO. 850 kcals.

BARLEY PASTRY

Barley flour gives a heavier texture to pastry than wheat flour, but has a nuttier flavour. Barley flour, like wholewheat flour, should be ground from the whole grain.

150g (5oz) barley flour
50ml (2 fl oz) oil
50–75ml (2–3 fl oz) cold
 water

Put the flour into a mixing bowl and pour in the oil, mixing well to form thick crumbs. Bind with as much water as is necessary to make a soft dough. Add the water little by little, and only use as much as you need to make a pliable dough. This pastry can be quite crumbly when rolled out and it is sometimes easier to pat it into shape in the tin.

Total pastry is 110g CHO. 975 kcals.

CAROB PASTRY

The dark brown hue of carob pastry makes it unusual and attractive. It tastes best if combined with fruit.

150g (5oz) wholewheat flour
25g (1oz) carob powder
50g (2oz) margarine or butter
50–100ml (2–4 fl oz) cold
 water

Combine the flour and carob powder in a mixing bowl and add the margarine. Cut the margarine into small pieces and rub the mixture into fine crumbs using the tips of your fingers. Add the water little by little to make a firm dough. Wrap in greaseproof paper and leave to chill in the fridge for half an hour before using.

Total pastry is 110g CHO. 895 kcals.

ALMOND PASTRY

The combination of nuts and flour makes this a very rich pastry and one to be kept for special occasions. Too many almonds sit heavily on your stomach although a healthy octogenarian of my acquaintance assures me that a few well-chewed almonds without the outer skin give immediate relief from heartburn.

150g (5oz) wholewheat flour
100g (4oz) ground almonds
3 tbs oil
1 egg, lightly beaten
25ml (1 fl oz) water

Combine the flour and ground almonds in a mixing bowl. Stir in the oil and egg. Add just enough water to make a pliable dough. Cover and leave in the fridge for one hour before using.

105g CHO. 1520 kcals.

HAZELNUT PASTRY

Hazelnuts were used in many of the cake and confectionery recipes made in late 19th century Vienna, the melting pot of Europe's south-eastern quarter whose inhabitants arrived from the farthest reaches of the Austro-Hungarian Empire.

100g (4oz) wholewheat flour
100g (4oz) ground hazelnuts
  (not roasted)
25g (1oz) butter
1 egg, lightly beaten

Combine the flour and ground hazelnuts in a mixing bowl. Rub in the butter, using your fingertips to make thick crumbs. Add the egg to the mixture to make a dough.

Cover with greaseproof paper and chill in the fridge for 45 minutes before using.

Total pastry is 75g CHO. 955 kcals.

SWEET SEED PASTRY

This is a useful pastry for anyone who needs to avoid flours milled from grains. It is made entirely from ground seeds, nuts and dried figs. All the ingredients in this recipe make their own special nutritional

*contribution – the seeds in particular are packed with minerals.
Pumpkin seeds are rich in iron and contain 15mg per 100g, an
amazing 32.5g of protein plus the additional bonus of linoleic
unsaturated fatty acids; the sesame seeds are high in calcium
containing an impressive 115mg per 100g and are also rich in lecithin;
the sunflower seeds provide a calcium booster plus a good supply of
magnesium and thiamin, one of the B vitamins. Almonds provide a
general mineral pick-me-up including a king-size dose of vitamin E.
The figs which bind the seeds and nuts together are high in potassium
and fibre.*

1 tbs boiling water
50g (2oz) dried figs, chopped
25g (1oz) sunflower seeds
25g (1oz) pumpkin seeds
25g (1oz) sesame seeds, toasted
25g (1oz) ground almonds (or
    ground hazelnuts)
½ tsp mixed spice (cinnamon,
    cloves and nutmeg)

Pour the boiling water over the figs and
leave to stand for 10 minutes. Then
purée using an electric coffee grinder (it
is particularly suitable for such small
amounts).

Grind all the seeds to powder.
Combine them in a mixing bowl with
the ground almonds and the mixed
spice. Bind with the fig paste to make a
dough. Sometimes it is necessary to add
a little extra water to make the crumbs
go into a dough. Chill in the fridge for
half an hour before using.

Total pastry is 40g CHO. 675 kcals.

YEAST PASTRY

*Yeast pastry is made much faster with vitamin C (ascorbic acid) and
yeast than with sugar. The vitamin C removes one of the proving
stages in the traditional approach and speeds up the rate at which the
dough rises. The first step is to mix the ingredients and knead. The
dough is left for a short space of time to rise, long enough to prepare
the filling and the baking tray. The second step is to roll out the pastry,
fill it and leave it to stand for about 15 minutes before baking.*

*The nutritional advantage of using yeast pastry is that the leavening
process helps the breakdown of phytates which are found in wheat
fibre. Phytates can limit the absorption of minerals such as calcium,
iron and zinc by the body. If your diet is made up of yeast-based bread
with occasional high-fibre biscuits or cakes this will not have any*

drastic effect, but if you suffer from a deficiency of these minerals then you should avoid unleavened bread and bran-based foods until the shortage has been made up. Many of the fillings in this section can be switched around and used with the yeast pastry.

If you cannot find a 25mg tablet of vitamin C buy the 50mg size and cut it in half. If you halve this recipe use 15g (½oz) fresh yeast.

400g (14oz) fine milled
  wholewheat flour
25g (1oz) fresh yeast
25mg tablet of vitamin C
75g (3oz) butter or margarine
200ml (7 fl oz) water
1 egg

Put the flour into a large mixing bowl. Crumble the yeast and crush the vitamin C tablet into a small bowl. Melt the butter in the water in a small saucepan until the temperature becomes lukewarm. Add a little of this liquid to the yeast and vitamin C to make a creamy mixture. Add the rest of the liquid and stir into the flour. Lightly whisk the egg and add. Work the mixture into a dough with your hands and turn on to a lightly floured board or work top and knead for about 5 minutes, or for about 1 minute in a food processor. Return to the bowl and cover the top with cling film and a clean teatowel and leave to rest for 10 minutes. The pastry is then ready to be rolled out thinly and used.

Total Yeast Pastry is 265g CHO. 1915 kcals.

APPLE AND PEAR PIE WITH CRUMBLE TOPPING

½ quantity of Hasty Pastry
  (see page 158)

Filling
350g (12oz) eating apples
350g (12oz) pears
100ml (4 fl oz) water
25g (1oz) dried apricots,
  chopped

Roll out the pastry thinly and line a 23cm (9in) diameter pie dish. Bake blind for 10 minutes in a preheated oven gas mark 5/190°C/375°F until a pale biscuit colour.

While the pastry is baking prepare the filling. Slice the apples and pears into a saucepan together with the water and apricots. Bring to the boil and simmer

Crumble topping
50g (2oz) oat bran and germ
50g (2oz) chopped almonds
2 tbs apple juice, unsweetened

Makes 16 small servings.

for 10 minutes. When the pastry is cooked pour the fruit and its juice into the pastry-lined dish.

Prepare the topping: combine the oat bran and germ and almonds with the apple juice to make thick crumbs. Sprinkle this over the top of the fruit.

Bake in a preheated oven gas mark 4/180°C/350°F for 15–20 minutes until it is browned all over.

Each serving is 10g CHO. 75 kcals.

APPLE AND ADUKI PIE

This may sound an improbable combination, but the result is very pleasant tasting and light on the stomach. It is a modified version of a macrobiotic recipe – the original would have rather more aduki beans and omit the few sultanas. The aduki bean and the juice it is cooked in is held in particularly high regard by macrobiotics; it is meant to be beneficial for the kidneys and less gaseous than other beans. The Japanese, whose cuisine seems to be the basis for many macrobiotic dishes, are also fond of this bean and use it for sweets and jelly, as well as cooked with rice. According to Lesley Downer, a writer on Japanese cuisine, aduki bean paste, which forms the basis for many of these dishes, used to be made unsweetened, with just a pinch of salt to bring out the natural sweetness. Today the bean paste is sweetened with sugar.

Aduki beans contain about 25 per cent protein, some iron, calcium and some of the B vitamins.

Filling
100g (4oz) dried aduki beans
25g (1oz) sultanas
350g (12oz) eating apples
1 tsp cinnamon

1 quantity of Hasty Pastry (see page 158)

Prepare the filling. Soak the aduki beans in cold water overnight. Cook in a pressure cooker or saucepan until they are soft and moist. Before using in the pie boil away most of the cooking liquid, but not so much that the beans dry out. Soak the sultanas in a little water for 30 minutes.

Makes 10 large servings.

Roll out the pastry thinly. Use a 20cm (8in) diameter pie dish to cut out 2 circles. The pastry base should be slightly larger than the top so that it covers the sides of the dish.

Pour the cold aduki beans evenly over the bottom of the pie. Place the sultanas at equal intervals over the beans and sprinkle the surface with ½ tsp cinnamon. Slice the apples thinly over the surface of the beans. Sprinkle with the remaining ½ tsp cinnamon. Lay the pastry lid on top and pinch the sides of the pie together.

Bake in a preheated oven gas mark 5/190°C/375°F for 30–40 minutes until the pastry is evenly browned.

Each serving is 20g CHO. 130 kcals.

MANGO PIE DELIGHT

This recipe is based on the traditional English approach to pies, of combining a fruit filling on a pastry base with a layer of meringue on top, but by using an exotic fruit the mundane is transformed into something quite mouthwatering. The puréed fruit looks like a creamy custard, waiting to ooze out with each mouthful.

½ quantity of Yogurt Pastry (see page 158)

Filling
1 small mango (weighing about 300g/11oz)
1 eating apple (weighing about 125g/4½oz)
2 tbs apple juice
1 egg yolk

Topping
1 egg white
25g (1oz) ripe banana, peeled

Roll out the pastry and line a (17.5cm/7in) baking dish. Bake blind for 10 minutes in a preheated oven gas mark 5/190°C/375°F.

While the pastry is baking prepare the filling. Peel the mango and slice the flesh. Slice the apple into the blender and add the mango and apple juice. Blend to make a thick purée. Add the egg yolk and blend for a few seconds more. Pour into the partly cooked pastry case and bake for 12–15

Makes 6 large slices.

minutes in a slightly cooler oven gas mark 4/180°C/350°F.

While the fruit filling is cooking prepare the topping. Whisk the egg white stiffly. Mouli or sieve the banana and fold in with a metal spoon. Spoon thinly over the top of the fruit and return to a cooler oven gas mark 3/170°C/325°F for about 10 minutes until it is lightly browned. Serve hot or cold.

Each slice is 20g CHO. 140 kcals.

APPLE STRUDEL

We used to be taught, 'An apple a day keeps the doctor away', but the lesson seems to have been forgotten. Despite the availability of an ever increasing number of varieties such as Discovery and Jonathan in the shops – or perhaps because of the confusion bred by this profusion – UK consumption has fallen to around one large apple per person a week. This strudel may help whet your appetite for larger doses of the fruit of paradise.

1 quantity of Strudel Pastry
(see page 159)

Filling
400g (14oz) eating apples,
  peeled and chopped
25g (1oz) sultanas
25g (1oz) raisins
50g (2oz) almonds, chopped
½–1 tsp cinnamon
½ tsp mixed spice
zest of ½ lemon
2 tbs orange juice,
  unsweetened
1 dessertspoon oil

Makes 12 slices.

Preheat the oven to gas mark 4/180°C/350°F. Lay the strudel pastry over a large baking tray so that it is ready for filling. This avoids having to lift it after filling.

Prepare the filling: mix the apples with the sultanas and raisins in a large bowl. Add the chopped almonds, spices, lemon zest and orange juice. Spoon this mixture along the entire length of the strudel leaving a margin of 4cm (1½in) at each end.

Lightly fold one side of the pastry over the fruit and then fold the other side to overlap it on top. This makes an oblong shape. Brush a little oil on one of the sides to help them stick together. Seal the two ends of the strudel.

Put a dessertspoon of oil in the bowl that the apple mixture stood in. Mix it up with the spices that are around the sides of the bowl and dribble the spiced oil along the top of the strudel. A little more cinnamon can be sprinkled on top according to taste.

Bake for 40–45 minutes until the pastry is browned and crisp.

Each slice is 10g CHO. 85 kcals.

PEACH AND APPLE STRUDEL

This recipe makes a low flat strudel. Roll the pastry thinly all over otherwise it will become a little spongy when baked.

1 quantity of Strudel Pastry
  (see page 159)

Filling
25g (1oz) ground almonds
½ tsp cinnamon
250g (9oz) eating apple, grated
200g (7oz) ripe peach, grated

Makes 10 thin slices.

Preheat the oven to gas mark 5/190°C/375°F. Lay the strudel pastry over a large baking tray so that it is ready for filling. This avoids having to lift it after filling.

Prepare the filling: combine the ground almonds and cinnamon and sprinkle over the base of the strudel. Mix together the apple and peach and spread over the centre of the pastry to cover an area about 25 × 12.5cm (10 × 5in).

Fold one side of the pastry over the fruit and then fold the other side to overlap it on top. This makes an oblong shape. Brush a little oil on one of the sides to help them stick together. Seal the two ends of the strudel. Sprinkle the top with cinnamon.

Bake for 35 to 40 minutes until the top

is browned and the other layers of pastry are cooked through.

Each slice is 10g CHO. 80 kcals.

APPLE DELIGHT

Apples appear again and again in mythology and literature. The fruit that Eve tempted Adam with was traditionally an apple and Snow White's wicked stepmother used an apple to poison her. In the Bible's 'Song of Solomon' there is the lovesick cry 'comfort me with apples: for I am sick of love'. This view of the apple is backed up by 16th century physician Thomas Cogan in his book Haven of Health:

Apples are thought to quench the flame of Venus, according to that old English saying,
'He that will not a wife wed,
must eat a cold apple when he goeth to bed.'

This very light pie with a thin pastry crust on top and a soft apple filling underneath is excellent hot or cold. If you are cooking for large numbers double the quantities so that half can be eaten when freshly baked and the other half served the next day.

Filling
800g (1lb 12oz) eating apples
1 tsp cinnamon

½ quantity Rough Puff Pastry (see page 160)

Makes 12 small servings.

Prepare the filling: grate the apples into a 20 × 25cm (8 × 10in) baking dish or tin. Mix well with the cinnamon.

Roll out the pastry top thinly and lay it over the apples. Bake in a preheated oven gas mark 4/180°C/350°F for 30–35 minutes until the pastry is well browned.

Each serving is 10g CHO. 60 kcals.

PECAN PIE

Pecan nuts are grown in the southern states of the USA and pecan pie is an American invention. The pecan, a very sweet tasting nut, is a good source of potassium, magnesium, iron and zinc and unusually for nuts contains a small amount of vitamin C.

Filling
100g (4oz) prunes, stoned and chopped
100ml (4 fl oz) water
150g (5oz) pecan nuts
250g (9oz) firm tofu
100g (4oz) banana, peeled
1 egg, lightly beaten
25g (1oz) oatmeal (or porridge oats ground to a fine flour)
a few drops of vanilla essence
½ tsp cinnamon

½ quantity of Rough Puff Pastry (see page 160)

Makes 12 servings.

Soak the prunes in the water for 15 minutes.

Roll out the pastry in a square so that it will cover the base of a 20cm (8in) square baking dish. Bake blind in a preheated oven gas mark 4/180°C/350°F for 10 minutes.

Prepare the filling: pour the prunes and water into a small saucepan and cook on a low heat until the water is absorbed and a thick paste is formed. Blend in the liquidizer if the paste looks too coarse.

Grind the pecan nuts and combine with the mouliéd tofu. The texture will be thick and a little coarse. Add the prune paste, mashed banana, egg, oatmeal, vanilla essence and cinnamon. (If using a food processor blend the prunes, nuts and tofu together.)

Spread the mixture as evenly as possible over the partly baked pastry shell. Bake in a preheated oven gas mark 4/180°C/350°F for 20 minutes until the filling has set firmly. Serve cold.

Each serving is 10g CHO. 160 kcals.

PEAR PIE

1 quantity of Rough Puff Pastry (see page 160)

Filling
150g (5oz) firm tofu
4 ripe pears weighing about 500g (1lb 2oz)
few drops of vanilla essence
50g (2oz) oat bran and germ

Roll out the pastry thinly so that a top and a base can be cut for a 25 × 20cm (10 × 8in) baking dish. The base needs to be cut about 1cm (½in) wider than the top.

Prepare the filling: in a liquidizer or food processor blend the tofu and

Makes 16 large slices.

pears until they become creamy. Add the vanilla essence and oat bran and germ. Pour the filling into the pastry base. Place the top sheet of pastry over it and pinch the edges together.

Bake in a preheated oven gas mark 4/180°C/350°F for 40 minutes until the pastry is evenly browned.

Each slice is 10g CHO. 80 kcals.

ORANGE CAROB PIE

Recent research in the USA has linked the three minerals magnesium, potassium and calcium with a reduction in blood pressure levels. The research suggests that magnesium helps protect against the development of high blood pressure in old age, while calcium and potassium have been most effective in counterbalancing high blood pressure in people who are salt-sensitive. In this recipe the seeds in the pastry are a source of magnesium and potassium while yogurt is a good source of calcium.

1 quantity of Sweet Seed Pastry
(see page 163)

Filling
225g (8oz) firm tofu
100g (4oz) banana
50g (2oz) carob powder
150ml (5 fl oz) low-fat natural
yogurt
1 egg
2 medium oranges, weighing
about 300g (11oz)

Makes 10 servings.

Press the pastry over the base of a 23cm (9in) baking dish. Bake in a preheated oven gas mark 4/180°C/350°F for 10 minutes.

Prepare the filling: use a liquidizer or food processor to blend the tofu and banana to a smooth cream. Add the carob, yogurt and lightly beaten egg.

Peel the oranges and remove the pith and seeds. Chop into small pieces and add them, together with any juice, into the tofu-carob mixture and stir gently. Pour into the pastry shell. The mixture has a thick custard-like texture.

Return to the oven for 30–35 minutes and bake until the tofu mixture is firmly set.

Each serving is 10g CHO. 120 kcals.

PEACH CUSTARD TART

Scrumptious slices of peach are set in a fruit custard on a thick cakey pastry base. The combination of fruit in this recipe makes it superbly sweet and useful to make when still trying to get used to doing without sugar.

Custard
50g (2oz) dried apricots
50ml (2 fl oz) boiling water
1 egg
150ml (5 fl oz) low-fat natural yogurt
50g (2oz) ground almonds

1 quantity of Yogurt Pastry (see page 158)

Fruit filling
200g (7oz) pears
2 tbs apple juice

Topping
400g (14oz) firm ripe peaches

Makes 10 slices.

Pour the boiling water over the dried apricots for the custard and leave to stand.

Prepare the pastry: there is no need to chill it before using. Roll it out thickly and line a 25cm (10in) diameter baking dish. Cut off any surplus pastry around the sides. Bake blind in a preheated oven gas mark 5/190°C/375°F for 10 minutes until a light biscuit colour.

While the pastry is baking prepare the fruit filling. Blend the pears and apple juice and put to one side.

Prepare the custard: grind the dried apricots with their soaking water to a paste, using a hand grinder or electric coffee grinder. Whisk the egg and fold in the yogurt, ground apricots and almonds.

Take the pastry out of the oven. Spread the pear purée thinly and evenly over the base. Spoon the custard on top. Return to a slightly cooler oven gas mark 4/180°C/350°F for 20–25 minutes until the custard is firm. By the time the custard is set the sides of the pastry will be brown but not burnt.

While the custard is baking prepare the topping. Pour boiling water over the peaches and leave for 15 seconds then remove the skins. Cut into thin, even slices. When the custard is firm and the tart has been removed from the oven lay the peaches in circles around the top, completely covering the custard. Return to the oven and bake for a further 5 minutes.

Each slice is 20g CHO. 175 kcals.

STRAWBERRY TART

Strawberries are set in jelly on a crisp thin pastry base in this tart, which tastes best if eaten the same day it is made.

½ quantity of Rough Puff Pastry (see page 160)

Filling
25g (1oz) ground almonds
500g (1lb 2oz) fresh strawberries, hulled
125ml (4½ fl oz) apple juice, unsweetened
25ml (1 fl oz) water
½ level tsp agar-agar powder

Makes 8 servings.

Roll out the pastry thinly to fit a circular 20cm (8in) diameter pastry dish. Bake blind in a preheated oven gas mark 5/190°C/375°F for 20–25 minutes until crisp and browned. Remove from the oven and leave to cool.

Prepare the filling: cover the base of the pastry with the ground almonds.

Cut the strawberries in half and place them flat side down around the pastry base, making two layers of fruit.

Combine the apple juice and water and dissolve the agar-agar powder in the liquid. Pour into a small pan and bring to the boil for 1½ minutes. Remove from the heat and allow to cool for a few minutes. Pour evenly over the fruit.

Each serving is 10g CHO. 95 kcals.

FRUIT TARTS

These rough puff pastry tarts are filled with cherries, but this recipe works just as well with whatever fruit is in season. A midsummer combination of raspberries, blackcurrants and strawberries looks very eyecatching. For midwinter thin slices of banana and grapes set in a layer of jelly work equally well. The tarts are fairly quick to make although stoning cherries can be laborious work — soft fruits are much quicker to prepare. These tarts look their best if eaten the same day, but still taste fine if eaten the day after.

1 quantity of Rough Puff
   Pastry (see page 160)

Filling
700g (1lb 9oz) black cherries
30g (1oz generous) ground
   almonds
½ tsp cinnamon

Jelly
150ml + 1 tbs (5 fl oz + 1 tbs)
   apple juice, unsweetened
50ml + 1 tbs (2 fl oz + 1 tbs)
   water
½ generous tsp agar-agar
   powder

Makes 24 tarts.

Roll out the pastry thinly enough to cut 24 circles 7.5cm (3in) in diameter. Press the circles into tart tins and bake blind in a preheated oven gas mark 5/190°C/375°F for 15 minutes until crisp and browned.

Prepare the filling: remove the stones from the cherries. Try and keep them whole because this looks more attractive than pieces.

Combine the ground almonds and cinnamon. Spoon out a little into the base of each tart. Place enough cherries in each one so that they look full.

Prepare the jelly: combine the apple juice and water in a small saucepan. Take 1 tbs of this liquid and mix with the agar-agar powder then pour it back into the saucepan. Bring to the boil and simmer for 1½ minutes. The jelly will take about 7–10 minutes to set. Leave it to cool for a few minutes. When cool put 2 tsp in each tart. With practice you will be able to gauge when the jelly is a few minutes from setting. The reason for waiting is that if you put boiling liquid jelly into a pastry case it will soften it and make it soggy. If you wait a little you will keep the contrast of a soft filling with a crisp outside.

Each tart is 10g CHO. 55 kcals.

CAROB CREAM TART

This is a very elegant tart. The combination of crisp pastry and firm carob mousse filling makes it a sensational but delicate dessert.

1 quantity of Rough Puff
   Pastry (see page 160)

Filling
200g (7oz) firm tofu
200g (7oz) ripe bananas,
   peeled
½ tsp vanilla essence
4 tbs orange juice
1 tbs brandy (optional)
100g (4oz) carob powder
200ml (7 fl oz) skimmed milk
200ml (7 fl oz) water
1 tbs agar-agar flakes or 2 tsp
   agar powder
2 egg whites, stiffly beaten

Makes 20 slices.

Roll out the pastry thinly to cover the base and a little of the sides of a 30 × 20cm (12 × 8in) baking tin. Bake blind in a preheated oven gas mark 5/190°C/375°F for 10–15 minutes until evenly browned, but be careful that it does not burn.

While the pastry is cooling prepare the filling. Use a food processor or food mill to blend the tofu and banana. Add the vanilla essence, orange juice and brandy. In a small saucepan combine the carob powder, milk, water and agar-agar flakes. Bring to the boil and simmer on a low heat for 5 minutes stirring all the time and making sure the mixture does not become too thick. If using agar-agar powder dissolve in a dessertspoon of water and add to the carob, milk and water in the saucepan after they have cooked gently for 3 minutes. Let the agar-agar solution simmer for a further 2 minutes.

Take the saucepan off the heat and add to the blended tofu-banana mixture. Fold in the egg whites and pour the mixture evenly over the pastry shell. Agar-agar does not require refrigeration to set and will become firm quite quickly. Chill the tart before serving.

Each slice is 10g CHO. 90 kcals.

APRICOT TART

Dried apricots have a very rich taste which always dominates whatever recipe they are used in. Many people prefer the strong taste of the dried variety to fresh ones. The vivid-coloured apricots are usually coated in sulphur, E220, in order to preserve that bright shade. Unsulphured apricots are available from wholefood shops although, of course, once additive-free the colour is a dark brown.

Dieters can bake the filling without the pastry.

Filling
400g (14oz) dried apricots
400ml (14 fl oz) water
200g (7oz) firm tofu
100ml (4 fl oz) apple juice, unsweetened

1 quantity of Barley Pastry (see page 162)

Makes 16 slices.

Soak the apricots in the water overnight. Put the apricots and soaking water in a saucepan and simmer on a low heat until the water has been absorbed. Leave to cool.

Remove and reserve a dessertspoon of the pastry then either roll or pat out the remainder to fit a 23cm (9in) diameter baking tin. Bake in a preheated oven gas mark 4/180°C/350°F for 15–20 minutes until lightly browned.

Prepare the filling: blend the softened apricots, tofu and apple juice to make a stiff paste. Spread it evenly over the partly-cooked pastry base.

Take the small piece of reserved pastry and make into little balls. Flatten between your fingers to form circles about 3cm (1¼in) in diameter. Dot these over the top of the apricot filling. Return to a slightly warmer oven gas mark 5/190°C/375°F for 15 minutes until the apricot has set and the pastry is brown at the edges.

Each slice is 20g CHO. 115 kcals.

CAROB PEAR TARTS

The Carob Pastry in this recipe goes particularly well with a moist fruit like pears, but others, such as mashed banana, could be substituted.

Filling
400g (14oz) ripe pears

1 quantity of Carob Pastry (see page 162)

Makes 14 tarts.

Prepare the filling by grating the pears.

Roll out the pastry evenly and cut 28 circles 7.5cm (3in) in diameter. Place 14 of them in tart trays, spoon in the grated pear and place the lids on top. Pinch the sides of the lids together with the bases so they stay on during baking.

Bake in a preheated oven gas mark 5/190°C/375°F for 25 minutes until lightly browned.

Each tart is 10g CHO. 70 kcals.

FRUTTI ALMOND TART

This is a rich concoction of softened winter fruit in layers of crisp Almond Pastry. This pastry keeps very well for at least 24 hours if it is stored in a tin after baking and cooling, so it can be prepared in advance and the filling completed later.

1 quantity of Almond Pastry (see page 163)
1 egg white
25g (1oz) ground almonds

Filling
275g (10oz) pears
325g (11½oz) eating apples
275g (10oz) satsumas, peeled
75g (3oz) banana, peeled
100ml (4 fl oz) apple juice
pinch of cinnamon

Makes 10 servings.

Divide the pastry into three equal pieces and roll out each one into a circle. Use an upturned 23cm (9in) bowl to cut the circles. If the pastry is difficult to handle place it on a 23cm (9in) baking dish which is covered with a sheet of greaseproof paper and use it as a mould. Press gently with your fingers so that the pastry fills the base of the dish. When you have the complete circular shape, lift up the greaseproof paper with the pastry on and place it on a baking tray. Repeat this process for the other two circles.

Whisk the egg white to stiff peaks. Choosing the pastry circle that looks the best spread the egg white over the top and then sprinkle ground almonds over the surface. This makes a very effective topping.

Bake the circles in a preheated oven gas mark 4/180°C/350°F for 15–20 minutes until the pastry is evenly browned. Make sure the circles do not start to burn at the edges. Remove from the baking trays when cool.

Prepare the filling: chop the fruit into medium-sized pieces and put in a heavy saucepan with the fruit juice and cinnamon. Cook over a low heat for about 10 minutes until the fruit is softened but not mushy. If there is too much liquid boil it down after removing the fruit with a slotted spoon.

When the filling is cool assemble the tart. Spread half the filling on one pastry circle. Place the second circle on top. Spread the remaining filling evenly across its surface. Place the third circle with the meringue and nuts on top to crown the tart.

Each portion is 20g CHO. 205 kcals.

ICE CREAM TORTE

This is definitely a special occasion cake. It has to be eaten on the same day so be sure you have a lot of people to help you! As the velvety ice cream is made with tofu rather than cream it is a very light cake.

Another attraction of this torte is that it can be prepared in advance and so reduce pressure on the cook. If you bake the pastry the day before it is needed then you only have to make the ice cream on the day.

1 quantity of Almond Pastry
  (see page 163)
1 quantity of Almond Carob
  Ice Cream (see page 284)
flaked almonds
a few strawberries or kiwi fruit

Makes 8 large servings.

Divide the pastry into three equal pieces and roll out each one into a circle. Use an upturned 23cm (9in) bowl to cut the circle. If the pastry is difficult to handle place it on a 23cm (9in) baking dish which is covered with a sheet of greaseproof paper and use it as a mould. Press gently with your fingers so that the pastry fills the base of the dish. When you have the complete circular shape, lift up the greaseproof paper with the pastry on and place it on a baking tray. Repeat this process for the other two circles.

Bake in a preheated oven gas mark 4/180°C/350°F for 20 minutes until the pastry is evenly browned. It should not be too brown, but it should be crisp when you eat it. Remove from the baking trays when cool. Store in a tin if they are to be used the next day.

Prepare the ice cream and store in the fridge until you are ready to put the torte together. Spread each circle of pastry with ice cream and put the layers on top of each other to give a three-tier torte, with the top layer also covered in ice cream. Sprinkle it with a few flaked almonds and decorate the sides with halved strawberries or slices of kiwi fruit.

Each serving is 20g CHO. 225 kcals.

SLICED APPLE TART

A friend surprised me with this recipe when I was invited for lunch with my daughters. It was her first attempt at a sugar-free dessert and it worked brilliantly. It is based on a French apple tart which is usually covered in a thick syrupy glaze. You can make a glaze with sugar-free jam, but it tastes just as good without.

1 quantity of Yogurt Pastry
 (see page 158)

Filling
625g (1lb 6oz) eating apples
100ml (4 fl oz) water
75g (3oz) sultanas
300g (11oz) eating apples
a little cinnamon

Glaze (optional)
50g (2oz) sugar-free apricot
 jam
100ml (4 fl oz) water

Makes 12 slices.

Roll out the pastry to fit the base and sides of a 25cm (10in) tart tin. Bake in a preheated oven gas mark 4/180°C/350°F for 10–15 minutes until lightly cooked.

Prepare the filling: slice the first quantity of apples thinly and cook with the water and sultanas over a low heat for about 10 minutes until the fruit is softened and the water is absorbed. Pour this evenly over the pastry base.

Cut the second quantity of apples into quarters, removing the cores. Slice the apples into thin half-moon pieces and place these on top of the soft cooked apple, letting them overlap. Repeat this over the whole surface of the soft apple so that it is completely covered. Sprinkle lightly with a little cinnamon.

Return the tart to the oven and bake for a further 20 minutes until the apples are lightly browned on top.

Prepare the glaze: heat the jam and water in a small saucepan. Let it bubble for a minute then spoon over the warm apples. Serve hot or cold.

Each slice is 20g CHO. 125 kcals.

DATE ROLLS

These are very sweet and light.

Filling
200g (7oz) dried dates
75g (3oz) prunes, stoned
250ml (9 fl oz) water
1 tbs lemon juice, freshly
   squeezed

1 quantity of Strudel Pastry
   (see page 159)

Makes 24 Date Rolls.

Prepare the filling first so that it can cool before being spooned on to the pastry. Chop the dates and prunes into a small saucepan together with the water. Cook on a low heat until all the water is absorbed. Mash the dried fruit with a fork to encourage the mixture to become really mushy. Remove from the heat and stir in the lemon juice.

Roll out the strudel pastry as thinly as possible. Spoon four lines of filling along the length of the pastry, about 7.5cm (3in) apart. Cut a dividing line between them, so that there are four long pieces of pastry with a date filling on one side. Roll them up lightly but firmly and cut into 24 rolls. Place these on an ungreased baking tray and bake in a preheated oven gas mark 4/180°C/350°F for 30–35 minutes until well browned.

Each roll is 10g CHO. 45 kcals.

BANANA AND WALNUT ROLLS

These are similar to date rolls. Although simple to prepare, the filling is not as sweet. This means that each roll contains less carbohydrate; but because of the oil content of walnuts the calorie content is not lower.

1 quantity of Strudel Pastry
   (see page 159)

Filling
400g (14oz) bananas
90g (3½oz) walnuts, chopped

Roll out the strudel pastry as thinly as possible.

Prepare the filling: mash the bananas with a fork and add the walnuts. Spoon four lines of filling along the length of

Makes 32 Banana and Walnut Rolls.

the pastry, with about 7.5cm (3in) between them. Cut a dividing line between them, so that there are four long pieces of pastry each with a banana filling on one side. Roll them up lightly but firmly and cut into 32 rolls. Carefully place these on an ungreased baking tray and bake in a preheated oven gas mark 4/180°C/350°F for 30–35 minutes until well browned.

Each roll is 5g CHO. 40 kcals.

ALMOND ROSE ROLLS

Almonds add something special to any dish whether it is sweet or savoury, and I use them in many recipes for the effect they have on texture rather than for their taste alone. These crisp rolls are filled with perfumed nuts.

Almonds often feature in vegetarian diets because they contain nearly 17g of protein and 20mg of vitamin E per 100g.

Filling
50g (2oz) dried figs, chopped
50ml (2 fl oz) water
150g (5oz) ground almonds
scant ½ tsp ground cardamom
2 tsp rosewater
1 egg white, stiffly beaten

½ quantity Rough Puff Pastry (see page 160)

Makes 24 Almond Rose Rolls.

Prepare the filling: put the figs in a small saucepan with the water. Heat slowly until about half the water has been absorbed. Leave to cool. Blend to make a liquid paste.

Combine the ground almonds, cardamom and rosewater. Add the fig paste and the mixture will become like thick crumbs. Bind with the egg white. Divide the filling into three equal amounts and put to one side.

Roll out the pastry thinly to a rectangular shape about 23 × 25cm (9 × 10in).

Take a third of the filling and make it into a long thin roll. Lay it along the length of the pastry. Repeat this process with the remaining two amounts of filling. Cut two lines about 4cm (1½in) from either side of the almond roll in the middle. Roll up the three thin rolls and cut each one into 8 slices. Place these on an ungreased baking tray and bake in a preheated oven gas mark 4/180°C/350°F for 30 minutes until lightly browned.

3 rolls are 10g CHO. 175 kcals.

BANANA AND ALMOND ROLL

Bananas and almonds are an unusual combination of flavours, but they work very well together in this rough puff pastry roll. It is satisfyingly filling and can be served in thin slices or large chunks. It tastes just as good the day after it is baked and also freezes well.

Filling
200g (7oz) firm tofu
400g (14oz) ripe bananas
100g (4oz) ground almonds
½ tsp almond essence

1 quantity of Rough Puff
Pastry (see page 160)

Makes 16 slices.

Prepare the filling: use a food processor or food mill to blend the tofu and bananas. Add the ground almonds and almond essence. The filling is very firm and holds its shape during baking.

Roll out the pastry to roughly 30 × 40cm (12 × 16in), but make sure that you have not rolled it so thin that it tears. Cut it in half so that each piece is about 30 × 20cm (12 × 8in).

Divide the filling in half and spread one half over one of the pieces of pastry, leaving a margin of 2.5cm (1in) all the way round. Gently roll up the pastry and seal the ends firmly, otherwise the filling will ooze out during baking. Mark off 8 slices along the length of the roll. Make another roll with the remaining piece of pastry and the rest of the filling. Transfer carefully to an ungreased baking tray. Bake in a preheated oven gas mark

5/190°C/375°F for 35–40 minutes until lightly browned and the pastry is cooked all the way through.

Serving suggestion: if you serve this roll as a dessert cut each roll into 16 slices and serve each one with a slice of kiwi fruit on top.

Each slice is 10g CHO. 115 kcals.

CAROB ROLL

Thin Rough Puff Pastry spread with a creamy carob filling and made into a long roll makes a delicious pastry for the tea table.

Filling
100g (4oz) raisins
100ml (4 fl oz) water
200g (7oz) firm tofu
40g (1½oz) carob powder
50ml (2 fl oz) orange juice, unsweetened

½ quantity Rough Puff Pastry (see page 160)

Makes 12 slices.

Prepare the filling: put the raisins and water in a small saucepan and simmer until all the water is absorbed. Blend to a paste in an electric coffee grinder.

Use a food processor or food mill to blend the tofu. Add the carob powder, orange juice and raisin paste.

Roll out the pastry to roughly 20 × 30cm (8 × 12in), but make sure there are no holes in the surface because the filling will leak out during baking. Spread the filling evenly over the surface of the pastry, leaving a margin of 2.5cm (1in) all the way round. Roll up the pastry loosely and seal firmly at each end and underneath. Transfer carefully to an ungreased baking tray.

Bake in a preheated oven gas mark 5/190°C/375°F for 35–40 minutes until the top is lightly browned and the pastry is cooked all the way through.

Each slice is 10g CHO. 75 kcals.

WALNUT CRESCENTS

Walnuts are loaded with nutrients. They contain protein, potassium, magnesium, calcium, iron and as much zinc as a tin of sardines. Zinc is said by some researchers to be beneficial for fertility, foetal growth and acne. Post-natal depression is also linked by some doctors with zinc deficiency.

When you eat a walnut you get a mineral and vitamin package made by nature, while if you dose yourself with supplements of different minerals it is quite likely that essential nutritive elements and balances that can only be found in foods are being omitted.

Filling
50g (2oz) dried dates, chopped
50ml (2 fl oz) water
200g (7oz) walnuts, chopped
½ tsp cinnamon

1 quantity of Yogurt Pastry
  (see page 158)

Makes 32 crescents.

Prepare the filling: heat the dates and water in a small saucepan until all the water is absorbed and a paste is formed. Leave to cool. Add the chopped walnuts and cinnamon to make a thick crunchy mixture.

Roll out the pastry thinly and cut 32 circles 7.5cm (3in) in diameter. Place an equal amount of filling on each one. Bring the two sides over to meet in the middle and pinch together to make a standing half-circle or crescent. Place on an ungreased baking tray.

Bake in a preheated oven gas mark 4/180°C/350°F for 20 minutes until lightly browned. Serve hot or cold.

2 crescents are 10g CHO. 135 kcals.

STRAWBERRY HATS

Crisp circles of sweet Hazelnut Pastry are sandwiched together over plump strawberries sitting in a bed of fromage frais.

1 quantity of Hazelnut Pastry
  (see page 163)

Roll out the pastry thinly on a lightly floured board and cut 16 circles 7.5cm (3in) in diameter. Place on a greased baking tray and bake in a preheated

Filling
300g (11oz) strawberries,
    hulled
150ml (5 fl oz) fromage frais

Makes 8 Strawberry Hats.

oven gas mark 4/170°C/350°F for
15–20 minutes until lightly browned.

When cool take eight of the circles and
lay them on a flat plate. Put a generous
teaspoon of fromage frais on each one.
Place about 3 whole strawberries on
each portion of fromage frais. On each
of the remaining eight pastry circles put
a teaspoon of fromage frais and place
each one this side down on top of the
strawberries so that they are
sandwiched with the cheese top and
bottom.

Each hat is 10g CHO. 140 kcals.

CINNAMON ROLL

Filling
200g (7oz) raisins, chopped
    coarsely
250ml (9 fl oz) water
5 tsp cinnamon
100g (4oz) ground almonds
50g (2oz) flaked almonds
100ml (4 fl oz) orange juice,
    freshly squeezed
a little beaten egg mixed with 1
    tsp water (for decoration)
cinnamon (for decoration)

½ quantity of Yeast Pastry (see
    page 164)
Coconut Icing (optional) (see
    page 82)

**Makes 24 slices, 12 in each
    roll.**

Prepare the filling: soak the raisins in
the water for half an hour. Put the
raisins and soaking water in a small
saucepan and heat gently until most of
the water has been absorbed. Leave to
cool. Combine the cinnamon, ground
and flaked almonds in a mixing bowl.
Add the raisins, the leftover cooking
juice and the orange juice. Mix to form
a thick paste.

Divide the pastry in half and roll out
each piece into a large thin rectangle.

Lay one of the pieces of pastry on a
lightly greased baking tray. Spread half
the filling over the pastry. Roll it up
tightly and seal the ends. Repeat this
process for the second piece of pastry.

Cover the rolls loosely with cling film and leave to stand in a warm room for 20 minutes while they increase in bulk. Brush with the egg and water. Sprinkle the cinnamon over the top.

Bake in a preheated oven gas mark 5/190°C/375°F for 30 minutes until the pastry is browned. Avoid overcooking or the roll will taste dry.

Make a little coconut icing (see page 82) and pour over the top (optional).

Each slice is 10g CHO. 100 kcals.

APRICOT RING

Filling
200ml (7 fl oz) water
225g (8oz) dried apricots
200g (7oz) sesame seeds
50g (2oz) ground almonds
50g (2oz) wheatgerm
2 tbs lemon juice
200ml (7 fl oz) skimmed milk

½ quantity of Yeast Pastry (see page 164)

Icing
50g (2oz) coconut cream
100ml (4 fl oz) water
½ tsp vanilla essence
½ tsp cinnamon
3 large dried apricots, weighing about 20g (¾oz), chopped

Makes 24 slices.

Prepare the filling: boil the water and soak the apricots in it for an hour. Chop the apricots and simmer in a small saucepan with the soaking liquid until all the water is absorbed. Leave to cool and prepare the pastry.

Lightly brown the sesame seeds under the grill. Combine them with the chopped apricots, ground almonds, wheatgerm, lemon juice and milk.

Roll out the pastry thinly into a large rectangle, about 60 × 30cm (24 × 12in). This is big enough to roll up into a ring after it has been filled, sealing the two ends together. If this size is too large for your pastry board or work top, roll out the pastry on a clean tablecloth on the kitchen table.

Spread the filling thinly over as much of the pastry surface as possible. Roll up swiss roll fashion, with the seam underneath. Join the ends and place on a lightly greased baking tray. Cover loosely with cling film and leave to stand in a warm room for 20 minutes until the bulk has increased. Bake in a preheated oven gas mark 5/190°C/375°F for 30–35 minutes until well browned.

Prepare the icing: chop up the coconut cream and heat in a small saucepan with the water. When it forms a thick paste add the vanilla essence and cinnamon. Spread over the top of the roll. Decorate the icing with the chopped apricots.

Each slice is 10g CHO. 135 kcals.

Cold fruit desserts depend on the quality of the fresh fruit you use. A favourite market stall or a fruitful relationship with your local greengrocer is essential. There is no reincarnation for sad and old bruised fruit by plunging them into the hopeful disguise of a fruit salad. It will only ruin the taste of the good fruit you use.

You may need to play the detective to find out the days your greengrocer goes to market. If you grow fruit in your own garden then no one can match you for freshness.

These recipes are all quick to make and look attractive.

CLEMENTINE CREAM DELIGHT

The ever-ready packet of tofu in your fridge can be called to service yet again in this dessert of segments of sweet clementine coated with a delicate-tasting orange cream. Prepare it at least four hours in advance as it improves with standing in the fridge while the tofu absorbs the fruit flavours. Either serve it by itself or with a light cake such as Walnut Cake (see page 247).

Clementines have a skin that is easily removed and are a sweet juicy fruit. Usually they can only be bought in the winter months. When choosing clementines pick the heaviest ones as these are the juiciest.

175g (6oz) firm tofu
juice and zest of 1 large orange, weighing about 250g (9oz)
450g (1lb) sweet clementines
1 heaped tsp desiccated coconut, unsweetened

Makes 4 servings.

Pour off the liquid from the tofu packet and either mouli or blend the tofu in a food processor to make a thick cream.

Squeeze the juice out of both halves of the orange and grate the zest Add the orange juice and zest to the tofu to make it into a creamy liquid.

Peel the clementines and remove the white pith around the segments before adding them to the bowl of creamy tofu. Stir together and lightly sprinkle the top with coconut. Chill in the fridge for at least 4 hours before serving.

Each serving is 10g CHO. 75 kcals.

DATE DELIGHT

When succulent fresh dates are available use them for this quick, light dessert.

200g (7oz) fresh dates, with stones
100g (4oz) almond flakes
1 pear, grated
a couple of mint leaves, for decoration

Makes 6 small servings.

Remove the stones from the dates and chop the fruit into small pieces with a knife. Combine with the flaked almonds and grated pear. Spoon into a shallow serving bowl and leave to chill in the fridge for one hour before serving. Decorate with a couple of mint leaves.

An alternative way of serving Date Delight is to spoon the mixture into paper cases.

Each portion is 10g CHO. 130 kcals.

POMEGRANATE DIP

Thy temples are like a piece of a pomegranate within thy locks.
Song of Solomon

. . . some 'pomegranate', which, if cut deep down the middle,
Shows a heart within blood-tinctured, of a veined humanity.
'Lady Geraldine's Courtship', Elizabeth Barrett Browning

The pomegranate is such an attractive fruit that it has often stimulated the imagination of poets. It is of a very round shape and when ripe it has a pinky red glow – this is probably what the 'Song of Solomon' is referring to. When it is cut open there are hundreds of red glistening seeds squeezed tightly next to each other. It would take a poet to compare the inside of the fruit to a heart – it is a romantic allusion rather than a literal one – but there is no denying that the luscious red seeds are a colourful addition to any fruit dish. A few sprinkled over a fruit salad make a very unusual garnish.

Pomegranates have become more available in the last few years and can be found in street markets as well as in the shops. When buying this fruit avoid those whose hard skin has split open. Look for a pinkish glowing skin, with deeper shades of red. If it is too pale the seeds will not be sweet enough, while if it is too red the seeds may be over-ripe with an unpleasant tang.

Pomegranates are high in potassium and chloride. The ancient Greeks and Romans used them for medicinal purposes. Today in parts of India the rind is used against chronic dysentery.

One of the simplest and most enjoyable ways to eat pomegranate is to cut the whole fruit, including the rind, into quarters. In this recipe the seeds are removed from the rind and placed in a large bowl – all your guests have to do is eat them.

2 large pomegranates
50g (2oz) almonds, with skins
2 medium-sized eating apples, weighing about 250g (9oz)

Makes 4 servings.

Remove the pomegranate seeds from the rind and put them in an attractive serving bowl. Keep back 1 tablespoonful and put in a glass. Crush these with the back of a spoon so that the juice runs out. Pour back into the bowl. Chop the almonds into chunky pieces and add.

Just before serving thinly slice the apples into rounds and put on a separate plate. Guests serve themselves by spooning the pomegranate on to a slice of apple.

This is a very sociable dessert!

Each serving is 15g CHO. 120 kcals.

FIGS AU FROMAGE FRAIS

The ancient Greek word for fig was sukon *and put together with* phaino, *meaning show, became the word for informer –* sukophantes. *This formed the basis for the English word 'sycophant' meaning an ingratiating flatterer. Why someone who shows the fig is an informer is not clear. One suggestion is that the original sycophants informed on fig smugglers as a way of ingratiating themselves with the authorities.*

This dish takes one minute to prepare. It is so delicious that you feel like throwing all caution to the wind and gorging yourself. The recipe uses dried figs because they are available all year round at considerably less cost than fresh figs. Having lived abroad and bought figs by the kilo in the local market I always find it painful to pay the equivalent price for one fresh fig. But if you can track down a shop or market stall that is not too expensive then do use them in this recipe.

Fromage frais has a light creamy taste. The amount of fat in the low-fat version differs according to the manufacturer.

100g (4oz) dried figs or 5 fresh figs	Chop the figs into smallish pieces. Combine in a bowl with the fromage frais. Leave to chill in the fridge for ½–2 hours before serving.
300g (11oz) fromage frais	
Makes 4 small servings.	

Each portion is 15g CHO. 85 kcals.

JULY FRUIT SALAD

This fruit salad uses fruit that is readily available in the shops during July.

We first ate this salad with a friend who lives in a tiny house with one room on each floor. It is opposite an Italian restaurant with only a narrow walkway between the two buildings. As it was a hot balmy July evening the restaurant tables had spilled out into the street almost up to our friend's front door. The room where we ate was on the first floor and opposite us on the restaurant balcony people stood drinking while waiting for a free table. While contemplating Italian culinary delights they couldn't keep their eyes off us devouring this delicious fruit salad, and were probably wishing their turn to eat would come quickly.

juice of 1 large orange, about 150ml (5 fl oz)
1 tbs cognac (optional)
1 nectarine
1 peach
1 pear
50g (2oz) banana, peeled
300g (11oz) galia or charantais melon without seeds
100g (4oz) dark red cherries
100g (4oz) strawberries, hulled

Makes 4 large servings.

Pour the orange juice into a fruit salad bowl and mix with the cognac.

Chop the nectarine, peach and pear flesh into small cubes and put into the juice. Slice the banana very thinly and add. Scoop the melon into balls, using a special cutter or a small teaspoon. Slice and stone the cherries and add. Turn the fruit over a few times with a large spoon so that it has all been soaked in the juice. Decorate the top with slices of strawberry. Leave to stand in the fridge for 1–2 hours before serving.

Each serving is 20g CHO. 90 kcals.

DRIED AND FRESH FRUIT SALAD

One winter evening, I was expecting nine people for supper and was very appreciative when one of the guests offered to make the dessert. Every cook gives their own special flavour to their food and I like the idea of combining mine with someone else's. My friend Vicky brought a massive bowl of this fruit salad. The unusual feature about it is that both the dried and the fresh fruit are very lightly cooked.

This dessert is high in carbohydrates because of the large amount of dried fruit. If you need to watch your carbohydrate intake, substitute 3 apples for the 50g (2oz) raisins – this will increase the size of the portions.

75g (3oz) dried apricots
75g (3oz) prunes
50g (2oz) dried peaches
50g (2oz) raisins
juice and zest of ½ lemon
1 stick cinnamon
2 medium-sized oranges
2 eating apples

Makes 6 servings.

Cover the dried fruit with spring water and leave to stand overnight. Simmer the dried fruit and the soaking water in a heavy saucepan with the cinnamon stick, lemon zest and lemon juice for about 20–30 minutes until the fruit is soft but not disintegrating. The dried fruit is so sweet that you can dilute the liquid by adding more water – and lashings of juice is what makes this dessert so good. Peel the oranges, slice them thinly and add to the saucepan with the sliced apples. Simmer for about 4 minutes until lightly softened. Cool before serving.

Each serving is 25g CHO. 110 kcals.

MELON BOWLS

Apart from being juicy and sweet this dish is aesthetically pleasing. It is a subtle blend of different shades of green. A matching tablecloth and bowls will make it look spectacular.

The kiwi fruit is thought of as being typically antipodean, but it originates from the Yangtze valley in China. In about 1900 a British botanist collected samples of a few plants in China and brought them to the West. The kiwi was one of these and was first grown in New Zealand in 1906. It is rich in vitamin C.

1 large ripe galia melon
  weighing about 1.5–1.7kg
  (3lb 5oz–3lb 12oz)
200g (7oz) seedless grapes
3 kiwi fruit

Makes 6 servings.

Cut the melon in half. The shells will be used as bowls for the fruit so when you cut the melon off the rind leave about 1.5cm (¾in) thickness all the way round, otherwise the rind will not be thick enough.

Scoop the melon flesh into balls using a special cutter or small teaspoon. Put all

the balls in a large fruit salad bowl.
Add the grapes. Slice the kiwi fruit
thinly and add. There should be rather
a lot of juice in the bowl from the ripe
melon. Pour this into a small saucepan
and bring to the boil until the liquid is
reduced by half. Leave to cool then
pour over the fruit. Chill in the fridge.
Just before serving spoon the fruit into
the two melon shells.

Each serving is 15g CHO. 65 kcals.

WILD HIMALAYAN APRICOTS IN ROSEWATER

*This item appeared on the menu of a favourite Indian vegetarian
restaurant. Images of Himalayan hunters hot in the pursuit of savage
apricots flashed across my mind – it was a dish I had to order. When
the bowl was set in front of me, I realized that the strange hard brown
nuts labelled as Hunza apricots I had half-noticed in my local health
food shop were the very same Himalayan apricots.*

*The Hunzas live in the foothills of the Himalayas and apricots form
an important part of their mostly vegetarian diet. They eat them fresh
in season and sun-dried out of season. Sir Robert McCarrison, in his
studies of diet in India early this century, writes about the Hunzas'
good health and 'freedom from disease in general'.*

*The seed inside the apricots can be cracked and a delectable-tasting
almond-shaped nut is found inside.*

225g (8oz) Hunza apricots
500ml (15 fl oz) spring water
1 tbs rosewater to taste

Makes 4 servings.

Wash the apricots and place them in an
attractive bowl. Pour the water and
rosewater over them. Leave them to
stand covered overnight in the fridge.
In the morning they will have swollen
up and become soft. If there is not
enough juice add more water and taste
to see if further rosewater is necessary.

Each serving is 20g CHO. 90 kcals.

CHILLED ALMOND GLOBES IN PASTEL PINK SAUCE

This unusual dessert requires no cooking and can be prepared in advance. The almond globes are quite substantial and go very well with the fruit sauce. This is a very nutritious dish as the tofu and almonds are both high in protein while the fruit sauce adds an injection of vitamin C.

Almond globes
150g (5oz) firm tofu
150g (5oz) ground almonds
75g (3oz) ripe banana, mashed
3 tsp rosewater

1 quantity of Pastel Pink Sauce
(see page 256)

Makes 6 servings.

Make the almond globes by using a food processor or by hand. If using a processor put all the ingredients in the mixing bowl and process until a thick paste is formed. If doing this by hand mash the tofu with a fork and continue to mash it as you work in the ground almonds, mashed banana and rosewater. Gradually a thick paste is formed.

Use an ice cream scoop to make six rounds. Put them in a freezer container with a lid and place them at the bottom of the freezer for about an hour so that they become very chilled but not frozen.

Use six small plates for serving. Spoon the sauce over each plate and place a chilled globe in the centre.

Each serving is 10g CHO. 190 kcals.

PEACH MILLET DELIGHT

This is a simple nutritious dish. Millet is not widely used in Europe, but is a staple in parts of India and Africa where it has been cultivated for 6000 years. In Britain the chief consumers are budgies – which seems a pity. Millet is a gluten-free cereal.
   The nutritional value of millet changes depending on the variety, but on average it contains 10g of protein, 180mg of magnesium, 80mg

of calcium, 6mg of iron, 2mg of niacin per 100g. *This compares well with wholemeal flour which contains 13.2g of protein, 140mg of magnesium, 35mg of calcium, 4.0mg of iron and 5.6mg of niacin per 100g.*

In this recipe millet is combined with fruit purée, nuts and chopped fruit to give a pleasing texture.

100g (4oz) millet
400–500ml (14–18 fl oz) water
50g (2oz) flaked almonds
2 peaches weighing about 300g (11oz), chopped
150g (5oz) strawberries, hulled and sliced
2 medium apples weighing about 300g (11oz)
100g (4oz) pineapple, without skin
1 star fruit (optional decoration)

Makes 8 small servings.

To give the millet a nutty taste heat it in a heavy cast-iron frying pan until it is lightly browned. Turn it over as it browns. Bring the water to the boil in a saucepan and pour in the millet. Simmer with the lid on over a low heat until the millet is soft and fluffy and all the water has been absorbed. If necessary add more water during cooking.

Mix the almonds, peaches and strawberries in a medium-sized bowl. Purée the apples and pineapple to make a sauce and stir with the millet into the chopped fruit and nuts. Chill in the fridge until ready to serve. For a special occasion garnish just before serving with thin slices of star fruit.

Each serving is 20g CHO. 120 kcals.

SUNSET OVER GREENLAND OR ICED GRAPES IN A FLAMING PINK SEA

A refreshing and easy dessert to make. Its effectiveness is in the contrast of tastes and flavours and it requires the bare minimum of preparation.

Iced grapes
225g (8oz) seedless green grapes (about 48 small grapes)

Place the grapes in a freezer bag and freeze for at least a couple of hours before you need them.

Assemble the dessert just before serving on four large dessert plates about

Strawberry sauce
200g (7oz) strawberries, hulled
2 tbs apple juice

Makes 4 servings.

17.5cm (7in) in diameter. Blend the strawberries with the apple juice in a liquidizer or food mill . Spoon the sauce over the plates. Arrange about 12 grapes on each plate. If the grapes have been in the freezer for a number of hours and are hard, leave the dessert to stand for a few minutes before serving.

Grapes assume a completely different character when frozen, astonishing the palate with sensations unmatched by any other fruit.

Each serving is 15g CHO. 50 kcals.

11 HOT FRUIT DESSERTS

Hot baked desserts, particularly puddings, are an intrinsic part of British cooking. Yet a sweet course at the end of a meal has only become part of our style of eating in the last two hundred years. Samuel Pepys, writing in his diary in the 17th century, frequently mentions what he dined on; hardly any of these meals include a dessert. It was the French who first began to eat a dessert-type course in the 15th century and the English eventually imitated them.

Puddings can be killers, often combining sugar and a high fat content. These recipes contain neither.

ORANGE FRITTERS

Oranges have long been promoted as a source of vitamin C, but marketing people seem unaware that they are also singularly rich in pectin, a type of soluble fibre. A medium-sized orange contains over 2g.

Pectin helps to reduce high blood cholesterol levels, acting like a sponge and mopping up bile salts. These are made from cholesterol, and are secreted in the small intestine after a meal to help with digestion. After they have completed their function they are partially reabsorbed. Water-soluble fibres, such as pectin, seem to engulf more of them and carry them into the large intestine where they can no longer be reabsorbed. The body then has to take cholesterol out of the blood to produce more bile salts, thus lowering the cholesterol level.

Some doctors in the USA have been prescribing doses of pectin supplements to achieve these results, but you can increase your body's intake of pectin through diet; oranges and pears are both a good source. 8–10g has been shown to be enough to lower cholesterol levels – the equivalent of eating four oranges a day.

Use a heavy well-seasoned frying pan to cook the pancakes in.

Pancake batter
75g (3oz) wholewheat flour
1 tbs wheatgerm
1 large egg
100ml (4 fl oz) skimmed milk
50–75ml (2–3 fl oz) soda
    water

Filling
2 oranges, weighing about
    375g (13oz)

lemon or yogurt for decoration

Makes 4 small servings.

Combine the flour and wheatgerm in a bowl. Make a well in the centre and break the egg into it. Whisk the egg with a fork and gradually add a little of the flour to make a smooth paste. Add the milk and beat in the rest of the flour. Add soda water and stand in the fridge for half an hour before using. If you leave the batter in the fridge for longer the mixture will become thick and you will need to add an extra 25ml (1 fl oz) soda water to make a consistency suitable for coating the oranges.

Peel the oranges and remove the pith and seeds. Use a sharp knife to slice them into circles. Heat a tablespoon of oil in the frying pan. Dip each orange circle in the batter and cook in the hot oil. The batter puffs up and browns quickly. Turn over to cook on the other

side. Garnish with lemon or yogurt.
Serve immediately.

Each portion is 20g CHO. 125 kcals.

SWEET OMELETTE

Omelettes taste best served immediately which makes this a difficult dish for a number of guests, but ideal for two. Sweet Omelette can either be baked in the oven or cooked on top of the stove.

3 eggs
75g (3oz) banana, peeled
zest of ½ lemon
fruit spread (see pages 78–9)
  or Cherry Compôte (see
  page 216)

Makes 2 servings.

If baking the omelette in the oven put a little butter in a 25cm (10in) diameter shallow baking dish and place in a preheated oven gas mark 5/190°C/375°F while you prepare the omelette mix.

Separate the eggs. Whisk the egg yolks well. Mouli or sieve the banana to make a fine liquid and add to the egg yolks together with the lemon zest. Whisk the egg whites stiffly and fold in with a metal spoon.

If baking in the oven pour the mixture into the heated greased dish and bake for 5–6 minutes until risen and lightly browned on top.

If making the omelette on top of the cooker put a little butter in a large frying pan, heat until moderately hot then pour in the egg mixture. Cook for just under 1 minute to allow the bottom to brown then place the frying pan under the grill so that the top becomes firm and lightly browned.

Fold in half and spread the inside with a fruit spread or a little Cherry Compôte.

Each serving without filling is 7.5g CHO. 250 kcals.

APPLE MERINGUE

This is a scrumptious light pudding.

500g (1lb 2oz) eating apples,
  thinly sliced
100ml (4 fl oz) water
¼ tsp cinnamon
100g (4oz) hazelnuts, finely
  chopped
2 egg whites
100g (4oz) ripe banana

Makes 6 servings.

Put the apples in a heavy saucepan with the water and cinnamon. Cook gently until the fruit softens and most of the water is absorbed.

Pour the hazelnuts into a 20cm (8in) diameter pie dish. Pour in the apple and cinnamon and combine to form a soft crumbly mixture.

Whisk the egg whites into stiff peaks. Sieve the banana or put through a food mill to make it fine and liquid. Gently fold the banana into the egg whites. Pour over the apple mixture.

Bake in a preheated oven gas mark 1/140°C/275°F for 30 minutes or until the meringue is set and lightly browned. Serve hot.

Each portion is 15g CHO. 120 kcals.

APPLE CUSTARD

This simple quick dish is nourishing for babies and children.

450g (1lb) eating apples
½ tsp cinnamon
150ml (5oz) water
2 eggs

Makes 4 large servings.

Slice the apples into a saucepan together with the water and cinnamon. Cook gently until the apple softens and most of the water is absorbed. Blend, using a liquidizer or food mill. Leave to cool.

Whisk the eggs and add. If you do this while the apple purée is still hot add a spoonful at a time so that the temperature of the eggs is not changed too dramatically and they become scrambled.

Pour the custard into a 20cm (8in)
diameter baking dish and bake
in a preheated oven gas mark
4/180°C/350°F for 25–30 minutes
until browned on top and firm. Serve
immediately.

Each serving is 10g CHO. 80 kcals.

ALMOND PUDDING

This fresh fruit pudding is baked with ground nuts. It is very quick to make and useful for those who wish to exclude all flours. For a really sweet taste serve with one of the fruit sauces such as cherry or peach (see pages 255 and 256).

150g (5oz) ground almonds
¼ tsp cinnamon
50g (2oz) bananas, peeled and
  finely mashed
100g (4oz) fresh dates with
  stones
100g (4oz) fresh pineapple,
  without skin
2 eggs
25g (1oz) brown rice flakes
sprinkling of cinnamon

Makes 6 servings.

Combine the ground almonds,
cinnamon and banana. Stone the dates
and slice into thin strips. Chop the
pineapple into smallish pieces and add
these and the dates to the nut and
banana mixture. Whisk the 2 eggs well
and fold in to make a thick paste.

Pour the pudding mixture into a
greased baking dish 20cm (8in) in
diameter. Mix the rice flakes with a
little cinnamon in a small bowl and
spoon them evenly and thinly over the
top. Bake in a preheated oven gas mark
4/180°C/350°F for 30–35 minutes
until browned on top. Serve hot.

Each serving is 10g CHO. 210 kcals.

NOODLE PUDDING

The Japanese wholewheat udon *noodles are very suitable for this dish and can be obtained from health food shops. These flat noodles are a creamy white colour with a delicate, light taste as the wholewheat flour used is very finely milled. Use ordinary wholewheat pasta if you cannot find these noodles.*

150g (5oz) udon noodles

Fruit sauce
100g (4oz) firm tofu
100g (2oz) banana
1 medium eating apple,
   weighing about 175g (6oz)
1 egg
50g (2oz) raisins
½ tsp mixed spice
15–20g (½–¾oz) poppy seeds

Makes 8 servings.

Place the noodles in a saucepan of boiling water and cook until they are swollen. The way to test them is either to remove a strand and taste it or to check that the inside and outside are the same colour. Avoid overcooking. Pour them into a colander and rinse under cold water to keep the firm texture.

Prepare the sauce while the noodles are cooking: blend the tofu with the banana, apple and egg in a liquidizer or food processor. Add the raisins and mixed spice. Stir the noodles into the fruit sauce and pour into a lightly greased baking dish, 17.5–20cm (7–8in) in diameter. Crush the poppy seeds slightly as this makes them a little stickier and sprinkle over the top.

Bake in a preheated oven gas mark 4/180°C/350°F for 40–50 minutes until well browned.

Each serving is 20g CHO. 125 kcals.

This dessert can be made without the raisins – each serving would then be 15g CHO. 110 kcals.

APRICOT SPONGE PUDDING

50g (2oz) dried apricots
100ml (4 fl oz) boiling water
500g (1lb 2oz) eating apples
100ml (4 fl oz) water
100g (4oz) wholewheat flour
50g (2oz) soya flour
1 tsp bicarbonate of soda
1 egg

Soak the apricots in the boiling water for about 15 minutes.

Slice the apples into a heavy saucepan with the 100ml water. Bring to the boil then lower the heat and simmer gently for about 10 minutes until the apples have become soft, but not mushy.

300ml (10 fl oz) low fat natural
  yogurt
1 heaped tbs desiccated
  coconut, unsweetened

Makes 8 large servings.

Leave to cool.

Prepare the sponge mixture: blend the
apricots and soaking water to a thick
paste. Combine the wholewheat flour,
soya flour and bicarbonate of soda in a
bowl. Add the apricot paste. Whisk the
egg and fold this in. Stir in the yogurt.

Grease a 20cm (8in) diameter baking
dish. Pour the cooked apples and juice
evenly over the bottom of the dish.
Spoon the coconut evenly over the top.
Spread the sponge mixture on top of
this and bake in a preheated oven gas
mark 4/180°C/350°F for 20–30
minutes until the sponge is brown and
firm on top. Serve either hot or cold.

Each serving is 20g CHO. 130 kcals.

Serving suggestion: serve with custard
(see page 258)

APPLE RICE PUDDING

100g (4oz) long grain brown
  rice
500ml (18 fl oz) water
225g (8oz) eating apples,
  chopped
30g (1oz, generous) prunes,
  stoned and chopped
½ tsp cinnamon
50g (2oz) flaked almonds
  (optional) for decoration

Makes 4 servings.

Place the well-washed rice in a
saucepan of boiling water and let it
continue to boil for about 5 minutes.
Skim off any foam that rises to the
surface. Add the apples, prunes and
cinnamon. Turn the heat down low,
put the lid on the pan and let it simmer
for about 30 minutes until all the water
is absorbed and the rice is soft. Brown
the almonds lightly under the grill and
use as a garnish. For a moister pudding
serve with Orange and Strawberry
Sauce (see page 255).

Each serving is 30g CHO. 195 kcals.
Each serving with sauce is 35g CHO.
220 kcals.

APPLE CRUMBLE

Fresh or dried dates can be used in this recipe. I prefer the taste of the fresh and recommend using them when they are cheaply available in the shops. The 150g of fresh dates with stones are the carbohydrate equivalent to 50g of dried dates without stones—illustrating how much water and bulk is lost from fruit when it is dried.

This is an ideal recipe to make when first beginning to get used to sugar-free foods.

Crumble
100g (4oz) wholewheat flour
100g (4oz) oat bran and germ
1 tsp cinnamon
50g (2oz) margarine or butter
1 small pear, weighing
    100–125g (4–4½oz), grated

Filling
50g (2oz) dried dates or 150g
    (5oz) fresh dates with stones
100ml (4 fl oz) boiling water
50ml (2 fl oz) apple juice
500g (1lb 2oz) eating apples

Makes 12 small servings.

Prepare the crumble by combining the flour, oat bran and germ and cinnamon. Rub in the fat to make thick crumbs. Stir in the pear. Put the crumble mixture to one side until it is needed.

Chop the dates and place them in the bottom of a 20cm (8in) diameter baking dish. Pour the boiling water over them and crush the dates with a fork so that they become partly dissolved in the water. (There is no need to do this with fresh dates.) Add the apple juice. Slice the apples very thinly on top of the date mixture and stir them together so the apples become well coated.

Pour the crumble over the apple and dates to form an even crust. Bake in a preheated oven gas mark 4/180°C/350°F for 40 minutes until evenly browned on top.

Each serving is 20g CHO. 120 kcals.

RHUBARB AND APPLE CRUMBLE

Carefully cultivated rhubarb can be bought in the greengrocer's, but most gardeners know how easily it flourishes, requiring little attention and spreading almost like a weed.

One version of the origin of the word rhubarb was that the ancient Greeks called it the plant of the 'foreigners (barbarians) beyond the Rha (Volga)'. That it came from beyond the Volga is certainly true; it was cultivated in China, Siberia and Mongolia where it was known for its medicinal properties. Herbalists used its lightly cooked roots to cure headaches, liver trouble, lack of appetite and bad breath. But it is worth noting that rhubarb leaves are poisonous. Rhubarb stalks eaten raw or lightly cooked have a gentle purgative effect.

Rhubarb became popular in the 19th century as a filling in puddings and pies – even Queen Victoria was said to have enjoyed it.

Crumble
100g (4oz) wholewheat flour
100g (4oz) oat bran and germ
1 tsp cinnamon
pinch of ground cloves
50ml (2 fl oz) oil
1 pear, weighing about 125g (4½oz), grated

Filling
450g (1lb) rhubarb
75ml (3 fl oz) water
½ tsp bicarbonate of soda
450g (1lb) eating apples, chopped
50ml (2 fl oz) orange juice, unsweetened
zest of 1 small orange
zest of ½ lemon
50g (2oz) banana, peeled and mashed
25g (1oz) ground almonds
1 tsp cinnamon

Makes 8 large servings.

Prepare the crumble: combine the flour, oat bran and germ and spices. Stir in the oil and mix in the pear with a knife to make thick crumbs.

Prepare the filling: wash and chop the rhubarb into pieces 2.5cm (1in) in length. Put it into a heavy saucepan with the water and bicarbonate of soda and simmer until the rhubarb has softened. (The bicarbonate of soda neutralizes the acidity of the rhubarb.) Add the apple, orange juice and zest, lemon zest and banana. Simmer for about 5 minutes until the fruit has added its own liquid to the juice in the pan, but the apples are still firm. Thicken with the combined ground almonds and cinnamon.

Pour the fruit into a deep 22.5cm (9in) diameter baking dish. Cover with the crumble and bake in a preheated oven gas mark 5/190°C/375°F for 30–40 minutes until browned.

Each serving is 25g CHO. 190 kcals.

STEWED FRUIT

Stewing or baking fruit is a basic part of the cooking repertoire. As all fruit contains a high proportion of water, if the fruit is cooked with a little liquid – either juice or water – this will serve to bring out the moisture in the fruit. Initially, while getting used to sugar-free fruit, you may wish to add an ounce of raisins or sultanas to give extra sweetness, but as your palate adjusts you will find that very little extra sweetener needs to be added to fresh sweet fruit.

STEWED PEARS

Surprisingly this juicy, sweet-flavoured fruit is not widely popular in Britain – we eat less per person than any other country in the EEC. Yet it is a fruit that has been valued throughout history. Homer, the Greek poet, called pears 'the gift of the gods' and in Switzerland tradition had it that dreaming of ripe pears symbolized future riches and happiness.

This is a very simple method for stewing firm pears in a delicate juice. If you can find comice pears use them in this recipe.

½ eating apple, weighing just over 50g (2oz), grated
1 tbs apple juice
250–300ml (9–10 fl oz) water
450g (1lb) firm pears
2 large sticks cinnamon

Makes 4 servings.

Put the apple in a medium-sized heavy saucepan with the apple juice and water. Bring to the boil and simmer on a low heat for 7–10 minutes until the apple has softened.

Slice the pears in half and cut out the pips. Place the pears in the pan with the insides touching the base and the skin showing outwards. Add the cinnamon sticks. Continue to simmer over a very low heat for 35–50 minutes, depending on the size of the pears. Add a little more water if the liquid seems to be disappearing.

This amount of cooking gives firm, moist stewed pears. If you prefer them softer then continue cooking longer, adding more water if necessary.

Remove the cinnamon sticks and serve hot or cold.

Each serving is 10g CHO. 40 kcals.

STEWED APPLE

This is a very simple way of stewing apples where the source of sweetener is the fruit themselves. Use your favourite variety of eating apple for best results. If you are in the early stages of adjusting to sugar-free food add 25g (1oz) raisins for a sweeter taste.

4 eating apples, weighing about 600g (1lb 5 oz), sliced
200ml (7 fl oz) water
1 tsp cinnamon

Serves 4.

Put the apples in a saucepan with the water and cinnamon. Bring to the boil and simmer on a low heat until the apple has softened and absorbed the water. Serve hot or cold.

Each serving is 15g CHO. 55 kcals.

Variation: Apple Purée – blend the cooked apple. The quantity can be doubled and stored in a jug in the fridge for a couple of days.

POACHED PEACHES

The peach was cultivated in China for many centuries and eventually travelled along the caravan routes to Persia, from where the Romans took it to Italy. The leaves and flowers of the peach have traditionally been used in herbal remedies. A mixture of peach flowers was said to be good for jaundice and Culpeper, the 17th century herbalist, wrote that 'if the kernels [seeds] be bruised and boiled in vinegar, until they become thick, and applied to the head, it marvellously makes the hair to grow again upon bald places.'

4 large peaches
200ml (7 fl oz) apple juice
½ tsp cinnamon

Makes 4 servings.

Cut the peaches in half. If you have difficulty removing the stones leave them in until the peaches are cooked, when they can be removed very easily.

Mix the apple juice and cinnamon together in a small heavy saucepan. Place the peaches, cut side down, into the saucepan. Simmer on a low heat for about 15 minutes until the peach flesh becomes soft but not mushy. Remove the loose skins. Serve either hot or cold with the juice.

Each serving is 15g CHO. 60 kcals.

CHERRY COMPÔTE

History has it that we should be grateful to the Romans for discovering this sweet, rich-tasting fruit in Asia Minor in about 70 B.C. and introducing it to Britain in the 1st century A.D. During the 15th and 16th centuries the fruit stalks were used for their medicinal properties.

Dessert cherries fall into two categories: the geans which have soft flesh and the bigarreaus which have firm flesh. When buying cherries always avoid those that are split or unripe. The brief cherry season in Britain is from June to August, but it is extended by imports which begin about the middle of May. Prices start off quite high, but gradually come down as the home-grown fruit appears in the shops.

450g (1lb) dark red cherries
200ml (7 fl oz) apple juice
2 tsp arrowroot
1 tbs kirsch (optional)

Makes 4 servings.

Stone the cherries carefully, trying to keep them whole. Use either a cherry stoner or a metal skewer to push the stones through. Put the cherries and apple juice in a heavy saucepan. Bring to the boil and simmer for about 7 minutes. The length of time depends on the size of the cherries. Watch them while they are cooking because the combination of heated cherries and apple juice produces a lot of foam which can easily spill over the side of the pan.

Remove a little of the juice and combine with the arrowroot to make a smooth liquid. Return to the liquid in the pan and simmer for a further two minutes until the juice has thickened. Take off the heat. Stir in kirsch if using. Serve hot or cold.

Each serving is 20g CHO. 85 kcals.

Serving suggestion: Cherry Compôte served warm goes very well with a firm ice cream such as Cherry Carob Ice Cream (see page 287).

BAKED APPLES

The sugar-free version of this standard dessert requires minimal thought and preparation – ideal qualities for the busy cook. Use eating apples as they are not nearly as sour as cooking apples and require very little sweetening.

4 medium-sized eating apples
30g (1oz generous) sultanas
1 tsp cinnamon
4 tbs apple juice

Makes 4 servings.

Remove the cores from the apples. Place the fruit on a baking tray. Fill the centre of each apple with sultanas. Sprinkle the outside lightly with cinnamon. Spoon a tablespoon of apple juice over each apple.

Bake in a preheated oven gas mark 4/180°C/350°F for 30 minutes until soft.

Each apple is 20g CHO. 80 kcals.

STUFFED PEARS

50g (2oz) dried apricots
100ml (4 fl oz) boiling water
4 medium-sized pears
50ml (2 fl oz) apple juice
50g (2oz) ground almonds
1 tbs apple juice, unsweetened

Soak the dried apricots in the boiling water for an hour.

Remove the cores from the pears using a potato peeler.

Pour the soaking water from the

Makes 4 servings.

apricots into a medium-sized baking dish and add the 50ml (2 fl oz) apple juice.

Chop the apricots finely and mix with the ground almonds using the 1 tbs of apple juice to form a paste. Stuff this filling into the pears and lay them in the baking dish. Make any leftover filling into small balls and place these alongside the pears in the dish.

Bake in a preheated oven gas mark 4/180°C/350°F for 30 minutes until the fruit is softened but not bursting. Most of the juice will be absorbed during cooking.

Each serving is 20g CHO. 145 kcals.

BAKED BANANAS

The combination of banana and sesame seed makes a soft, crunchy dessert.

A friend told me she was warned by a health visitor about giving her young child too many bananas because of their high potassium level. However, bananas contain other minerals including magnesium, small amounts of iron, copper and zinc. The potassium content in bananas is 350mg per 100g which is not a great deal more than grapes and cantaloupe melon which are close behind with 320mg per 100g. They are also particularly high in vitamin B6 with 0.51mg per 100g compared to 0.10 in grapes or 0.07 in melons.

The misleading advice she received illustrates the risks of taking random pieces of nutritional information out of context.

400g (14oz) bananas
4 tbs orange juice, freshly
  squeezed
100g (4oz) sesame seeds
sprinkling of cinnamon

Makes 6 servings.

Slice the bananas into slices about 0.5cm (¼in) thick. Place in an ovenproof dish. Spoon the orange juice over the banana. Cover well with the sesame seeds. Sprinkle a little cinnamon over the bananas.

Bake in a preheated oven gas mark

4/180°C/350°F for 15 minutes until the banana has softened.

When serving garnish the plates with any sesame seeds that have stuck to the baking dish.

Each serving is 15g CHO. 155 kcals.

Cakes are the crowning glory of the tea table, the centrepiece of a well-celebrated birthday. There is a special place in one's memory for vivid images of past teas, the table adorned with the best china, an abundance of sandwiches and scones, and in the centre one glorious, mesmerizing cake.

Excluding sugar from one's life does not mean that these delights must be banished. In fact, one can enjoy cakes even more knowing that they are made healthily, that they not only look good but also actively promote well-being. Of course it is still better to eat lots of fresh or lightly cooked fruit and vegetables than lots of cake, but then cakes are special and would hold little excitement if we were to eat them every day of the week.

For me, tea with family or friends is a comfortable affair sitting around the kitchen table. My daughters enjoy any kind of gathering over a meal and are keen to help, laying the table with serviettes and any fanciful additions I will allow them. Open sandwiches or rolls with do-it-yourself fillings are the norm and a cake is, of course, essential. The atmosphere is relaxed and usually rather noisy. It is very different from the At Home days that the young Constance Spry remembers at the turn of the century when visiting ladies wore white kid gloves, swishing glacé silk petticoats and immense feather boas – and children were to be seen and not heard. Preparations began first thing in the morning:

The kitchen hummed with activity. The fire had to roar, the oven get hot, and there was to be no nonsense on the part of any one . . .
Hanging over the banisters we children might see the feathers and hear the frou-frou and get a nice sense of party goings-on.
Sometimes, indeed, unnaturally clean and restrictingly dressed, one of us might be called down 'to say how do you do'. On such occasions, until observed and called to order, I have watched with

unwavering concentration miracles of sleight of hand. I have seen tightly gloved women balance a cup and saucer in the air, negotiate a knotted veil, and convey a tremulous cucumber sandwich from hand to mouth without a fault. Seldom have I had the satisfaction of seeing even a bit of tomato misfire. The white gloves, in consideration of which the bread and butter had been rolled, might come to grief over buttery toast or too-soft sugar icing, but what of it? Such offerings on the altar of delicate behaviour only added lustre to a reputation for refinement.

Times have changed and sugar is superfluous, but the pleasures of a handsome tea are an abiding joy.

The cakes in this section are quick to make. The main work involved is the preparation of ingredients, and the actual mixing takes very little time. Food processors, blenders and electric coffee grinders can all help in speeding up the preparation process. I prefer to mix the ingredients by hand because then I know exactly what is happening to them, but the recipes will work as well if made completely by machine.

Many of the recipes are very straightforward. They combine dry ingredients with wet and have no delicate balance between the weight of sugar, eggs and flour, so it is almost impossible for them not to succeed. Bicarbonate of soda is often used as a raising agent. The only precaution to remember is to include no more liquid than specified.

The cakes stay fresh for 2–3 days unless the recipe specifies a shorter period. They should be wrapped with greaseproof paper and foil or stored in a tin. Their life-span is a little shorter than conventional cakes because sugar acts as a preservative. The cheesecake is best stored in the fridge.

All the cakes freeze well and should be wrapped in greaseproof paper and foil or cling film then put in a plastic freezer bag. If you intend to decorate a cake then do so after defrosting. The decoration usually looks better if freshly made.

Some of the recipes are based on the torte model and include up to 3 eggs; not a great many in terms of Sachertorte, say, but more than I included in my previous book which was designed for diabetics and dieters. The attraction of eggs to the cook is that they aid lightness and to the nutritionist is that they add protein. Four eggs a week is the average British weekly consumption. However, eggs are a source of dietary cholesterol and people with some heart conditions are usually advised not to eat too many. In an experiment at the Radcliffe Infirmary in Oxford healthy volunteers ate 7 eggs a week, while adjusting the rest of their diet to one that was high in fibre-rich carbohydrates and low in saturated fats. Under these conditions the eggs had no effect on their blood cholesterol concentration. The study concluded that it was unnecessary to reduce dietary cholesterol by cutting down on eggs if people had already cut back on saturated fats and increased the fibre in their diet – as proposed throughout this book.

If you are a vegan or have been told by your doctor to avoid eggs there are a number of recipes in the cake and pastry section which contain no eggs at all.

When eggs are used in a recipe beat them extremely well with a mixer or a hand whisk. They can become thick and creamy without adding sugar. After the beaten egg has been added, fold in the remaining ingredients by hand; do not use a mixer or the air incorporated in the egg will be beaten out.

The guiding principle behind many of the recipes in this book is to create cakes and biscuits which are light and in the patisserie style of baking rather than heavier cakes in the farmhouse tradition. Hazelnut Gateau (see page 244) is a perfect example of this type of cake.

APPLE CAKE

This very moist cake is made with apple purée and dotted with sultanas.

50g (2oz) sultanas
300g (11oz) eating apple,
  sliced
50ml (2 fl oz) water
100g (4oz) wholewheat flour
25g (1oz) soya flour
50g (2oz) oat bran and germ
50g (2oz) ground almonds
½ tsp cinnamon
¼ tsp mixed spice
½ tsp bicarbonate of soda
25g (1oz) banana, peeled and
  mashed
1 egg
150ml (5 fl oz) low-fat natural
  yogurt

Makes 16 slices.

Soak the sultanas in a little water.

Combine the apple with the water in a blender or food processor. Blend until a thick purée is formed. Alternatively cook the apples and water over a low heat until the water has been absorbed and the fruit is softened, then put through a food mill.

In a large bowl mix the wholewheat flour, soya flour, oat bran and germ, ground almonds, cinnamon, mixed spice and bicarbonate of soda. Stir in the sultanas, apple purée and banana. Whisk the egg until it is creamy and add to the mixture. Fold in the yogurt, making sure all the ingredients are mixed well.

Grease and flour a 20cm (8in) diameter baking tin and pour in the cake mixture. Bake in a preheated oven gas mark 5/190°C/375°F for 30–40 minutes until the cake comes away from the sides of the tin.

Each slice is 10g CHO. 80 kcals.

APPLE CHERRY CAKE

The cherry season is so short that it is worth making a few of these cakes for cooler days and freezing them. The rich flavour of the cloves combines well with the apples and cherries. Cloves are very popular in Indonesia, not as one would expect for use in the local cuisine, but for combining with tobacco and smoking.

100g (4oz) wholewheat flour
25g (1oz) soya flour
100g (4oz) ground almonds
25g (1oz) wheatgerm
½ tsp bicarbonate of soda
1 tsp cream of tartar
½ tsp cinnamon
pinch of ground cloves
75g (3oz) sultanas
2 large eating apples, weighing
    300g (11oz), grated
150g (5oz) cherries, stoned
1 egg white, stiffly beaten

Makes 16 slices.

Combine the flours and ground almonds, wheatgerm, bicarbonate of soda, cream of tartar and spices in a large bowl. Add the rinsed and dried sultanas to the flour mixture. Grate the apples into the bowl and stir in. Stone the cherries, cut into halves and add to the cake mixture. Bind with the stiffly beaten egg white.

Lightly grease and flour a 20cm (8in) baking tin and pour in the cake mixture. Bake in a preheated oven gas mark 4/180°C/350°F for 30–35 minutes until a knife inserted in the centre comes out cleanly.

Each slice is 10g CHO. 90 kcals.

Serving suggestion: serve with Cherry Sauce (see page 255) or spread with Cherry Cream (see page 81).

APPLE SLICE

This moist cake uses chopped apple and a few tablespoons of apple purée as the main sweeteners. It freezes well.

½ quantity of Yeast Pastry (see page 164)

Filling
225g (8oz) eating apples
50g (2oz) wheatgerm
2 tsp cinnamon
700g (1lb 9 oz) eating apples, chopped
50g (2oz) sultanas
little beaten egg for decoration

Makes 24 slices.

Roll out the pastry thinly to make two rectangles of about 30 × 20cm (12 × 8in) to fit a large baking tin. Lightly grease the base of the tin and cover with one of the layers of pastry.

Prepare the filling: blend the 225g (8oz) apples with a little water to make a thick purée. Combine the wheatgerm with the cinnamon and sprinkle it over the pastry base. Spread the 700g (1lb 9oz) of chopped apples over this. Cover the apples with the sultanas and dot teaspoonfuls of apple purée over the top. Put the pastry lid on and pinch the sides together. Leave to stand in a warm place for 20 minutes until the bulk has increased.

Brush with a little beaten egg and bake in a preheated oven gas mark 6/200°C/400°F for 15 minutes then turn the oven down to gas mark 5/190°C/375°F for a further 15–20 minutes until browned on top.

Each slice is 10g CHO. 65 kcals.

BANANA CAKE

Our local newspaper reported last year that Gwenty Cannon, prizewinner of the sugar-free cake section of the local Horticultural Society Show, had considered her own successful entry tasted revolting. I promptly challenged her to a bun-fight over tea. She fudged the Pecan Pie and minced words over my Carob Kisses, but yielded to the Poppy seed and Apple Cake and was altogether vanquished by the Banana Cake, rating it supremely light with a delicate texture. I was bowled over when she called me some days later for advice on decoration: she was making my Banana Cake for her grandson's birthday.

75g (3oz) dried dates
100ml (4 fl oz) water
225g (8oz) bananas, peeled and finely mashed
1 egg
75g (3oz) wholewheat flour
25g (1oz) soya flour
50g (2oz) ground almonds
1 tsp bicarbonate of soda
½ tsp vanilla essence
150ml (5 fl oz) low-fat natural yogurt

Makes 16 slices.

Cook the dates in the water in a small saucepan over a low heat until the water has been absorbed. Blend to a smooth paste. Leave to cool.

Add the cooled date paste to the bananas. Add the well-beaten egg. Fold in the flours, ground almonds and bicarbonate of soda. Stir in the vanilla essence and yogurt.

Lightly grease and flour a 20cm (8in) diameter baking tin, and pour in the mixture. Bake in a preheated oven, gas mark 4/180°C/350°F if your oven is a 'quick' one, but gas mark 5/190°C/375°F if it is not especially hot. The heat ensures that the cake rises quickly. Bake for 35–45 minutes until the cake is browned on top and the sides come away from the tin.

Each slice is 10g CHO. 70 kcals.

PINEAPPLE TANG CAKE

The fresh pineapple used in this recipe gives it a light sweet quality. The riper the pineapple is, the sweeter the taste will be. When testing for ripeness a good sign is if one of the fruit's inner leaves can be pulled out easily.

The actual mixing of the ingredients is very quick, but preparing them does take a little time, so it might be worth doubling the ingredients and freezing half the cake.

This is a useful recipe for anyone unable to eat wheat flour.

50g (2oz) prunes, stoned and finely chopped
25g (1oz) dried pear (use dried figs if not available)
150ml (5 fl oz) water
275 g (10oz) fresh pineapple, without skin
25g (1oz) raisins
40g (1½oz) pumpkin seeds
2 eggs
40g (1½oz) ground almonds
75g (3oz) brown rice flour

Makes 12 slices.

Cook the prunes, pear and water in a saucepan over a low heat until the water has been absorbed and the fruit has become soft. Leave to cool.

Chop the pineapple into 1cm (½in) square pieces and combine with the raisins and dried fruit paste. Grind the pumpkin seeds. Whisk the eggs with a fork and add to the fruit mixture, together with the ground almonds, ground pumpkin seeds and brown rice flour. Avoid crushing the pineapple as you stir it in with the other ingredients. The mixture will be fairly thick.

Grease a 20cm (8in) baking tin and sprinkle the surface of the tin with brown rice flour to avoid sticking. Pour in the cake mixture, smoothing the top with the back of a tablespoon. Bake in a preheated oven gas mark 4/180°C/350°F for 40 minutes until browned on top and a knife inserted in the centre comes out cleanly.

Each slice is 10g CHO. 95 kcals.

POPPY SEED AND APPLE CAKE

A thick layer of poppy seed filling and a layer of apple are packed between crisp pastry to make this unusual cake. During cooking the juice of the apples seeps down to the poppy seed filling and makes it very sweet and moist. I am not sure where the cake originates from; probably Poland or the region that used to be known as Transylvania.

I first came across this cake while studying to be a librarian. The tedium of lectures on subjects such as Bibliography of Bibliographies was broken by a visit to the warm, friendly students' cafeteria for a moan with friends and a huge slice of this cake, accompanied by a pot of yogurt. This diet sustained me through many boring lectures.

The fillings are quite time-consuming to make and all electrical aids that you possess should be enlisted to help. Failing these another pair of hands is just as good, or you could prepare the pastry in advance so that only the fillings remain to be made.

This cake improves with standing. A day after baking, the apple filling turns very jammy and is quite irresistible.

1 quantity Rough Puff Pastry (see page 160)

Poppy seed filling
75g (3oz) prunes, stoned and finely chopped
75g (3oz) dried dates, finely chopped
200ml (7 fl oz) water
150g (5oz) poppy seeds
50g (2oz) ground almonds
200g (7oz) firm tofu
1 egg
2 tbs orange juice
1 tbs brandy (optional)

Apple filling
500g (1lb 2oz) eating apples
50ml (2 fl oz) apple juice

Makes 14 slices.

Prepare the pastry and while it is chilling in the fridge prepare the poppy seed filling. Cook the prunes and dates in the water in a saucepan over a low heat until the water has been absorbed. The dried fruit should be quite soft and paste-like; mash it with a fork, to improve the texture.

Poppy seeds should be ground when used in a cake, to make them moister and softer. Use an electric coffee grinder, although because of its small size you will have to repeat the process a few times.

Combine the ground poppy seeds with the softened dried fruit and the ground almonds. Blend or mouli the tofu so that it becomes creamy and add. Lightly whisk the egg and fold in together with the orange juice and brandy. Put to one side.

Prepare the apple filling: thinly slice the apples and put in a saucepan with the apple juice. Simmer over a low heat with the lid on for about 10 minutes until the apples are softened. Remove from the heat and leave to cool while rolling out the pastry.

Divide the pastry into two halves, one slightly larger than the other. Roll out the larger one to a 28 × 23cm (11 × 9in) rectangle. Take a baking dish which is about 25.5 × 20cm (10 × 8in) and line with the pastry. There will be extra pastry to cover the sides of the baking dish. Roll out the smaller piece of pastry to make a lid.

To assemble: spread the poppy seed filling evenly over the base of the pastry. Pour the apples and their juice over the top of the poppy seed filling. Put the pastry lid on top and pinch the pastry together at the sides.

Bake in a preheated oven gas mark 5/170°C/350°F for about 40–45 minutes until the pastry is browned.

Each slice is 20g CHO. 190 kcals.

SPICY APPLE TOFU CAKE

This cake comes out of the oven with the filling ready baked in the middle and more filling decorating the top. All you have to do is eat it!

90g (3½oz) dried dates, chopped
150ml (5 fl oz) water

Cook the dates and water in a saucepan over a low heat until all the water has been absorbed and a thick

125g (4½oz) wholewheat flour
25g (1oz) soya flour
1 tsp bicarbonate of soda
1 tsp cream of tartar
2 tsp cinnamon
1½ tsp ground ginger
2 tsp mixed spice
50ml (2 fl oz) oil
2 eggs
150 ml (5 fl oz) low-fat natural
 yogurt

Filling
200g (7oz) firm tofu
275g (10oz) eating apple,
 grated
2 tsp cinnamon
25g (1oz) sultanas
25g (1oz) flaked almonds

Makes 10 large slices.

paste has formed. Blend if necessary to make smooth. Leave to cool.

Combine the flours, bicarbonate of soda, cream of tartar and spices in a large bowl. Stir in the oil and then add the date paste to the flours. Whisk the eggs well until creamy, fold them in, then add the yogurt to give the mixture a thick consistency.

Prepare the filling: the firm tofu will be in the form of a block. Put it in a clean tea towel and bring the sides of the tea towel together to make a bag. Twist the tea towel ends round and round so that the bag around the tofu becomes tighter and tighter and excess liquid is squeezed out. Do this for a few minutes then empty the tofu into a bowl and mash with a fork. The texture will now be quite crumbly. Stir in the apple with the cinnamon and sultanas.

Assemble the cake by pouring half the cake mixture into a greased and floured baking tin 20–23cm (8–9in) in diameter. Cover this with half the apple-tofu filling. Pour the remaining cake mixture evenly over the top. Cover with the remaining apple-tofu mixture and sprinkle the flaked almonds on top of this. Bake in a preheated oven gas mark 4/180°C/350°F for 50–60 minutes. If the cake is quite deep put a sheet of greaseproof paper over the top after about 35 minutes to stop it burning.

Each slice is 20g CHO. 180 kcals.

CAROB CAKE

75g (3oz) raisins
100ml (4 fl oz) water
125g (4½oz) wholewheat flour
15g (½oz) wheatgerm
30g (generous 1oz) low fat
  soya flour
50g (2oz) carob powder
1 tsp bicarbonate of soda
2 tsp cream of tartar
50ml (2 fl oz) oil
200g (7oz) pear, grated
2 eggs
100ml (4 fl oz) low-fat natural
  yogurt

Makes 10 large slices.

Cook the raisins and water in a saucepan over a low heat until all the water has been absorbed. Blend to make into a paste. Leave to cool.

In a large bowl mix together the wholewheat flour, wheatgerm and soya flour, carob powder, bicarbonate of soda and cream of tartar. Stir in the oil. Add the raisin paste and grated pear. Whisk the eggs well until creamy and add to the cake mixture. Add the yogurt to make a mixture with a thick pouring consistency.

Pour into a greased and floured 20cm (8in) diameter baking tin and bake in a preheated oven gas mark 4/180°C/350°F for 30–35 minutes until a knife inserted in the centre comes out cleanly.

Each slice is 20g CHO. 155 kcals.

Variation: cover with Carob Icing (see page 82) and sprinkle 1 tbs of desiccated coconut over the top.

CAROB MOUSSE LAYER CAKE

This impressive multi-layered cake has four layers of carob mousse set between four layers of sponge. It is a small rectangular shape about 12.5cm (5in) high.

75g (3oz) dried dates
100ml (4 fl oz) water
150g (5oz) wholewheat flour
25g (1oz) soya flour
25g (1oz) wheatgerm
1 tsp bicarbonate of soda
2 tsp cream of tartar

Cook the dates and water in a small saucepan over a low heat until all the water has been absorbed. Blend to make a smooth paste. Leave to cool.

Combine the flours, wheatgerm, bicarbonate of soda and cream of

½ tsp vanilla essence
50g (2oz) banana, peeled and
  mashed
2 eggs, size 3
300ml (10 fl oz) low fat natural
  yogurt

½ quantity of Carob Mousse
  (see page 267)

Makes 20 slices.

tartar. Add the cooled dates, vanilla essence, mashed banana and well-beaten eggs. Fold in the yogurt to make a creamy mixture.

Grease and flour a swiss roll tin about 30 × 23cm (12 × 9in) square. Spoon the cake mixture evenly over the tin. Bake in a preheated oven gas mark 4/180°C/350°F for about 30 minutes until the cake has browned and is firm. Remove carefully with a palate knife and leave to cool.

Prepare the Carob Mousse.

Cut the cake in quarters, so that each piece is about 15 × 11cm (6 × 4½in). Spread the Carob Mousse over each layer of cake, and place the layers one on top of another, with a layer of Carob Mousse on top. Ensure that the top layer is slightly thicker than the others because if it is too thin it will dry out and spoil the effect. Some of the filling will ooze out because of the weight of the layers, but simply spread this around the sides.

Each slice is 10g CHO. 75 kcals.

CARROT CAKE

This light Carrot Cake is perfumed with orange peel, giving off a fragrant orange scent while it bakes. The smell always reminds me of cold winters spent working in a library in Jerusalem. The old stone building was wonderfully cool in the long hot summer, but bitterly cold in the winter months. We used two regulation pot-bellied open paraffin stoves to heat the library, which were quite effective although they gave off suffocating fumes. The window should have been opened to allow the fumes to escape, but that would have allowed the cold to come back in. We found our way round this problem by eating seasonal oranges and balancing the peel precariously on the metal bars covering the flames. After a few moments the heat would draw out the orange perfume from the skin and we were intoxicated by the powerful odour.

100g (4oz) dried dates, chopped
100ml (4 fl oz) water
225g (8oz) carrots, grated finely
75g (3oz) wholewheat flour
25g (1oz) wheatgerm
25g (1oz) desiccated coconut
50g (2oz) ground almonds
1 tsp bicarbonate of soda
½–1 tsp mixed spice
1 egg
1 tsp grated orange zest
150ml (5 fl oz) low fat natural yogurt

Makes 12 slices.

Cook the dates and water in a small saucepan over a low heat until the water has been absorbed. Mash with a fork to make a smooth paste, and blend if necessary. Put them to one side to cool. Grate the carrots and mix with the cooled date paste.

Combine the flour, wheatgerm, coconut, ground almonds, bicarbonate of soda and spice. Stir in the carrots and dates. Add the well-beaten egg and the orange zest. Fold in the yogurt.

Pour into a greased and floured 20cm (8in) diameter baking tin. Bake in a preheated oven gas mark 5/190°C/375°F for 40 minutes until the cake has browned on top and the sides have begun to come away from the tin.

Each slice is 10g CHO. 100 kcals.

PARSNIP CAKE

This is a very fragrant light cake although a parsnip may sound an unlikely candidate for providing such qualities!

Parsnip contains, per 100g, 1mg of vitamin E, 10mg of vitamin C, very small amounts of the B vitamins and a number of minerals, including potassium, phosphorus and magnesium. Parsnip, and particularly wild parsnip, was used for medicinal purposes. The root was chopped into a pulp and used as a poultice to relieve and heal abscesses and swellings, while the juice was claimed by Culpeper, the 17th century physician and astrologer, to cure jaundice.

225g (8oz) parsnip
75g (3oz) wholewheat flour
50g (2oz) soya flour

Scrub the parsnip well then grate.

Combine the flours, ground almonds,

50g (2oz) ground almonds
1 tsp bicarbonate of soda
2 tsp cream of tartar
1 tsp cinnamon
75g (3oz) dried dates, chopped
50g (2oz) prunes, stoned and
    chopped
100ml (4 fl oz) water
6 tbs orange juice, freshly
    squeezed
1 heaped tsp of orange zest
1 egg
150ml (5 fl oz) low fat natural
    yogurt

Makes 8 large slices.

bicarbonate of soda, cream of tartar
and cinnamon. Stir in the grated
parsnip.

Cook the chopped dates, prunes and
water in a small saucepan over a low
heat until the water has been absorbed.
If necessary blend to make a smooth
paste.

Add the date-prune paste, orange juice
and zest to the flours. Whisk the egg
well and add. Stir in the yogurt.

Pour into a greased and floured 20cm
(8in) diameter baking tin and bake
in a preheated oven gas mark
5/190°C/375°F for 30–40 minutes
until firm.

Each slice is 20g CHO. 160 kcals.

CHERRY CHEESECAKE

*This is a delicious cheesecake. The cherries make it very sweet and
special.*

Crust
10g (½oz) carob powder
6 tbs water
15g (½oz) sultanas, chopped
    (use dried dates if not
    available)
50g (2oz) shredded wheat

Filling
2 eggs
150g (5oz) bananas, peeled
200ml (7 oz) skimmed milk
    quark
75g (3 fl oz) low fat natural
    yogurt
25g (1oz) ground almonds
a few drops of vanilla essence
100g (4oz) cherries

Prepare the base: put the carob
powder, water and chopped sultanas in
a small saucepan. Place over a low heat
stirring all the time. The carob powder
will dissolve in the liquid and the
sultanas will become mushy. Take the
pan off the heat and add the shredded
wheat, crumbling it in with your
fingers. Stir until all the shredded
wheat is coated with the carob sauce.
Press into a 20cm (8in) diameter
greased baking tin, patting the soft
mixture with your fingertips so that it
is distributed over the whole tin.

Prepare the filling: whisk the eggs well.
Mouli or sieve the bananas to a fine

Topping
½ tsp agar-agar
100ml (4 fl oz) apple juice
200g (7oz) cherries

Makes 12 slices.

liquid and add to the eggs. Whisk for a further minute. Fold in the quark and yogurt. Add the ground almonds and vanilla essence. Add the 100g (4oz) of cherries, stoned and halved. Stir carefully so that they do not become mashed or the cake mixture turns pink. This is the reason that they are added at the end.

Spoon the filling over the base and bake in a preheated oven gas mark 4/180°C/350°F for 25–30 minutes until the mixture becomes firm and slightly browned at the edges. Cheesecake continues to set even when taken out of the oven so do not overcook.

Prepare the topping: combine the agar-agar with a dessertspoon of the apple juice, then add the remainder. Bring to the boil in a very small pan and allow it to bubble gently for one minute. Pour the jelly over the surface of the cold cake. Quickly arrange the 200g (7oz) of stoned and halved cherries on top of the cheesecake. They will set firmly in the jelly.

Each slice is 10g CHO. 70 kcals.

YEAST CHEESECAKE

Use fromage frais with just under 4 per cent fat for this recipe. If you cannot obtain it from your local grocers or supermarket substitute skimmed milk quark.

For a really sweet taste spread 25g (1oz) of sugar-free apricot jam over the pastry base.

½ quantity Yeast Pastry (see page 164)

Roll out the pastry thinly to make two equal-sized rectangles to fit a 25 × 20cm (10 × 8in) baking tin. Lightly

Filling
100g (4oz) cottage cheese
400g (14oz) low-fat fromage
   frais
150g (5oz) raisins
2 tsp lemon zest
1 egg
little beaten egg for decoration

Makes 24 slices.

grease the base of the tin and cover it with one of the pastry sheets.

Put the cottage cheese through a food mill so that it becomes fine and combine with the fromage frais. Add the raisins, lemon zest and well-beaten egg.

Spread the cheese mixture over the base of the pastry. Place the lid on top. Leave to stand in a warm room for 20 minutes until it has increased in size. Brush the lid with a little beaten egg and make a few slashes across the top of the pastry.

Bake in a preheated oven gas mark 6/200°C/400°F for 15 minutes then turn the oven down to gas mark 5/190°C/375°F and cook for a further 15 minutes until browned.

Each slice is 10g CHO. 75 kcals.

PERSIMMON CHEESECAKE

Persimmons, round, smooth, orange-skinned fruit, have a unique taste if they are eaten when just ripe. The kaki variety was originally found growing in Japan and China, and is sometimes known as a Chinese apple, probably because of its origins. The Israelis grow sharon fruit which are smaller versions of persimmons and can be substituted for them in this recipe.

The persimmon is a nutritious fruit. Each one contains about 500mcg of carotene (vitamin A) and 10mg of vitamin C. This compares well with an apple which contains only 30mcg of carotene and 3mg of vitamin C.

This recipe has a very delicate taste as it is sweetened solely with the ripe fruit. The persimmon is ready for use when it is a little soft to the touch and may even have a slight tinge of brown in the orange skin. If it is eaten when unripe and still hard it has an unpleasant astringent taste. The Chinese extract a fluid from it when it is in this state and use it to make cosmetics.

The filling is not baked but set with agar-agar.

1 quantity of Sweet Seed Pastry
  (see page 163)

Filling
600g (1 lb 4oz) ripe
  persimmon, peeled
200g (7oz) skimmed milk
  quark
100g (4oz) Greek yogurt
1 egg, separated
2 heaped tbs agar-agar flakes
100ml (4 fl oz) apple juice,
  unsweetened
50ml (2 fl oz) water

Makes 12 slices.

Lightly grease a 23cm (9in) diameter baking tin or deep baking dish, and pat the pastry around the base. Bake in a preheated oven gas mark 4/180°C/350°F for 20–25 minutes until the pastry is cooked and lightly browned all over.

Prepare the filling: blend the persimmon to make about 350ml (12 fl oz) of fruit purée. Combine with the quark, yogurt and well-beaten egg yolk.

Mix the agar-agar flakes with the apple juice, water and about 100ml (4 fl oz) of the fruit purée in a small saucepan. Bring to the boil and simmer for at least 5 minutes, stirring all the time. Add to the fruit and cheese mixture, stirring the setting liquid in well. Whisk the egg white and fold in. Pour over the cooked pastry base and leave to set. Chill in the fridge before serving.

Each slice is 15g CHO. 130 kcals.

TOFU APPLE CHEESECAKE

Tofu is a very effective non-milk substitute for curd cheese. The main difference in texture is that tofu is firmer.

1 quantity Sweet Seed Pastry
  (see p. 163)

Filling
500g (1lb 2oz) eating apples,
  chopped
100ml (4 fl oz) water

Prepare the pastry. Take a 23cm (9in) baking tin. Pat the dough around the base of the tin. Bake blind in a preheated oven gas mark 4/180°C/350°F for 10 minutes.

Prepare the filling: combine the apple

200g (7oz) firm tofu
1 egg
2 tbs lemon juice, freshly
    squeezed
1 tsp cinnamon
1 tsp vanilla essence
30g (1oz generous) ground
    almonds
25g (1oz) brown rice flakes

Makes 12 large slices.

with the water and blend in a liquidizer to make a purée. Add the tofu and continue to blend until a thick paste is formed. Fold in the whisked egg, lemon juice, cinnamon, vanilla essence and ground almonds.

Pour the filling into the partly baked crust. Sprinkle the top with the brown rice flakes. Return to the oven at gas mark 4/180°C/350°F for 30 minutes until browned around the edges.

Each slice is 10g CHO. 115 kcals.

Sponges and Light Cakes

SWISS ROLL

Traditional recipes for Swiss Roll are always precise, with the weight of the dry ingredients often balanced against the weight of the eggs. Swiss Roll is basically a light, flexible sponge and it presents particular problems for the sugar-free cook. It is not possible to use dried fruit, even if it is blended, because it will affect the lightness of the sponge and the degree of ease with which it can be rolled up without cracking at each turn. To overcome the problem this recipe uses sieved banana for sweetness.

The texture of the Swiss Roll is also improved by the amount of air beaten in with the eggs. Although the sponge is simple to make it is sensitive, so it is important to avoid delays when mixing and baking. When you take the Swiss Roll out of the oven have everything you need ready at hand so that you can roll it up quickly while it is still warm.

Spread with a sugar-free jam or for special occasions fill with Creme aux Marrons (see page 275).

125g (4½oz) bananas, peeled
50g (2oz) fine milled
    wholewheat flour
3 eggs
25g (1oz) ground almonds

Grease or oil the base of a 23 × 30cm (9 × 12in) swiss roll tin and place a sheet of grease-proof paper on top. Oil the top surface of the grease-proof paper so that it fits snugly into the

½ tsp almond essence
2 tbs desiccated coconut,
  unsweetened
50g (2oz) sugar-free jam

Makes 12 thin slices.

corners and sides of the tin. Preheat the oven to gas mark 6/200°C/400°F.

Prepare the ingredients: put the banana through a food mill or sieve it into a small bowl. Sieve the flour, after which there will be a small residue of coarse grains at the bottom of the sieve. Try and force them through. Toss back whatever remains into the sieved flour.

Separate the yolks and whites of the eggs into two bowls. Whisk the egg yolks until pale and creamy. Add the liquid banana and continue to whisk for a little longer. Whisk the egg whites stiffly and fold these into the banana and egg yolk mixture. Add the sieved flour, ground almonds and almond essence and stir in gently with a metal spoon.

Pour into the prepared swiss roll tin and spread evenly making sure you do not skimp near the corners. Bake for 7–10 minutes in the centre of the oven until the mixture has set and is beginning to brown. If it becomes too brown or overcooked it will crack when rolled up.

Have ready prepared a sheet of greaseproof paper the same size as the baking tin and placed on top of a clean tea towel. Sprinkle the greaseproof sheet with desiccated coconut.

Take the Swiss Roll out of the oven and turn it top side down on to the coconut-covered paper. Using a sharp knife gently ease the greaseproof lining paper off the back of the Swiss Roll. The corners and the sides are often the most brittle spots so approach these first. While the Swiss Roll is still warm swiftly roll it up in the greaseproof paper and tea towel. When cool ease open, lightly spread the jam over the surface and roll up again.

Each slice is 5g CHO. 65 kcals.

CAROB SWISS ROLL

This recipe shatters the usual image of heavy wholefood cakes. Fill it with Hazelnut-Carob Cream (see page 81) and it can shoulder its way on to a tea table with the best.

It can also be used as a basis for a Yuletide log. Fill with fromage frais mixed with seasonal fruit such as sliced bananas or chopped clementines and decorate the outside with half the recipe for Carob Mousse (see page 267).

3 eggs
125g (4½oz) bananas, peeled
50g (2oz) wholewheat flour, finely milled
25g (1oz) carob powder
few drops of vanilla essence
2 tbs desiccated coconut, unsweetened
50g (2oz) sugar-free jam

Makes 12 slices.

This recipe is prepared in the same way as Swiss Roll. The basic outline for preparing this cake is given below, but the Swiss Roll recipe (see page 240) provides a more detailed explanation.

Prepare a swiss roll tin by greasing the base, covering it with greaseproof paper then greasing the top of the paper. Preheat the oven to gas mark 6/200°C/400°F.

Separate the eggs. Whisk the egg yolks until pale and creamy. Add the sieved or mouliéd banana and whisk a little longer. Whisk the egg whites stiffly and fold in. Add the sieved flour, carob powder and vanilla essence. Fold in with a metal spoon.

Pour into the prepared swiss roll tin and spread evenly making sure you do not skimp near the corners. Bake for 7–10 minutes in the centre of the oven until the mixture has set. If it is overcooked it will crack when rolled up.

Remove from the oven and turn on to a sheet of greaseproof paper resting on a tea towel. The greaseproof paper should be sprinkled with desiccated coconut. Using a sharp knife gently ease the greaseproof lining paper off the back of the Swiss Roll. Swiftly roll up the Swiss Roll in the greaseproof lining paper and tea towel while it is still warm. When cool ease open, lightly spread the filling over the surface and roll up again.

Each slice without filling is 5g CHO. 60 kcals.

APRICOT FAIRY CAKES

These little sponge cakes are very light. Cook in paper cases, decorate with Coconut Icing and a little blob of apricot jam in the middle and they look and taste quite mouthwatering.

50g (2oz) dried apricots
3 eggs, separated
125g (4½oz) bananas
25g (1oz) ground almonds
50g (2oz) wholewheat flour, finely milled
1 quantity Coconut Icing (see page 82)
1 dessertspoon strawberry jam

Makes 15 cakes.

Pour a little boiling water over the dried apricots and leave to stand for half an hour. Put the apricots and soaking water in a small saucepan and heat until the water has been absorbed. Chop the apricots finely.

Whisk the egg yolks until they are thick and creamy. Whisk in the moulied banana. (Sieve if you do not have a mouli – the aim is to remove all lumps.) Whisk the egg whites until stiff and fold in. Fold in the ground almonds, sieved flour and chopped apricots with a metal spoon. Spoon the mixture into 15 paper cases.

Bake in a preheated oven gas mark

5/190°C/375°F for 8–10 minutes. The little cakes will puff up and turn brown on top in that short space of time, although they drop slightly after being taken out of the oven.

2 cakes with Coconut Icing are 10g CHO. 110 kcals.

HAZELNUT GATEAU

This recipe is a light nut gateau which is sandwiched together with a creamy filling and a nut carob topping. This is more work than a straightforward fruit cake such as banana or apple, but the results will stun your guests.

This gateau does not have as long a life as some of the other recipes so double the quantity only if you know that you will have enough people to eat it within two days of baking.

The hazelnuts in this recipe are not roasted. Try and buy the whole hazelnuts and grind them yourself. The grated orange zest should ideally come from organically grown oranges.

Gateau
50g (2oz) sultanas
250g (9oz) hazelnuts, ground
25g (1oz) wheatgerm
25g (1oz) soya flour
150g (5oz) bananas, peeled
juice and zest of 1 orange
    weighing about 225g (8oz)
3 eggs, separated

Grease and flour two 20cm (8in) sandwich tins and preheat the oven to gas mark 4/180°C/350°F.

Pour a little water over the sultanas and leave them to soak for 15 minutes. Combine the hazelnuts, wheatgerm and soya flour. Dry the sultanas and stir in.

Mash the bananas and add to the nut mixture together with the orange juice and zest to make a thick paste. Whisk the egg yolks and fold in. Whisk the egg whites until they are stiff and fold in with a metal spoon.

Divide the mixture equally between the two prepared tins and bake for 25 minutes until lightly browned. Test the cake by inserting a knife in the middle and checking that it comes out cleanly.

Hazelnut cream filling
50g (2oz) hazelnuts, ground
75g (3oz) low-fat fromage frais
juice and zest of 1 small orange weighing about 125g (4½oz)
1 tbs brandy (optional)

Mix the ground hazelnuts with the fromage frais in a small bowl. Moisten this mixture with the orange juice and zest and optional brandy. When the two cakes are cool spread the filling over one side and sandwich them together.

Carob hazelnut icing
25g (1oz) carob powder
15g (½oz) butter
100ml (4 fl oz) skimmed milk
25g (1oz) hazelnuts, ground

Put the carob powder, butter and milk in a small saucepan over a low heat and stir until the ingredients have dissolved. Take off the heat and add the ground hazelnuts. Spread the icing over the top of the cake and coat the sides with any that is left over.

Makes 12 slices.

Each slice is 10g CHO. 185 kcals.

POPPY SEED TORTE

Poppy seeds are often used in cakes in Eastern Europe, but in Britain are mostly used for decorating bread or rolls. The blue-black seeds are high in thiamin, one of the B vitamins. Herbalists recommend them as a general tonic food and in parts of Turkey they are mixed into a health-boosting cake.

50ml (2 fl oz) boiling water
75g (3oz) dried dates, chopped
25g (1oz) prunes, stoned and chopped
175g (6oz) poppy seeds
175g (6oz) ground almonds
50g (2oz) soya flour
500g (1lb 2oz) ripe pears, grated
1 tbs brandy (optional)
4 eggs, separated

Makes 12 slices.

Pour the boiling water over the dates and prunes. Leave to stand for 15 minutes then purée in a blender. Alternatively increase the quantity of water to 150ml (5 fl oz), chop the dried fruit finely and put them in a small saucepan to simmer over a low heat until the water is absorbed and the dried fruit has become a thick paste.

Grind the poppy seeds in an electric coffee grinder. Combine them with the ground almonds and soya flour. Add the pear to the dry ingredients together with the dried fruit purée, brandy and beaten egg yolks. Whisk the egg whites until stiff and fold into the mixture.

Grease and flour two 20–23cm (8–9in) diameter sandwich tins. Divide the mixture equally between them and bake in a preheated oven gas mark 4/350°F/180°C for about 25–30 minutes until the cakes are brown on top and a knife inserted in the middle comes out easily. Leave to cool before removing from the tins.

When cool the cake can be filled with fromage frais mixed with sieved banana or Apricot-Almond Spread (see page 78).

Each slice without filling is 10g CHO. 235 kcals.

GINGER FIG CAKE

Rye flour adds its distinctive flavour to this spicy tea cake made without eggs.

125g (4½oz) dried figs
100ml (4 fl oz) water
100g (4oz) rye flour
25g (1oz) soya flour
75g (3oz) porridge oats
1 tsp bicarbonate of soda
1–2 tsp ground ginger
½ tsp cinnamon
pinch of nutmeg
pinch of ground cloves
50ml (2 fl oz) oil
1 large orange, weighing about 250g (9oz)

Makes 10 slices.

Soak the figs in a little water for an hour or chop them and put with the 100ml (4 fl oz) water in a small saucepan over a low heat until the water is absorbed. Leave to cool.

Combine the flours, oats, bicarbonate of soda and spices in a mixing bowl. Add the chopped and softened figs and the oil and stir in.

Peel the orange and remove any remaining pith and pips and blend. It should make about 225ml (8 fl oz) of thick liquid orange. Stir this in with the other ingredients to make a sticky paste. Pour into a greased and floured 17.5cm (7in) baking tin and bake in a preheated oven gas mark 3/170°C/325°F for 40 minutes until the cake is browned all over and a knife inserted in the middle comes out cleanly.

Each slice is 20g CHO. 150 kcals.

MINCEMEAT CAKE

This is based on a Belgian recipe. When you make mincemeat double the quantity then you will have enough for this cake waiting ready in your fridge.

3 eggs
1 quantity Mincemeat (see page 80)
75g (3oz) wholewheat flour
25g (1oz) soya flour
25g (1oz) wheatgerm

Makes 16 slices.

Whisk the eggs well so that they are thick and creamy. Stir in the mincemeat. Fold in the sieved flours and wheatgerm.

Grease and flour a shallow baking tin which measures about 20 × 30cm (8 × 12in). Pour in the mixture. Bake for 40 minutes in a preheated oven gas mark 4/180°C/350°F for about 40 minutes until the cake is browned all over.

Each slice is 15g CHO. 115 kcals.

WALNUT CAKE

This moist cake can be eaten by itself or served with a fruity cream such as Clementine Cream Delight (see page 194).
Walnuts are a high source of Omega 3 fatty acids. These are mostly found in fish oils and come from very few plant sources. The beneficial effects of these oils include lowering of blood cholesterol levels and reducing certain types of arthritic pain. A survey of heart disease mortality in Holland showed a 50 per cent lower death rate from heart

disease amongst men eating at least one fish meal a week compared to those who eat none. Walnuts contain 1.9g of Omega 3 per 100g, not as high as mackerel which contains 2.6g, but rather higher than soya beans which contain 0.85g.

50g (2oz) dried dates, finely chopped
200g (7oz) walnuts, ground
50g (2oz) soya flour
25g (1oz) wheatgerm
¼–½ tsp cinnamon
1 tsp bicarbonate of soda
2 tsp cream of tartar
150g (5oz) bananas, peeled and finely mashed
3 eggs

Makes 10 large slices.

Cover the dates with a little water and leave to soak for 20 minutes.

Combine the ground walnuts, soya flour, wheatgerm, cinnamon, bicarbonate of soda and cream of tartar. Mix the banana with the soaked dates. Separate the eggs and whisk the egg yolks until they are thick and creamy and add to the nut mixture. Whisk the egg whites stiffly and fold into the mixture. Grease and flour a 20cm (8in) square baking tin and pour in the mixture. Bake in a preheated oven gas mark 4/180°C/350°F for 25 minutes until evenly browned.

Each slice is 10g CHO. 180 kcals.

ADUKI BEAN CAKE

The main ingredient of this moist and sweet cake is not as strange as it first sounds. Aduki beans are quite widely used in Japan and South-East Asia as a basis for sweets – they are usually mixed with sugar and made into sticky blocks which are cut into slices for eating. It is not unknown for white beans to be used in cakes in central Europe, and in this recipe I have married the two traditions. Aduki beans have been used rather than other types because they are meant to be particularly beneficial for the kidneys – and the idea of enjoying food and benefiting one's internal organs at the same time seems eminently sensible.

Aduki beans also make a delicious soup using sweet vegetables such as onions and carrots.

100g (4oz) dry aduki beans
450ml (16 fl oz) water
75g (3oz) raisins
150g (5oz) hazelnuts, ground

Pour boiling water over the aduki beans and leave to soak for an hour. Cook the beans: if you have a pressure cooker they will be ready after about

1 large eating apple, weighing about 175g (6oz), grated
50g (2oz) bananas, peeled and mashed
¼ tsp vanilla essence
zest of 1 lemon
3 eggs, size 2, separated

Makes 12 large slices.

15 minutes of cooking at pressure. Only a little water will remain at the bottom of the pressure cooker. When you have removed the weighted lid let the water boil lightly so that most of it evaporates. Do not try to boil it all away or the beans can become dried up.

If you cook the beans in an ordinary heavy saucepan soak them overnight. Bring the beans to the boil for 10 minutes then simmer for about an hour until they are soft. Let any excess water boil away, but be careful not to overdo it and burn the beans.

Purée the beans and the remaining cooking water in a blender or a food mill. Their combined weight is roughly about 350g (12oz).

Soak the raisins in a little water for about 15 minutes.

Grind the hazelnuts and combine with the aduki bean purée. The purée will become considerably thicker. Fold in the apple and banana. Add the few drops of vanilla essence and lemon zest.

Dry the raisins, remove any stalks and purée in an electric coffee grinder. Add to the cake mixture.

Whisk the egg yolks until they are creamy and fold into the cake mixture with a large spoon. Whisk the egg whites until stiff and fold in lightly. Pour into a large greased and floured baking tin about 23 × 23cm (9 × 9in). The shallower the cake is the quicker it cooks.

Bake in a preheated oven gas mark 4/180°C/350°F for 45–55 minutes. The cake is ready when the edges are browned and a knife inserted in the centre comes out cleanly.

Each slice is 10g CHO. 114 kcals.

FRUIT CAKE

Fruit cake is often the basis for a festive cake for a wedding or anniversary or for a Christmas tea. Everyone has their favourite combinations of dried fruit. This recipe uses the traditional raisins and dates, but also includes dried apricots and dried bananas. Dried bananas are sticky and sweet and contain 2mg of vitamin B6 per 100g.

Baking a fruit cake can be a long slow process and I have come across various tips to avoid it drying out. Some people swear by putting a baking dish of hot water in the oven which adds moisture to the cooking environment, while others cover the top with greaseproof paper throughout cooking. If you are not keen on a hard crust then a sheet of greaseproof paper cut to size and put on the top of the cake after the first 50–60 minutes is a useful protection. Another method is not to make the fruit cake too deep so that it does not require such extensive baking.

The attraction of a fruit cake is that it can be prepared in advance for a special occasion. This still holds true for a sugar-free version, but it keeps for less time. A method for encouraging its preserving qualities is to pour fruit juice or spirits such as brandy slowly over the top of the finished cake so that it soaks through. Wrap well with greaseproof paper and foil and leave to mature in a tin for a couple of weeks.

100g (4oz) dried figs
75g (3oz) dried apricots
75g (3oz) dried bananas
100g (4oz) dried dates
100g (4oz) seedless raisins
100g (4oz) sultanas
100ml (4 fl oz) water
100g (4oz) firm tofu
50g (2oz) butter
1 tbs tahini
2 large eggs
50g (2oz) whole almonds, with outer skins, chopped

Soak all the dried fruit except the dates in the water for 30 minutes. After soaking, rinse, dry and chop the dried figs, apricots and bananas. Put the dates with a little water in a separate bowl.

If you are using a food processor combine the dates with the tofu, butter, tahini and eggs to make a sweet batter. Alternatively chop the dates very finely and mash as much as you can with the back of a fork and add to the

50g (2oz) ground almonds
100g (4oz) wholewheat flour
25g (1oz) soya flour
1 tsp bicarbonate of soda
2 tsp cream of tartar
1 tsp mixed spice
1 tsp lemon zest
1 large orange weighing about
    175g (6oz) or 100ml (4 fl oz)
    orange juice
brandy (optional)

Makes 16 slices.

well-whisked eggs, moulied tofu, creamed butter and tahini. Pour this mixture over the dried fruit together with the chopped almonds. Stir well and add all the remaining ingredients except for the orange. This should make a very stiff cake mixture.

Pour into a 20cm (8in) diameter cake tin which has been oiled and lined with oiled greaseproof paper. Flatten the top with the back of a spoon.

Bake in a preheated oven gas mark 3/170°C/325°F for 60 minutes until the top is well browned and a knife inserted in the centre comes out cleanly.

When the cake has cooled squeeze the juice from the orange, which should make about 100ml (4 fl oz). Make a few light cuts on the top of the cake and slowly pour the juice over until it has all soaked in. If you prefer your fruit cake more alcoholic then substitute a little brandy for the orange juice. Wrap the cake in greaseproof paper and foil and store in a tin for one week to mature before using.

Each slice is 25g CHO. 185 kcals.

CHERRY SAUCE

This sauce requires no cooking. Try and use the dark red cherries as these have the sweetest flavour. Cherries are high in potassium and contain magnesium, a small amount of calcium and some of the B vitamins.

150g (5oz) cherries, stoned
1 tbs apple juice

Makes 150ml (5 fl oz)

Blend the cherries with the apple juice to make a thick liquid. Serve immediately or chill until needed later the same day.

Sauce is 15g CHO. 70 kcals.

Serving suggestion: serve with Apple Cherry Cake (see page 226) or Cherry Carob Ice Cream (see page 287).

ORANGE AND STRAWBERRY SAUCE

This is a thick jam-like sauce. Use English strawberries because they are the sweetest.

1 large orange, weighing about
    200g (7oz)
100g (4oz) strawberries, hulled
1 scant tsp arrowroot
1 dessertspoon brandy

Makes 4 servings.

Peel the orange and remove all the pith and any pips. Blend the orange and strawberries in a liquidizer. The purée will be a salmon colour. Pour it into a small saucepan, removing a small amount to mix with the arrowroot. Pour this into the pan with the rest of the purée. Heat on a low light until the purée thickens. Serve either hot or cold.

Sauce is 20g CHO. 100 kcals.

Serving suggestions: this sauce goes well with ice cream. It can also be used to make a speedy dessert – serve the sauce with firm fresh fruit such as apricots, sliced bananas or quartered pears.

PASTEL PINK SAUCE

350g (12oz) strawberries, hulled
1 eating apple, weighing about 125g (4½oz)
1 tbs apple juice

Blend the strawberries, apple and apple juice in a liquidizer and chill in the fridge until needed. Use the same day.

Sauce is 35g CHO. 140 kcals.

Serving suggestion: serve with Chilled Almond Globes (see page 200).

PEACH SAUCE

An apple is an excellent thing – until you have tried a peach!
George du Maurier, 19th-century French-English artist and novelist.

There is something special about peaches, whether it is the texture, colour or smell of the fruit, or a combination of all three. When buying peaches make sure they are firm and a rich warm colour – a sign that they are ready for eating.

3 peaches, weighing about 375g (13oz)
2 tbs apple juice
⅛ tsp ground ginger
1 dessertspoon brandy

Wash two of the peaches and slice into the liquidizer. Blend with the apple juice and ground ginger to make 300ml (½pt) liquid.

Pour boiling water over the remaining peach. Remove the skin, cut the fruit into thin slices and add to the sauce.

Heat in a small saucepan and bring to the boil. Take off the heat and stir in the brandy.

Sauce is 35g CHO. 160 kcals.

Serving suggestion: serve with Peach Ice Cream (see page 285) or Apple Crumble (see page 211).

RASPBERRY SAUCE

The raspberries sold in the shops are all cultivated, but if you live near woods where raspberries grow wild it is worth searching them out. Herbalists regard wild raspberries and their leaves as having considerable medicinal powers. Raspberry leaf tea is a well known tonic taken during pregnancy and sometimes during labour.

Cultivated raspberries also have a high mineral and vitamin content – 220mg of potassium, 41mg of calcium, 22mg of magnesium, 1.2mg of iron, 17mg of selenium, 25mg of vitamin C, some carotene and some of the B-complex vitamins. They are also low in calories.

1 small eating apple, weighing about 100g (4oz)
75ml (3 fl oz) apple juice, unsweetened
275g (10oz) raspberries

Slice the apple into a medium-sized saucepan with the apple juice. Bring to the boil and simmer until the apple has softened. Add the raspberries and mash slightly with a fork. Bring to the boil and remove from the heat. Sieve the sauce and serve cold.

The sauce is 35g CHO. 140 kcals.

Serving suggestions: serve with Melon and Raspberry Ice Cream (see page 283). If you double the quantity Raspberry Sauce can be served by itself in little bowls.

SAVOURY APPLE SAUCE

This sauce goes well with a meat dish such as roast lamb, or with a mixed vegetable pie.

250g (9oz) eating apples
150ml (5 fl oz) vegetable stock (or water and 1 small tsp of vegetable concentrate such as Vecon or a vegetable soup cube)

Chop the apples into a liquidizer and blend with the vegetable stock. Pour into a small saucepan and bring to the boil. Simmer for about 5–10 minutes until the sauce has thickened. Either serve immediately or reheat the same day when needed.

Sauce is 20g CHO. 100 kcals.

CUSTARD

It was a particularly difficult task to work out how to sweeten custard subtly without affecting its pure yellow colour and texture. I turned to Judy Jackson, a cookery writer and demonstrator, who had the original idea of infusing the sweet flavour of dried apricots into the custard – without using the fruit itself.

50g (2oz) dried apricots
75ml (3 fl oz) boiling water
2 large egg yolks
1 tsp arrowroot
150–175ml (5–6 fl oz) skimmed milk

Pour the boiling water over the apricots and leave to stand for an hour.

Lightly beat the egg yolks with a fork then add the arrowroot. Carefully pour the water off the dried apricots into a measuring jug (keep the dried apricots as they will be used for further infusion) and add enough of the milk to make the liquid up to 225ml (8 fl oz).

Heat the milk and apricot water in a small saucepan to just below boiling point. Pour over the yolks and arrowroot, stirring. Pour the mixture back into the pan and cook on a very low heat stirring continuously with a wooden spoon until it thickens and coats the back of the spoon. The slow thickening is very important. If the contents of the pan seem to be getting too hot and it is not possible to lower the cooking heat any more, lift the saucepan a little way above the heat for a couple of seconds to slow down the cooking. Another alternative is to use a double saucepan, but this is not essential. The custard should not be allowed to boil as this causes curdling.

When the custard has thickened pour it over the apricots and leave for 20–30 minutes. Sieve before using.

Custard is 15g CHO. 180 kcals.

BANANA CUSTARD

This custard goes very well with crumbles and pies and requires less preparation than the plain custard recipe.

2 large egg yolks
1 tsp arrowroot
225ml (8 fl oz) skimmed milk
50g (2oz) ripe banana, peeled

Lightly beat the egg yolks with a fork then add the arrowroot.

Heat the milk in a small saucepan to just below boiling point. Pour over the yolks, stirring. Pour the egg and milk mixture back into the pan and cook on a very low heat. Stir continuously with a wooden spoon until the mixture thickens and coats the back of the spoon. The slow thickening is very important. If the contents of the pan seem to be getting too hot lift it a little way above the heat for a couple of seconds to slow down the cooking. The custard should not be allowed to boil as this causes curdling. (If that does happen some cooks recommend pouring the mixture immediately into a bowl and whisking it in order to get back to a fairly smooth texture.)

When the custard has thickened pour it into a bowl and add the finely mashed banana. Sieve the custard and either use hot or leave to cool.

Banana custard is 25g CHO. 240 kcals.

14 MOUSSES, JELLIES AND CREAMS

Agar-Agar

Agar-agar is a seaweed and a very effective setting agent for mousses and jellies; it comes in either powder form or flakes. Powder is the form most readily available in health food chains, while specialist health food shops will stock the flakes. Both are soluble in hot water but not in cold. They set quickly and do not need to be refrigerated to speed up the gelling process.

Agar-agar flakes are a less processed product than the powder. They are prepared by slow cooking, filtering and, according to the manufacturers, being placed out 'in the winter snow to be naturally bleached and freeze dried into dry fibrous strips'. These are then cut into flakes. The quantity of flakes used is normally double that of powder.

I find the flakes work best with mousses while the powder, which requires a shorter cooking time, is more suited for jellies. The flakes set more slowly which can be useful when other ingredients have to be added after the agar-agar. With experience you may find that you have a greater preference for one or other of these forms of agar-agar.

How to use agar-agar flakes: mix the flakes with the liquid in a small pan. Slowly bring to the boil and simmer for 5 minutes, stirring all the time. Use a very small pan if the quantity of liquid is below 200ml (7 fl oz) so that less water evaporates during the simmering. If the liquid seems to be evaporating too fast, quickly add a little more to the pan.

How to use agar-agar powder: dissolve the powder in a little liquid to make a thick paste then gradually add the rest of the liquid. Bring to the boil in a pan, the size depending on the amount of liquid, and boil for 1½ minutes. This sets very quickly. If only using a little liquid with the powder be careful that it does not evaporate too fast or you will be left with a glutinous mass instead of liquid in the pan.

STRAWBERRY MOUSSE

Strawberries 'cool the liver, the blood and the spleen, or a hot choleric stomach; refresh and comfort fainting spirits and quench thirst', wrote Culpeper in the 17th century. A modern-day herbalist, Juliette de Bairacli Levy, claims that strawberries act as a nerve tonic and are good for treating anaemia, lowered vitality and lack of appetite. Interestingly she suggests that 'strawberry rash' is not an allergic reaction, but evidence of the cleansing action of strawberries, driving excess acid from the body more speedily than the body can remove it by other means. Wild strawberries are richer in iron, but any kind make this marvellous mousse.

300g (11oz) strawberries, hulled
150g (5oz) Greek yogurt
100ml (4 fl oz) water
100ml (4 fl oz) apple juice
1 tbs agar-agar flakes
150g (5oz) strawberries, hulled and sliced

Makes 4 small servings.

Blend the 300g (11 oz) strawberries to make a purée. Combine with the yogurt.

Put the water, apple juice and agar-agar flakes in a small saucepan. Bring to the boil and stir for 5 minutes while it simmers. Keep on stirring to avoid the agar-agar sticking to the sides of the pan. Take off the heat and add to the strawberry and yogurt mixture. Add the 150g (5 oz) sliced strawberries. Spoon into 4 glasses or bowls and leave to set.

Each serving is 10g CHO. 90 kcals.

PINEAPPLE AND APPLE MOUSSE

This is a delicate, fluffy dessert. Make sure the pineapple you use is ready for eating. An unripe one will not only sour the dessert, but for some people can act as a stomach irritant. A sign that the pineapple is ripe is if one of the inner leaves pulls out easily.

250g (9oz) fresh ripe pineapple, without skin
1 eating apple, weighing about 125g (4½oz)
200g (7oz) firm tofu

Chop the pineapple, apple and tofu and blend in a liquidizer or food processor. Put to one side while you prepare the agar-agar which will make it set.

1 tbs agar-agar flakes
50ml (2 fl oz) water
100ml (4 fl oz) orange juice
1 egg white

Makes 6 small servings.

Heat the water and orange juice with the agar-agar flakes in a very small saucepan and let it simmer for 5 minutes stirring all the time. Take off the heat and add the agar-agar liquid to the blended fruit and tofu mixture.

Whisk the egg white stiffly and fold it into the fruit mixture. Pour into a bowl to set. An optional decoration is to sprinkle the top with a little cinnamon. Chill in the fridge before serving.

Each serving is 10g CHO. 50 kcals.

APRICOT MOUSSE

Dried apricots are so nutritious that they are often recommended in ordinary and special diets by dietitians. This is because of their high vitamin A content and because a portion of dried apricots contains more iron than the same weight of rump steak.

An unusual way to serve this mousse is to place peeled lychees around the sides of the serving dish.

175g (6oz) dried apricots
300ml (11 fl oz) water
75g (3oz) low-fat natural
  yogurt
150ml (5 fl oz) apple juice
50ml (2 fl oz) water
1 tbs agar-agar flakes
1 egg white

Makes 4 servings.

Soak the apricots overnight in the 300ml (11 fl oz) water. Put the apricots and soaking water in a heavy saucepan and simmer gently until the water is absorbed, making sure that the apricots do not burn. Cool. Blend in a food processor or liquidizer to make a smooth cream. Fold in the yogurt.

Combine the apple juice, water and agar-agar flakes in a small saucepan and simmer for 5 minutes, stirring all the time. Stir the cooked agar-agar liquid into the apricot mixture. Whisk the egg white stiffly and fold in. Pour into 4 bowls and leave to set.

Each serving is 15g CHO. 70 kcals.

CAROB MOUSSE

200g (7oz) firm tofu
200g (7oz) ripe banana, peeled
½ tsp vanilla essence
4 tbs orange juice,
    unsweetened
1 tbs brandy (optional)
100g (4oz) carob powder
200ml (7 fl oz) skimmed milk
200ml (7 fl oz) water
1 tbs agar-agar flakes or 2 tsp
    agar-agar powder
2 egg whites

Makes 6 servings.

Blend the tofu and banana in a food processor or food mill. Add the vanilla essence, orange juice and brandy and put to one side. In a small saucepan combine the carob powder, milk, water and agar-agar flakes. Bring to the boil and simmer on a low light for 5 minutes, stirring all the time and making sure the mixture does not become too thick.

If using agar-agar powder dissolve in 1 dessertspoon of water and add to the carob powder, milk and water in the saucepan after they have cooked gently for 3 minutes. Let the agar-agar solution simmer for a further 2 minutes.

Take the pan off the heat. Stir the agar-agar liquid into the tofu and banana mixture. Whisk the egg whites stiffly and fold in. Pour the mousse into 6 bowls and leave to set.

Each serving is 20g CHO. 100 kcals.

STRAWBERRY JELLY

The sweetness of this jelly is affected by the sweetness of the strawberries used. The English strawberries which appear in July and August seem to be sweeter than any of the imported ones on sale at other times of the year. When using those that do not have such a rich taste it is a good idea to include a few fresh dates or ripe banana for added flavour.

450g (1lb) strawberries, hulled
100g (4oz) fresh dates weighed
    with stones or 100g (4oz)
    ripe banana, peeled
    (optional)

Blend the strawberries (and dates or banana) to make a bright pinky red purée. The small seeds on the outside of Spanish strawberries seem to be

150ml (5 fl oz) apple juice
50ml (2 fl oz) cold water
2 tsps agar-agar powder

Makes 4 servings.

coarser than the English ones, so if you use this variety sieve the purée.

Combine the apple juice and water in a small saucepan. Use 1 tbs of this liquid to dissolve the agar-agar powder. Pour into the saucepan with the rest of the juice and water. Bring to the boil, add a little of the strawberry purée and simmer for 1½ minutes. Mix with the rest of the purée and pour into a wetted mould or bowls. The agar-agar powder sets very quickly. If you plan to pour the strawberry jelly into a mould have it ready beforehand so that it can be filled immediately after combining the agar-agar with the purée.

Each serving without added dates or banana is 10g CHO. 45 kcals.
Each serving with dates or banana is 15g CHO. 70 kcals.

STRAWBERRY JELLY RING

The way food is presented makes a huge difference to its appeal, and good presentation can make an ordinary dish festive. A simple strawberry jelly is transformed into an extraordinary dessert by setting it in a ring mould with fruit piled up in the middle.

1 recipe Strawberry Jelly (see page 267)
150g (5oz) strawberries, hulled
3 ripe kiwi fruits

Makes 6 servings.

Wet the 20cm (8in) ring mould before making the jelly. As soon as the fruit purée has been combined with the agar-agar liquid pour it into the mould. It will set very quickly. Store in the fridge until needed.

Before serving the jelly slice the strawberries. Peel and thinly slice the ripe kiwi fruits and combine these fruits in a bowl.

Remove the ring mould from the

fridge. Immerse it for 5 seconds in a bowl of warm water, then dry its outside. Place a plate over the top and invert the mould so that it is sitting on the plate. Give the mould a few taps around the side and it should lift off the jelly easily. Fill the hole in the centre of the strawberry ring with the fresh fruit. The vivid colours are very eye-catching.

Each serving is 10g CHO. 50 kcals.

HONEYDEW JELLY

400g (14oz) honeydew melon, without seeds
50g (2oz) fresh dates, with stones
2 tsp agar-agar powder
100ml (4 fl oz) orange juice, unsweetened
100ml (4 fl oz) water
1 kiwi fruit for decoration

Makes 4 large servings.

Scoop out the melon flesh from the rind and put in a blender with the sliced and stoned dates.

Mix the agar-agar powder with a little of the combined orange juice and water to make a thick paste then pour it into a small saucepan with the rest of the liquid and a little of the melon purée. Bring to the boil and continue to boil gently for 1½ minutes.

Combine with the rest of the melon and date purée and pour into glass bowls. (An alternative way of serving this jelly is to pour it into half the empty melon shell and use it as a large serving bowl.)

Decorate the jelly by placing slices of kiwi fruit on top. Chill before serving.

Each serving is 10g CHO. 45 kcals.

PEAR AND GRAPE JELLY

450g (1lb) ripe pears, peeled
1½ tbs lemon juice, freshly
   squeezed
2 tsp agar-agar powder
100ml (4 fl oz) apple juice
50ml (2 fl oz) water
75g (3oz) seedless grapes,
   halved, for decoration

Makes 4 servings.

Cut the pears into chunks and blend
with the lemon juice.

Mix the agar-agar powder with a little
of the combined apple juice and water
to make a thick paste. Add the rest of
the liquid and pour into a saucepan
with a little of the pear purée and boil
for 1½–2 minutes. Add the agar-agar
liquid to the remaining pear purée.

Pour into 4 serving glasses and
decorate with halved grapes. Leave to
set. Chill in the fridge before serving.

Each serving is 5g CHO. 70 kcals.

PINEAPPLE AND CHERRY JELLY

*Using fruit juice is a quick way to prepare a jelly and I have included
this recipe as an example of this method. It should be remembered that
juice is a concentrated form of natural sugar, so for this reason chunks
of whole fruit are introduced to provide some fibre and bulk to
counteract the effects of the juice. Use the cartons of unsweetened
pineapple juice that can be bought at most grocers.*

300g (11oz) fresh pineapple,
   without skin
100g (4oz) cherries, stoned
1 tsp agar-agar powder
400ml (14 fl oz) pineapple
   juice

Makes 6 small servings.

Before weighing the pineapple remove
the skin. Make sure there are no
remnants of the skin on the outside.
Slice into bite-sized chunks. Slice the
cherries in half. Put these two fruits on
separate plates ready for use.

Mix the agar-agar powder with a little
of the pineapple juice to make a thick
paste. Gradually add more juice to
make it into a runny liquid. Pour this
together with any remaining juice into
a medium-sized saucepan. Boil for 1½
minutes then pour immediately into a
dampened mould.

Once the jelly is in the mould add the pineapple chunks then place the halved cherries around the outer edge of the mould. When the jelly has set and been removed from the mould the edges around the base will be red. This has a particularly delicate effect with a fluted mould.

Each serving is 15g CHO. 65 kcals.

ORANGE CUPS

Oranges are associated with Mediterranean climates, but in fact originate from India. Nor are they naturally orange. In their native habitat they are often sold when the skin is still green – yet they still taste just as sweet. Oranges are particularly high in vitamin C – 50mg per 100g – and because of this are recommended for people who have colds.

4 oranges weighing about 600g
  (1 lb 5 oz)
100ml (4 fl oz) apple juice
2 tsp agar-agar powder

Makes 8 small or 4 large servings.

Cut the oranges in half. Remove the flesh carefully so as not to break the orange peel cups, and put them on a plate ready to be filled with the orange jelly.

Remove the pith and pips from the fruit. Blend the fruit and put it to one side in a bowl. Mix the agar-agar powder with a little of the apple juice. Pour this into a saucepan together with the rest of the juice and add a little of the blended orange. Bring to the boil and cook gently for 1½ minutes.

Take off the heat and add the agar-agar liquid to the rest of the puréed orange juice. Leave to stand until it cools a little then pour into the 8 orange halves.

Each orange half is 5g CHO. 25 kcals.

MANGO FOOL

This velvety dessert can be whizzed up in a matter of minutes. The mango originated in India and in recent years has become easier to obtain in Europe. Many different kinds of mangoes are grown, but only a few varieties are seen in the shops. Mostly they are either oval or kidney-shaped, about 10–15cm (4–6in) long. They are usually yellow, with orange or red tinges in their skin when ready for eating, and give slightly to the touch when ripe. You can ripen a mango yourself at home by putting the fruit in a brown paper bag until ready. As soon as it is ripe store in the fridge.

The one problem about mangoes is that they are amazingly messy to eat. The central stone is covered in hairs that cling on to the fibrous flesh around it and make it difficult to slice all the fruit off easily. It is a kindness on your part to prepare this fruit for your guests! The mango makes a superb fool and because it is a tropical fruit it is an unusual dessert.

Mangoes are high in carotene and vitamin C, although if the fruit is unripe it will not contain nearly as much carotene. It also contains small amounts of minerals.

2 large mangoes weighing
about 550–600g (1lb
4oz–1lb 6oz)
1 tbs lemon juice, freshly
squeezed
200ml (7 fl oz) Greek yogurt

Makes 6 servings.

Peel the mango. Carefully slice the flesh around the stone into a bowl, making sure you do not lose any of the juice. Pour into the liquidizer with the lemon juice. Blend to make a purée.

Combine with the yogurt and spoon the fool into 6 bowls or glasses. Chill in the fridge before serving. Decorate with a few flaked almonds.

Each serving is 10g CHO. 80 kcals.

GOOSEBERRY FOOL

Gooseberries have a lower carbohydrate and calorie content than other soft summer fruit such as strawberries because they are much less sweet.

In Britain there are records of gooseberries being grown in the time of Henry VIII. Gooseberry juice was used as a medicine for the treatment of fevers and for preventing and curing the plague. They contain small amounts of different minerals including potassium and calcium. When raw they contain only 10g less vitamin C than oranges.

400g (14oz) ripe gooseberries
400ml (14 fl oz) apple juice,
  unsweetened
100g (4oz) firm tofu

Makes 4 servings.

Wash and top and tail the gooseberries. Put them in a heavy saucepan with the apple juice and simmer on a low heat until most of the juice is absorbed. The gooseberries will have become very soft. Blend with the tofu to make a thick creamy mixture. Leave to cool. Pour into 4 bowls or glasses and chill in the fridge.

Each serving is 15g CHO. 95 kcals.

PINEAPPLE-TOFU CREAM

This is light, creamy and swiftly thrown together.

200g (7oz) firm tofu
200g (7oz) fresh pineapple,
  with the skin removed
75g (3oz) ground almonds
cinnamon
almond flakes

Makes 4 servings.

Blend or process the tofu and pineapple together. To achieve a really creamy texture you may need to put this mixture through a sieve or food mill. Add the ground almonds. Spoon into 4 bowls or glasses. Sprinkle lightly with cinnamon and a few almond flakes. Chill in the fridge before serving.

Each serving is 10g CHO. 160 kcals.

STRAWBERRY CREAM

'Doubtless God could have made a better berry, but doubtless God never did.'

Dr William Butler (1536–1618), English physician
regarded as 'the Aesculapius of our age'.

Strawberries taste so perfect it seems a shame to liquidize or purée them. Eat them with a little fromage frais and they are extra delicious. Fromage frais is a soft cheese produced from skimmed milk which tastes somewhere between yogurt and soft white cheese. It has a thick consistency and a creamy taste. There are two types available – a low fat version and a richer creamier one. The recipes in this book use the low-fat version which contains only 0.4 per cent fat – considerably less than the 21 per cent fat that single cream, the usual accompaniment to strawberries, contains. This means that fromage frais is lighter on the stomach and the conscience.

550g (1lb 4oz) strawberries, hulled
600g (1lb 5oz) fromage frais

Makes 4 servings.

Combine the strawberries and fromage frais in a bowl. Leave to chill in the fridge for an hour. The cream will turn a little pink while standing. Serve chilled.

Each serving is 10g CHO. 105 kcals.

GREEK RASPBERRIES

Although raspberries grow wild all over Britain, two-thirds of the cultivated variety are grown in Scotland. Until recently raspberry picking was like hop-picking in Kent – an opportunity to combine a holiday with earning money. Nowadays south of the border it is a different story with three-quarters of English raspberries being grown on pick-your-own farms.

Raspberries are not a new hybrid fruit. Pliny, the Roman botanist, wrote that the Greeks called them Idea, named after Mount Idea in Asia Minor where the fruit grew. Cookery writers in Britain began to give recipes for raspberries as early as the 18th century.

When buying raspberries only buy as many as you need to use the same day. They do not keep well and do not taste nearly as fresh if kept for more than a day.

Raspberries are delicious eaten straight off the bush, but when mixed with a cream they can taste a little tart so here a sweet fruit purée is added to the thick Greek yogurt.

100g (4oz) ripe banana, peeled
300g (11oz) raspberries
200ml (7 fl oz) Greek yogurt

Makes 4 servings.

Sieve the banana or put it in a food mill. Combine with the yogurt.

Divide the raspberries between 4 bowls, spooning them over the sweetened yogurt.

Each serving is 10g CHO. 105 kcals.

CRÈME AUX MARRONS

This quickly-made chestnut cream is versatile. It can serve as a cream dessert served in tall glasses or as a fancy filling for a swiss roll or cake.

50ml (2 fl oz) boiling water
50g (2oz) dried apricots
200g (7oz) chestnut purée, unsweetened
100ml (4 fl oz) skimmed milk
100g (4oz) skimmed milk quark
1 tbs brandy

Makes 4 dessert servings.

Pour the boiling water over the apricots and leave to stand for 15 minutes. Grind the apricots finely in an electric coffee grinder. Put them together with the chestnut purée and milk in a small saucepan. Cook over a very low heat and stir continuously until the milk has been absorbed and the whole mixture takes on a thick paste-like consistency.

Remove from the heat and add the quark and brandy. The cream is now a light honey-brown colour and ready for use.

As a dessert: spoon the cream into 4 glass bowls. Serve with a Cinnamon Hazelnut Stick (see page 100) in the middle of each dish.

As a cake filling: halve the ingredients. Spread the cream over the cake's surface. This quantity provides enough cream to cover the surface of a 22.5 × 30cm (9 × 12in) swiss roll.

Each serving is 25g CHO. 145 kcals.

CAROB CREAM

This thick cream makes a delicious dessert.

2 tsp arrowroot
10g (¼oz) carob powder
300ml (10 fl oz) skimmed milk
150g (5oz) ripe banana, peeled
½ tsp vanilla essence

Blend the arrowroot and carob powder in a small saucepan with enough milk to make a paste. Stir in the rest of the milk and slowly heat. Bring the mixture to the boil, stirring

Makes 6 servings.

continuously. Cook for 3–4 minutes until the mixture thickens.

Take off the heat and add the finely mashed or sieved banana and the vanilla essence. Pour into glasses ready for serving. Leave in the fridge for a few hours to become firmer and chilled.

Each serving is 10g CHO. 45 kcals.

TRIFLE

Trifle, when you think about it, is nothing more than a combination of jelly, custard, fruit and cake. But, to take Alexander Pope's famous line from 'An Essay on Man' out of context, 'all are but parts of one stupendous whole'. Two versions of trifle are given here: one uses fruit that is available in the summer and the other uses fruit that is available in the winter.

½ quantity Swiss Roll (see page 240)
4 tbs orange juice (or 2 tbs orange juice and 2 tbs brandy)

Summer fruit trifle

2 small eating apples weighing 200g (7oz)
250g (9oz) cherries, with stones
200g (7oz) peach

Jelly

3 oranges weighing about 550g (1lb 4oz) with skin
scant 2 tsp agar-agar powder
100ml (4 fl oz) apple juice

2 quantities Banana Custard (see page 259)

Bake the swiss roll sponge. Half will be used in this recipe and half can be frozen for future use. Cut the sponge into small bite-sized pieces and lay around the base of an attractive serving bowl. Pour the orange juice or juice and brandy over the top. Chop the apples and spread them evenly over the sponge. Chop the cherries and spread these over the apple. Chop the peach and spread thinly over the cherry layer.

Prepare the jelly: peel the oranges and remove any pith or seeds. Blend in the liquidizer to make 400ml (14 fl oz) liquid. Mix the agar-agar powder with the apple juice and pour into a small saucepan. Add a little of the blended orange pulp. Bring to the boil. Add the rest of the orange pulp and simmer for 1½–2 minutes. Pour over the fruit and sponge. This will hold it in place.

Topping
300g (11 oz) strawberries, hulled
300ml (11 fl oz) fromage frais

Prepare the Banana Custard and pour over the jelly, which will have set quite quickly.

Prepare the topping: combine the sliced strawberries with the fromage frais and spread over the top of the custard, which should be fairly firm. Leave to chill in the fridge for a couple of hours before serving. The trifle still tastes very good, some say even better, after a night in the fridge.

Winter fruit version

2 small eating apples weighing 200g (7oz)
5 kiwi fruit
150g (5oz) seedless grapes, halved

Follow the instructions for the summer trifle but substitute the different fruit where appropriate.

Each portion is 25g CHO. 200 kcals.

Jelly
3 oranges weighing about 550g (1lb 4oz) with skin
100ml (4 fl oz) apple juice
scant 2 tsp agar-agar powder

2 quantities Banana Custard (see page 259)

Topping
200g (7oz) mango
300ml (11oz) fromage frais

Makes 8 large servings.

When Richard the Lionheart of England was wounded in Palestine in the Third Crusade, his adversary Saladin called off the fight and chivalrously despatched snow, ice and chilled fruits from the slopes of Mount Hermon to hasten his recovery. Richard soon resumed his pursuit of the infidel but, having taken Jaffa, failed to storm Jerusalem and in 1192 signed a truce with the Saracen chieftain. On the long march home, he was captured by his fellow-Christians, Duke Leopold of Austria and Emperor Henry IV, and held to a 150,000-mark ransom.

The total cost of his ice cream break in the Holy Land shattered the English economy, gave the barons greater power and paved the way to Magna Carta and the earliest stirrings of parliamentary democracy.

Nevertheless, for the next five hundred years, ice cream remained the exclusive preserve of monarchs. In the mid-18th century Hannah Glasse, in *The Complete Confectioner*, gave the following instructions:

> To make ice cream. Take two pewter basons, one larger than the other; the inward one must have a close cover, into which you put your cream, and mix it with what you think proper, to give it a flavour and colour, as raspberries, etc. then sweeten it to your palate, cover it close, and set it in the larger bason; fill it with ice, and a large handful of salt under and over and roundabout; let it stand in the ice three quarters of an hour, uncover, and stir it and the cream well together, then cover it again; let it stand half an hour longer, and then turn into your plate . . .

This remains one of the basic approaches in many home-made recipes. The refinement that the Americans brought to ice cream making was the invention of the hand-cranked ice cream freezer in 1846. This machine kept the ice cream mixture moving so that it was evenly cooled, preventing the growth of large ice crystals and at the same time incorporating air. From this point on Americans continued to put their own special stamp on ice cream. By the early 1920s they had invented such technological wonders as ice cream on a stick, ice cream in a chocolate shell and lemonade on a stick.

Proof of the Americans' commitment to ice cream was reported by the *New York Times* in 1943. US Air Force pilots stationed in Britain during the Second World War were so determined not to be deprived of it that they anchored a large container of ice cream mixture to the rear gunner's compartment of their planes and by the time they returned to base from a bombing mission over Germany it was 'well shaken up and nicely frozen by flying over enemy territory at high altitudes'.

Home-made ice cream usually has a dense texture. If you own an ice cream machine this makes a great difference because the mixture is kept in continuous motion throughout the freezing time which results in a smooth, light texture. The alternative method is to remove the ice cream from the freezer after about an hour, beat it and return it again to the freezer. This can be repeated a few times although the result will be icier than ice cream made with a machine. I find that if there is a lot of fruit in the ice cream this compensates for the firmer texture. A third method, which also originates from the USA, is to freeze the fruit first then mix with yogurt or cream in a food processor. This gives a very satisfactory texture, as in Banana Velvet Ice Cream (see page 283) and Melon and Raspberry Ice Cream (see page 283).

When the ice cream is made, avoid thawing and refreezing as this will make its texture coarser. Ideally make as much as you need at one go or else divide the quantity into two freezer containers.

BANANA VELVET ICE CREAM

This ice cream is as soft as the kind that comes flowing out of commercial vending machines – the only difference is that the ingredients are all natural. It can either be served as soon as it is made or prepared a couple of hours before it is needed and stored in a covered container in the bottom of the freezer – this gives it a thicker and firmer texture.

The secret of this recipe lies in its use of frozen bananas. If bananas are particularly cheap one week I buy extra and freeze them in quantities of 200g (7oz) in freezer bags so that they are on hand for the arrival of unexpected hot weather.

200g (7oz) bananas, peeled
150ml (5 fl oz) low-fat natural
  yogurt

Makes 4 servings.

Cut the bananas into thin slices, place them in a freezer bag and freeze until they are hard.

Use the sharp blade of a food processor. Place the frozen banana pieces and yogurt in the food processor and pulse gently, switching it on and off for short bursts. At the beginning the machine responds jerkily to the frozen banana, but after a while this is converted into a rich cream.

Each serving is 10g CHO. 60 kcals.

MELON AND RASPBERRY ICE CREAM

The fragrant galia melon blends well with raspberries in this scrumptious pink-coloured ice cream. It is not as sweet as Banana Velvet Ice Cream. If you need extra sweetness scatter a few chopped sultanas across the top.

600g (1lb 5oz) ripe galia melon
175g (6oz) raspberries, frozen
150ml (5 fl oz) low-fat natural
  yogurt

Makes 6 servings.

Cut the melon off the rind and discard the seeds. Slice the melon into chunks and freeze in a freezer bag until they become hard.

Use the sharp blade of a food processor. Place the frozen melon and raspberries with the yogurt in the food processor and pulse gently, switching it on and off for short bursts until the fruit becomes creamy.

Each serving is 5g CHO. 35 kcals.

Serving suggestion: the thick creamy texture of this ice cream makes it suitable for pouring on to a sweet pastry base to make a delicious ice cream tart (see following recipe).

Melon and Raspberry Ice Cream Tart

1 quantity Sweet Seed Pastry (see page 163)
1 quantity Melon and Raspberry Ice Cream (see recipe above)
100g (4oz) fresh raspberries

Makes 8 servings.

Roll out the pastry to fit a 22.5cm (9in) tart tin. Bake blind in a preheated oven gas mark 5/190°C/375°F for 25 minutes until browned. Cool and put to one side until needed.

Prepare the ice cream and store at the bottom of the freezer for no more than an hour. Spread the ice cream evenly over the base of the cooked pastry and decorate with fresh raspberries. Serve immediately.

Each serving is 10g CHO. 110 kcals.

ALMOND CAROB ICE CREAM

The advantage of this recipe is that the ice cream keeps its thick creamy form and can be kept in the fridge for a few hours until needed. It also works well as an unusual filling for pastry or plain cakes, such as Ice Cream Torte (see page 184). The hint of carob in this recipe colours the ice cream a pale brown, but does not overload the taste-buds.

Because frozen banana is used you will need to use a food processor to blend it to a cream.

150g (5oz) firm tofu
200g (7oz) banana, sliced and
  frozen
15g (½oz) carob powder
few drops of almond essence

Makes 4 generous servings.

Use the sharp cutting blade of a food
processor. Put all the ingredients in the
food processor and pulse gently,
switching it on and off for short bursts
for as long as necessary until the
ingredients form a thick cream. Store in
the fridge until needed.

Each serving is 15g CHO. 70 kcals.

STRAWBERRY ICE

*This very fruity ice can be made with either yogurt or, if you prefer,
with tofu for a milk-free version.*

400g (14oz) strawberries,
  hulled
4 tbs apple juice, unsweetened
100g (4oz) banana, peeled
100ml (4 fl oz) low-fat yogurt
  or 100g (4oz) firm tofu

Makes 4 large servings.

Blend the strawberries in a liquidizer
with the apple juice. Add the banana
and yogurt or firm tofu and blend to
make a creamy liquid.

Pour the mixture into a freezer
container. Cover with the lid and freeze
for about 1–1½ hours until the sides of
the ice cream have become frozen.
Take it out of the freezer and blend
again, beating air into it. Pour back
into the container and return to the
freezer for a further 2 hours or until
needed. Put in the fridge 45 minutes
before serving to thaw slightly.

Each serving is 15g CHO. 65 kcals.

PEACH ICE CREAM

*For a really special dessert serve this ice cream with hot peach sauce
(see page 256). This recipe uses the skin of the peaches to keep the
fibre content high.*

400g (14oz) peaches
100g (4oz) fresh dates, with
  stones

Chop the peaches into a blender. Stone
the dates and blend with the juices.

1 tbs lemon juice
1 tbs apple juice
100ml (4 fl oz) low-fat natural
  yogurt

Makes 4 servings.

Add the yogurt and blend for a few seconds.

Pour the ice cream mixture into a freezer container. Cover with the lid and freeze for about 1 hour until the sides are just beginning to set. Take the ice cream out of the freezer and blend again, beating air into it. Pour back into the container and return to the freezer for a further 2 hours or until needed. Put in the fridge 45 minutes before serving to thaw slightly.

Each serving is 15g CHO. 70 kcals.

MANGO CHERRY ICE CREAM

A delicious fruit ice cream that is quick to make and ideal for those on a milk-free diet.

1 mango weighing about
  300–325g (11–11½oz)
100g (4oz) firm tofu
3 tbs apple juice, unsweetened
50g (2oz) dark red cherries

**Makes 4 medium-sized
  servings.**

Peel the mango and slice the fruit away from the inner stone. Put in a blender with the tofu and apple juice. Blend until a thick creamy purée is formed. Pour into a freezer container. Chop the cherries and stir them in so that they are well distributed in the ice cream. Cover with the lid and freeze until almost ready to serve. Place in the fridge 30–45 minutes before serving to thaw slightly. Alternatively leave in the freezer for 2½–3 hours and serve before the ice cream is frozen solid.

Each scoop is 10g CHO. 55 kcals.

OAT ICE CREAM

The custard base of this ice cream gives it a creamy richness.

50g (2oz) porridge oats
2 egg yolks
1 tsp arrowroot
150ml (5 fl oz) skimmed milk
150ml (5 fl oz) low-fat fromage
  frais
100g (4oz) banana, peeled

Makes 6 servings.

Pour the oats onto a shallow ovenproof dish and bake in a preheated oven gas mark 4/180°C/350°F for 15 minutes or until lightly browned.

Combine the egg yolks and arrowroot in a bowl. Put the milk in a small saucepan and bring almost to the boil. Take it off the heat and slowly pour over the yolks, mixing them together. Pour this mixture back into the pan and stir with a wooden spoon until the mixture has thickened enough to coat the back of the spoon. (For tips on making custard, see page 258.)

Pour the custard into a bowl and add the fromage frais and the sieved or moulied banana. Fold in the roasted oats and leave to cool for 15 minutes before freezing. Place in a freezer container, cover with the lid and freeze until thick (about 2 hours).

Each serving is 10g CHO. 100 kcals.

CHERRY CAROB ICE CREAM

Cherry ripe, cherry ripe, ripe, I cry,
Full and fair ones; come and buy:
If so be, you ask me where
They do grow? I answer, there,
Where my Julia's lips do smile;
There's the land or cherry-isle
'Cherry Ripe', Robert Herrick (1591–1674)

Summer fruit and romance go hand in hand, and ripe cherries are one of the pleasures of summer. If you use them in this ring-shaped ice cream they can still be eaten later in the year.

If carob is not your favourite taste leave it out and substitute ½ tsp vanilla essence.

50g (2oz) seedless raisins
2 tbs brandy
50g (2oz) flaked almonds
225g (8oz) skimmed milk quark
100ml (4 fl oz) low-fat natural yogurt
150g (5oz) bananas, peeled
2 egg yolks
150ml (5 fl oz) skimmed milk
25g (1oz) carob powder
200g (7oz) ripe black cherries

Makes 8 servings.

Put the raisins in a small cup together with the brandy.

Place the almonds on a flat dish or tin and lightly brown under the grill. Leave to cool.

Combine the quark, yogurt and mashed banana in a medium-sized bowl.

Beat the egg yolks with a fork. Put the milk and carob powder in a small saucepan and bring almost to the boil. Remove from the heat and stir into the eggs. Pour this mixture back into the pan over a very low heat and stir until it thickens. Leave to cool for a few minutes then add to the quark and banana mixture.

Stone and halve the cherries. Add these, together with the raisins and brandy, to the ice cream mixture.

Line the base of an angel tin (ring mould) with the toasted almonds. Pour the ice cream mixture on top. Cover and freeze for a few hours until firm. When you are ready to serve the ice cream place the base of the tin in a bowl of boiling water for 30 seconds. Then invert the tin on a plate. Serve with cold Cherry Sauce (see page 255) poured into the middle of the ice-cream ring.

Each serving without sauce is 15g CHO. 150 kcals.
Each serving with sauce is 17.5g CHO. 160 kcals.

FROZEN STRAWBERRY SUNDAES

Liqueur-flavoured strawberry ice cream sitting in a frozen strawberry case decorated with a lustrous green grape makes a colourful and unusual dessert.

350g (12oz) large strawberries, hulled
about 90–100g (3½–4oz) hulled strawberries
1 tbs apple juice
1 tbs calvados
25g (1oz) banana, peeled
25g (1oz) firm tofu
small green seedless grapes

Makes 4 servings.

Prepare the strawberry cases: hollow out the 350g (12 oz) large strawberries, leaving their outer shells quite thick. Before doing this observe which way they sit because when served they should stand upright. It might be more practical to hollow out some of the strawberries slightly off-centre.

Prepare the ice cream: combine the insides of the strawberries with the 90–100g (3½–4 oz) quantity to make up a total weight of 100g (4oz) strawberries. Blend with the apple juice, calvados, banana and tofu. Stand this fruit purée in a shallow dish in the freezer for about 30 minutes or until it has begun to set around the sides and has become thick and creamy.

Place the large hollowed-out strawberries in a shallow freezer container. Spoon the fruit ice into each strawberry. If it is thick enough pile it up on top, but avoid it running down the sides and coating the outside of the strawberry.

Return to the freezer for about 30 minutes then remove and place one small grape on the top of each strawberry. Cover and return to the bottom of the freezer, where the strawberries will freeze more slowly and after a few hours the ice will be set but the fruit will not be rock hard. If you prepare this dessert the day before, remove the sundaes from the freezer to the fridge 30 minutes before serving.

Each serving is 10g CHO. 45 kcals.

FRUIT ICE LOLLIES

Fresh fruit can be frozen to make quite delicious ices. Use either the whole fruit or slices of fruit and freeze until solid. This is an even simpler method than mixing juice and water and pouring it into a mould, and the fruit lollies are such a novelty that they are an instant success with everyone.

When choosing fruit for freezing always use fruit that is fresh and not bruised or over-ripe for the best results. Very sweet fruits are ideal since the sweet flavour usually diminishes during freezing.

The carbohydrate and calorie value of the individual lollies is very low and because they are frozen they take longer to eat.

Strawberry Ice Lollies
These are very simple to make and popular with everyone. Use fresh beautifully rounded strawberries in season. Hull and wash the fruit. Cut a brightly coloured plastic straw in half or insert a wooden cocktail stick in the centre of each strawberry. Place the strawberries in a container, putting greaseproof paper between the layers, and freeze until hard (this will vary with size – a few hours at most).

Freezing changes the texture of the strawberry, but it does not affect its bright colour.

150g (5oz) strawberries is 10g CHO. 40 kcals.

Melon Ice
Honeydew or galia melons freeze well. Remove the seeds and rind and cut the melon into chunks. Lay them out on a freezer tray, making sure that they are not touching, and freeze until hard.

Red watermelon looks very attractive when frozen and makes a very icy mouthful because of its high water content, but it is fiddly work removing all the seeds.

200g or 7oz melon without the rind is 10g CHO. 40 kcals.

Peach Ice Pops

Peaches have a firm texture and freeze well. Cut thick slices and spear them with a cocktail stick through the middle then freeze.

100g (4oz) peaches is 10g CHO. 40 kcals.

Iced Fruit Kebab

For this unusual end to a meal, use wooden skewers. Put 3 seedless grapes at each end of the skewers and alternate 2 whole strawberries with 2 slices of peach, 2 slices of honeydew melon and 2 thin slices of banana, then freeze.

16 CHILDREN'S PARTIES

Ices, lollies, jellies, biscuits and cakes – the traditional ingredients of a children's party – can all be found in the pages of this book.

The sweet treats that children enjoy most at a party are ices and lollies. Biscuits and cakes are never in great demand. They are visually appealing, but it is usually parents who eat them rather than children. It is the savoury foods that are always the most popular – crisps, fish fingers, and pizzas and quiches for older children. Sandwiches have a solid minority appeal. Titbits such as salted popcorn, raisins and their carob-coated cousins also go down well.

A midday party shifts the emphasis even more towards savoury foods. Fish fingers or coated chicken served with chips, crisps or potatoes in their jackets are top favourites. Follow them up with Strawberry Ice Lollies or ice cream and all will be content. The pleasurable side of lunch parties is that the guests are hungry and eat most of the food, unlike tea where they tend to take one bite and move on to the next delicacy.

Popular party recipes which are simple to make are:

– *Strawberry Ice Lollies* (see page 290). These are always a huge success. Even children who usually eat strawberries doused in sugar ask for seconds.

– *Banana Velvet Ice Cream* (see page 283). Prepare this a couple of hours beforehand and store it in the bottom of the freezer so that when it is needed it will be firm but not frozen solid. If there are not too many guests sprinkle the round scoops of ice cream with desiccated coconut and use carob-coated raisins for eyes.

– *Strawberry Jelly* (see page 267).

– *Apricot Fairy Cakes* (see page 243). Bake these in petits fours cases and decorate with a blob of coloured coconut icing in the centre.

— *Jam Tarts*. Use one of the simple pastry recipes (see page 158). Cut the pastry into circles, place in a jam tart tray, fill with sugar-free jam and bake in a quick oven.

— *Carob Balls* (see page 94).

— *Cinnamon Drops* (see page 97).

— *Carob Secrets* (see page 95). Serve these in miniature paper cases.

— *Gingerbread Men* (see page 88).

— *Marzipan Mice* (see page 105).

The Birthday Cake

Banana Cake (see page 228), Apple Cherry Cake (see page 226) or Carrot Cake (see page 234) make a scrumptious base with a texture that is firm enough to be cut into shapes. Swiss Roll (see page 240) filled with sugar-free jam is excellent for any design that requires a cylindrical shape, and is popular with children.

Decorating birthday cakes

There are five toppings you can use for decorating a birthday cake:

— *Carob Icing* (see page 82).

— *Coconut Icing* (see page 82).

— spreading the cake's surface with sugar-free jam and sprinkling *desiccated coconut* all over. The coconut can be used as it is or coloured.

— sprinkling *carob flakes* over the cream surface of a cake. Make them by melting a good quality carob bar (see Carob Apricot Treats page 102). Spread the carob thinly over a sheet of greaseproof paper. After a few minutes cut long thin lines across the surface and when you remove it from the paper the carob will break into thin flakes.

— *quark* or *fromage frais* can be coloured and used to cover the surface of the cake. By itself it is not particularly sweet and you will find that the addition of a little puréed dried apricot or puréed banana with a drop of lemon juice to avoid discolouring makes a considerable difference to the taste.

To emphasize details on the cake choose either:

— *Fresh fruit*, particularly the bright ones such as kiwi fruit, strawberries, oranges and green grapes. They look very effective but need to be prepared on the day of the party because they will not look so fresh and bright if prepared earlier.

— *Dried fruit*: raisins, sultanas, slivers of prune, dried apricots and long strips of dried banana, circles of dried pear or peach can all be used to enhance letters or a design.

— *Marzipan*: this can be used for lettering, railway lines or trimming around the edge of a cake. The sugar-free version will not take as much detail as marzipan made with sugar so avoid a design that requires dense detail.

Colouring

Colouring that uses natural ingredients is available in the shops. If you prefer to make your own try raspberry concentrate or the juice of fresh blackberries for pink, turmeric or carrot juice for yellow, cinnamon for light brown.

Simple ideas for cakes

There is an infinite number of designs that you can make using the five basic icings.

Happy Birthday Cake: This is very quick to decorate. Cover the cake either in carob icing or sugar-free jam with tinted desiccated coconut sprinkled over the top. Pipe the child's name or 'happy birthday' in plain white quark which can be flavoured with a few drops of vanilla essence. Decorate the sides with halved strawberries or kiwi fruit slices.

Name Cakes: Alphabet letters made of cake provide a strong visual effect.

Bake a double quantity of cake in a rectangular tin about 30 × 20cm (12 × 8in). Cut in half lengthways. Use one half to cut into equal lengths – these will provide the straight part of such letters as l, t, h, d, b, k, and half-size will provide 'i'. Use the second section of the cake for the rounded shapes such as a, o, u, c (see diagram on p. 298). One way of making this easier is to place a toy letter in front of you while cutting it out or to draw it on a piece of greaseproof paper, cut it out and place it on the cake as you cut around it.

Cover a large tray with silver foil on which to assemble the letters needed to write the child's name. Jam is a useful glue for sticking together the different sections of the letters. Coat with carob icing and sprinkle with desiccated coconut.

If you have leftover cake an extra touch that goes down well is to use a gingerbread cutter to make a boy or girl and decorate them, adding a few fruit details for eyes, hands and feet.

Train Cake: An old favourite. Bake two swiss rolls about 30 × 20cm (12 × 8in). Roll one up, spreading the inside with jam. This will be the basis for the engine.

Cut the remaining swiss roll into five strips crossways, each one about 5cm (2in) wide. Place one of these under the completed swiss roll so that it will have the same width as the railway wagons. Cut the remaining strips in half so that each one is about 10 × 5cm (4 × 2in). Build these up to make three low wagons.

Cover the engine in carob icing. Use coloured skimmed milk quark for the wagons. Most children will not enjoy quark by itself. A simple sweetener is to add 25g (1oz) ground dried apricots per 100g (4oz) quark or 50g (2oz) puréed banana with a few drops of lemon juice. Colour each wagon a bright colour – yellow, green and pink go well together.

Cover a large tray with silver foil to assemble the train on. For railway tracks use either coloured straws or strips of dried banana. Place the engine and its wagons on the railway lines. Use slices of banana dipped in lemon juice as wheels and a thicker piece to sit on top of the engine as

SWISS ROLL X 2

ENGINE

STRIP TO GO UNDER ENGINE ▼

W A G O N

P A R T S

WAGONS ▶

BASIC ROUND CAKE

BUILT-UP AREA UNDER
EYES TO NOSE AND
DOWN TO MOUTH MADE
FROM CUT-OFF CAKE

the funnel. Use strips of dried apricot to connect the engine and wagons together. Pile the wagons high with colourful cargo such as strawberries or cherries. Decorate the window of the engine with pieces of dried apple. A small engine driver or guard can be placed on the appropriate part of the train.

Cat's Face: The central part of the cat's face is built up to give a three-dimensional effect. This makes a much greater impact than a flat one-dimensional shape. There is no need for it to be a perfect likeness, but only to suggest the part of a cat's face that protrudes the most, from the eyes to the nose.

Bake the cake in a round, shallow 22.5–30cm (9–12in) baking tin. Cut around the cake according to the diagram (see page 300). Use the cut-off pieces to build up the area under the eyes. It should gradually reach up to a peak for the nose then rapidly descend to the mouth.

Cover the cake with a double quantity of carob icing. Because the built-up area will have an irregular surface let the icing harden and pour an extra batch on top to give a smoother finish.

The facial details bring the cat to life so use brightly coloured fruit. Place a little icing underneath the fruit to set it firmly on the cake's surface:

EYES – slanted slices of peach or orange segments with a seedless green grape propped up against the middle for a pupil.

NOSE – place a blob of quark or Greek yogurt on the highest point for the base of the nose. Use either a cherry or the round end of a strawberry for the nose.

WHISKERS – take 4 large dried apricots and cut them round and round with a sharp knife to make long curly strips. Gently unfurl them and place two on each side of the nose.

MOUTH – at the base of the built-up section, directly under the nose, place a round piece of plum with the skin side showing.

EARS – spread the inside of the ears with a little quark or Greek yogurt. Either leave them white or tint a pale pink.

If the carbohydrate or calorie count has to be watched remember to add on the value of the icing and the dried or fresh fruit.

NATURAL SUGAR AND FIBRE IN FOOD

(n/a = not available, tr = trace, neg = negligible)

100g	fibre	natural sugars	calories
Almonds, shelled	14.3g	4.3g	565
Apple, eating	1.5g	9.1g	35
Apple juice, unsweetened	neg	12.0g	45
Apricots, dried	24.0g	43.4g	182
Apricots, fresh	1.9g	6.2g	25
Apricots, hunza	21.2g	38.3g	160
Arrowroot	n/a	tr	355
Banana, peeled	3.4g	16.2g	79
Banana, dried	9.4g	53.0g	210
Barley flakes	6.0g	n/a	315
Barley flour	2.4g	n/a	360
Beans, aduki, raw	9.0g	n/a	280
Beansprouts, mixed	3.0g	0.4g	9
Braising beef	0g	0g	121
Bran, wheat	44.0g	3.8g	180
Brazil nuts, shelled	9.0g	1.7g	619
Brown lentils	11.7g	2.4g	305
Butter	0g	0g	740
Carob powder	55.2g	n/a	200
Carrots, raw	2.9g	5.4g	25
Cherries, fresh whole	1.5g	10.4g	40
Chestnut purée	6.8g	7.0g	170
Chicken	0g	0g	121
Chicory	n/a	n/a	9
Clementine	1.3g	8.0g	23

100g	fibre	natural sugars	calories
Coconut cream	n/a	n/a	330
Coconut, desiccated	23.5g	6.4g	604
Cod fillet	0g	0g	76
Dates, dried, stoned	8.7g	63.9g	248
Dates, fresh	n/a	18.0g	80
Eggs	0g	0g	145
Figs, dried raw	18.5g	52.9g	213
Figs, fresh	2.5g	9.5g	41
Flour, brown rice	8.0g	n/a	310
Flour, soya	15.0g	13.5g	375
Flour, wholewheat	9.6g	2.3g	318
Fromage frais, low-fat	0g	n/a	50
Gooseberries	3.2g	3.4g	17
Grapes, green seedless	0.9g	16.1g	63
Hazelnuts without shells	6.1g	4.7g	380
Jam, sugar-free	5.6g	34.0g	120
Kiwi fruit	n/a	7.0g	35
Lamb, fillet, lean	0g	0g	200
Leeks, cooked	3.9g	4.6g	24
Lemon, whole	5.2g	3.2g	15
Lemon juice	0g	1.6g	7
Mango	1.5g	15.3g	59
Margarine, polyunsaturated	0g	0.1g	730
Melon, honeydew with skin	0.6g	3.1g	13
Melon, watermelon with skin	n/a	2.7g	11
Milk, skimmed	0g	5.0g	33
Millet	5.0g	n/a	380
Millet flakes	5.0g	n/a	380
Oats, porridge	7.0g	tr	401
Oat bran with germ	18.0g	n/a	420
Oil (sunflower, soya bean, olive oil, sesame seed)	0g	0g	900

100g	fibre	natural sugars	calories
Onions, raw	1.3g	5.2g	23
Orange, with peel	1.5g	6.4g	26
Orange juice	0g	9.4g	38
Parsnip, cooked	4.0g	8.8g	56
Passion fruit with skin	6.7g	2.6g	14
Peach with stone	1.2g	7.9g	32
Peanut butter	7.6g	6.7g	630
Peanuts, without shells	8.1g	3.1g	570
Pears, fresh	2.3g	10.6g	41
Pecan nuts	5.0g	n/a	680
Pepper, green	0.9g	2.2g	15
Pineapple, fresh	1.2g	11.6g	46
Pine nuts	4.0g	n/a	580
Poppy seeds	n/a	n/a	560
Prunes, dried, stoned	16.1g	40.3g	161
Pumpkin seeds	n/a	n/a	555
Pomegranate	n/a	9.1g	35
Quark, skimmed milk	0g	n/a	80
Raisins	6.8g	64.4g	246
Raspberries	7.4g	5.6g	25
Redcurrants	8.2g	4.4g	21
Rhubarb, raw	2.6g	1.0g	6
Rice, brown, raw	4.2g	n/a	360
Rice flakes, brown	4.2g	n/a	360
Rosewater	neg	neg	neg
Rye flakes	6.0g	n/a	315
Rye flour	n/a	tr	335
Salmon	0g	0g	182
Satsuma	1.9g	8.0g	35
Sesame seeds	3.9g	n/a	500
Shredded wheat, 1 biscuit	3.3g	neg	80
Soya bean flakes	15.0g	n/a	385
Soya milk	0g	n/a	60
Spinach, cooked	6.3g	1.2g	30
Split peas, dried raw	11.9g	1.9g	310

100g	fibre	natural sugars	calories
Spring onions	3.1g	8.5g	35
Strawberries, fresh	2.2g	6.2g	26
Sultanas	7.0g	64.7g	250
Sunflower seeds	3.6g	n/a	560
Tahini	5.2g	n/a	600
Tofu, firm	0g	n/a	70
Tomatoes, raw	1.5g	2.8g	14
Walnuts, shelled	5.2g	3.2g	525
Wheat flakes	12.3g	0.4g	325
Wheatgerm	n/a	16.0g	345
Wholewheat noodles	11.0g	n/a	340
Yeast, baker's	6.9g	tr	53
Yogurt, Greek	0g	4.0g	135
Yogurt, low-fat natural	0g	6.2g	52

BIBLIOGRAPHY

Blacklock, Norman J., 'Sucrose and idiopathic renal stone' in *Nutrition and Health*, vol. 5, no. 1/2, 1987.

Brekhman, I. I. and Nesterenko, I. F., *Brown Sugar and Health*, Oxford, Pergamon, 1983.

Bristol, J. B. et al, 'Sugar, fat, and the risk of colorectal cancer' in *British Medical Journal*, 23 November 1985.

'Britain tops lung, heart death list' in *The Times*, 8 January 1987.

British Medical Association, *Diet, Nutrition and Health*, March 1986.

British Nutrition Foundation Task Force, *Sugar and Syrups*, London, BNF, 1987.

Burkitt, D. P. and Trowell, H. C., eds, *Refined Carbohydrate Foods and Disease*, London, Academic Press, 1975.

Cannon, Geoffrey and Walker, Caroline, *The Food Scandal*, London, Century, 1985.

Chipping, John, *Your Teeth*, London, Cottrell, 1975.

Cleave, T. L., *The Saccharine Disease*, Bristol, J. Wright, 1974.

Cohen, A. M., 'Change of diet of Yemenite Jews in relation to diabetes and ischaemic heart-disease' in *The Lancet*, 23 December 1961.

Cooper, Derek, 'A question of analysis' in *The Listener*, 23 July 1987.

Cooper, Derek, 'Sugaring the medicine' in *The Listener*, 17 September 1987.

Cooper, Derek, *The Food Programme*, BBC Radio 4, 27 March 1987.

Cooper, Derek, 'Uneatable at any price' in *The Listener*, 13 November 1986.

The Coronary Prevention Group, *Statistics*, Briefing Paper 1, London, CPG, n.d.

The Coronary Prevention Group, *Healthy Eating*, Briefing Paper 5, London, CPG, n.d.

Culpeper's Complete Herbal: consisting of a comprehensive description of nearly all herbs, with their medicinal properties, and directions for compounding the medicines extracted from them, London, W. Foulsham, n.d.

David, Elizabeth, *English Bread and Yeast Cookery*, London, Penguin, 1977.

Davies, Stephen and Stewart, Alan, *Nutritional Medicine. The drug-free guide to better family health*, London, Pan, 1987.

Davis, Adelle, *Let's Eat Right to Keep Fit*, London, Unwin, 1986.

De Bairacli Levy, Juliette, *The Illustrated Herbal Handbook*, London, Faber and Faber, 1982.

Deerr, Noel, *The History of Sugar*, vols I, II, London, Chapman and Hall, 1949.

Dinnage, Paul, *The Book of Fruit and Fruit Cookery*, London, Sidgwick and Jackson, 1981.

Downer, Lesley, *Japanese Vegetarian Cookery*, London, Jonathan Cape, 1986.

Drummond, J. C. and Wilbraham, Anne, *The Englishman's Food: five centuries of English diet*, London, Jonathan Cape, 1969.

Dufty, William, *Sugar Blues*, Radnor, Penn., Chilton Book Company, 1975.

Edington, J. et al, 'Effect of dietary cholesterol on plasma cholesterol concentration in subjects following reduced fat, high fibre diet' in *British Medical Journal*, 7 February 1987.

European Community: Green Europe, *Cheaper Raw Materials for Europe's Industries: sugar and starch*, February 1987.

Europe Information. Développement. Commission des Communautés Européennes. *Le sucre, la communauté européenne et la Convention de Lome*, February 1983.

Feingold, B. F., *Why Your Child is Hyperactive*, New York, Random House, 1975.

Fisher, Hans, 'Dietary fats: a primer' in *Prevention*, March, 1987.

Flour Advisory Bureau, *Introduction to Yeast Cookery*.

Francis, C. and Gontier, F., *The Book of Honey*, London, Robert Hale, 1981.

Gillie, Oliver, 'Sugar report leaves sour taste with diet experts' in *The Independent*, 22 October 1986.

Glasse, H., *The Complete Confectioner: or the whole art of confectionery made plain and easy*, London, J. Cooke, 1770?

Gledhill, Ruth, 'No stomach for victory' in *The Times*, 17 September 1987.

Goldman, J. A. et al, 'Behavioral effects of sucrose on preschool children' in *Journal of Abnormal Child Psychology*, vol. 14, 1986.

Graham, J. and Odent, M., *The Z Factor*, Wellingborough, Thorsons, 1986.

Griggs, Barbara, *The Food Factor*, Harmondsworth, Viking, 1986.

Hackett, A. F., Rugg-Gunn, A. J., Appleton, D. R., 'Sugars consumption of Northumbrian children aged 11–14 years' in *Nutrition and Health*, vol. 5, no. 1/2, 1987.

Harris, Derek, 'The sweetest tooth in Europe' in *The Times*, 15 March 1988.

Health Education Council, *A discussion paper on proposals for nutritional guidelines for health education in Britain*, NACNE, September 1983.

Heasman, Michael, *One lump or two? Current issues and challenges facing sugar in the United Kingdom*, University of Bradford, 1987.

Heaton, K., 'Tough line on sugar' in *World Medicine*, 18 October 1978.

Heaton, K. W., 'Dietary fibre in perspective' in *Human Nutrition: Clinical Nutrition*, 37C, 1983.

Hume, Rosemary and Downes, Muriel, *Cordon Bleu Desserts and Puddings*, Harmondsworth, Penguin, 1976.

'Informing food manufacturers' in *Sugar Times*, no. 3, May 1987.

Kaplan, H. K. et al, 'Behavioral effects of dietary sucrose in disturbed children' in *American Journal of Psychiatry*, July 1986.

Kavanagh, M. K. et al, 'Does sucrose damage kidneys?' in *British Journal of Urology*, no. 58, 1986.

Keynote report, *Confectionery, an Industry Sector Overview*, London, Keynote, 1987.

Kinderlehrer, Jane, *Cooking Kosher the Natural Way*, New York, Jonathan David, 1980.

Kohrman, Katherine, *The Common Ground Dessert Cookbook*, Berkeley, Calif., Ten Speed Press, 1983.

Lebrecht, Elbie, *Sugar-free Cakes and Biscuits*, London, Faber and Faber, 1985.

Lebrecht, Elbie, 'Sweet reason' in *The Sunday Times Magazine*, 16 November 1986.

Liebman, B. F. and Mayer, G., 'The case against sugar' in *Nutrition Action*, December 1980.

Light, Marilyn, *Hypoglycemia: one of man's most widespread and misdiagnosed diseases*, New Canaan, Conn., Keats Publishing, 1983.

London Food Commission, *Pesticides Broadsheet*, London, n.d.

Marshall, J., 'Heaven preserve us' in *The Sunday Times Magazine*, 1 November 1987.

McCallum, Cass, *The Real Food Guide*, vols I, II, Glasgow, Molendinar Press, 1981.

McCarrison, Sir Robert, *Nutrition and Health*, London, McCarrison Society, 1982.

McCarrison Society Conference, *Sugars: a menace to public health?* Summaries of presentations by Geoffrey Cannon, July 1986.

McGee, Harold, *On Food and Cooking: The Science and Lore of the Kitchen*, London, Unwin Hyman, 1987.

Maleskey, Gale, 'Pectin – the super fiber' in *Prevention*, March 1987.

Mann, J. I., 'What carbohydrate foods should diabetics eat?' in *British Medical Journal*, 7 April 1984.

May, Tony, 'Raising the peanut's performance' in *The Guardian*, 21 March 1988.

'Media file' in *The Guardian*, 7 December 1987.

Millstone, Eric and Abraham, J., *Additives, a Guide for Everyone*, Harmondsworth, Penguin, 1988.

Mintz, Sidney W., *Sweetness and Power: the place of sugar in modern history*, New York, Viking, 1985.

Moore, Toby, 'Brown rice and orange juice to fight violence' in *The Sunday Times*, 16 November 1986.

Moore, Toby and Leigh, Lis, 'Sugar experts' soft line sours the health lobby' in *The Sunday Times*, 22 February 1987.

Nichols, Naomi, M., *Food Drying at Home*, Newton Abbot, David and Charles, 1978.

Organic Farmers and Growers, *The Organic Handbook*, OF&G, 1987.

Painter, Mary, 'Beware waxed fruits and vegetables!' in *Food Monitor*, no. 42, Fall, 1987.

Passmore, R. and Eastwood, M. A., *Human Nutrition and Dietetics*, Edinburgh, Churchill Livingstone, 1986.

Patten, Marguerite, *500 Recipes for Bread and Scones*, London, Paul Hamlyn, 1965.

Paul, A. A. and Southgate, D. A. T., *McCance and Widdowson's The Composition of Foods*, London, HMSO, 1979.

Penny, W. J. et al, 'Relationship between trace elements, sugar consumption and taste in Crohn's disease' in *Gut*, 24 (4), April 1983.

Philpott, W. H. and Kalita, D. K., *Victory over diabetes; a bio-ecologic triumph*, New Canaan, Conn., Keats Publishing, 1983.

Rabinovitch, Dina, 'Sour aftertaste from the tale of a wonder sweetener' in *The Independent*, 7 April 1987.

Roden, Claudia, *A Book of Middle Eastern Food*, Harmondsworth, Penguin, 1979.

Royal College of Physicians, *Medical Aspects of Dietary Fibre*, Pitman, 1980.

Royal College of Physicians, *Obesity*, London, 1983.

Rugg-Gunn, A. J., 'Sugar consumption in the United Kingdom' in *British Dental Journal*, 22 November 1986.

Schauss, Alexander, *Nutrition and Behavior. How what you eat affects what you do – and can even prevent or promote delinquency and anti-social acts*, New Canaan, Conn., Keats Publishing, 1985.

Schoenthaler, Stephen J., 'The effect of sugar on the treatment and control of anti-social behavior: a double-blind study of an incarcerated juvenile population' in *International Journal of Biosocial Research*, vol. 3, no. 1, 1982.

'Score another one for the Mediterranean diet' in *Prevention*, May 1987.

Sheiham, Aubrey, 'Sucrose and dental caries' in *Nutrition and Health*, vol. 5, no. 1/2, 1987.

Sheiham, Aubrey, 'Sugars and dental decay' in *The Lancet*, 5 February 1983.

Sherman, Jill and Prentice, Thomson, 'Prevention rather than cure seen as the way forward' in *The Times*, 26 November 1987.

Shurtleff, William and Aoyagi, Akiko, *The book of tofu – food for mankind*, New York, Ballantine, 1979.

Spencer, Colin, 'Out for an oil change' in *The Guardian*, 12 June 1987.

Spry, Constance, *Come Into the Garden, Cook*, London, J. M. Dent, 1942.

Steiner, J. E., Sgan-Cohen, H. D. and Nahas, J., 'Sweet preference and dental caries among Bedouin youth in Israel' in *Community Dentistry and Oral Epidemiology*, Dec 12 (6), 1984.

'Sugar intake advice turned upside down' in *Health Express*, June 1987.

'Sugar sense' in *Which?*, November 1987.

Sugars Task Force, *Evaluation of Health Aspects of Sugars Contained in Carbohydrate Sweeteners*, Washington, Food and Drug Administration, 1986.

Taitz, L. S., 'Foods, fads and fats in under fives' in *Nutrition and Health*, vol. 5, no. 3/4, 1987.

Thompson, Sarah, 'Disturbed pupils to test diet theory' in *The Times*, 10 November 1987.

Trowell, H., Burkitt, D. and Heaton, K., eds, *Dietary Fibre, Fibre Depleted Foods and Diseases*, London, Academic Press, 1985.

Yudkin, John, 'Metabolic changes induced by sugar in relation to coronary heart disease and diabetes' in *Nutrition and Health*, vol. 5, no. 1/2, 1987.

Yudkin, John, *Pure, White and Deadly*, Harmondsworth, Viking, 1986.

Yudkin, John and Kang, S. S., 'Effects of high dietary sugar' in *British Medical Journal*, 22 November 1980.

Aduki and apple pie, 166
Aduki bean cake, 248
Agar-agar, 263
Almond
    and banana roll, 184
    and pine crescents, 98
    apricot spread, 78
    carob balls, 94
    carob ice cream, 284
    frutti tart, 178
    globes, chilled, in pastel pink sauce,
        200
    pastry, 163
    pudding, 209
    rose rolls, 183
Apple(s)
    and aduki pie, 166
    and peach strudel, 169
    and pear pie with crumble topping,
        165
    and pineapple mousse, 265
    and poppy seed cake, 230
    and rhubarb crumble, 212
    and wheatgerm, 46
    baked, 217
    cake, 226
    cherry cake, 226
    crumble, 212
    custard, 208
    delight, 170
    fibre content, 10
    juice, 7
    meringue, 208
    muffins, 74
    rice pudding, 211
    slice, 227
    sliced apple tart, 181

    spicy tofu cake, 231
    stewed, 215
    strudel, 168
Apricot(s)
    almond spread, 78
    carob treats, 102
    dried, fibre content, 9
    fairy cakes, 243
    mousse, 266
    ring, 188
    sponge pudding, 210
    tart, 177
    wild Himalayan, in rosewater, 199
Artificial sweeteners, 15–16
Ascorbic acid (Vitamin C), 31, 55
Aspartame, 16, 28

Baby foods, 26
    sugar-free packaged, 29
Bagels, 62
Baked
    apples, 217
    bananas, 218
Banana(s)
    and almond roll, 184
    and walnut rolls, 182
    baked, 218
    cake, 228
    custard, 259
    drops, 89
    fibre content, 9
    tahini spread, 79
    velvet ice cream, 282, 283
Barley
    loaf, 70
    pastry, 162
Beans, baked, sugar-free, 27

Belfast City Hospital, 19
Biscuits, 4
  carob oat, 92
  sugar-free packaged foods, 26, 28
Bladder tumours, 16
Bread
  basic method of making, 54
  brown, 7
  kneading, 55–6
  rolls, 55
    without Vitamin C, 57
  Rye, 58
Breakfast cereals, 26
Bristol University Medical School, 18
British Dental Association, 17
British Federation of Bakers, 53
British Medical Association, 18
British Nutritional Foundation (BNF),
  19
Butter, peanut, 28, 78

Cake(s), 4, 27
  Aduki bean, 248
  apple, 226
  apple cherry, 226
  apple slice, 227
  apricot fairy, 243
  banana, 228
  birthday, 296
  carob, 233
  carob mousse layer, 233
  carrot, 234
  fruit, 250
  ginger fig, 246
  hazelnut gateau, 244
  mincemeat, 247
  parsnip, 235
  pineapple tang, 229
  poppy seed and apple, 230
  spicy apple tofu, 231
  Swiss roll, 240, 242
  walnut, 247
Cancer of the large bowel, 1, 20–21
Canderel, 16
Carob
  almond balls, 94
  almond ice cream, 284
  and prune crescents, 101
  apricot treats, 102
  bars, 27
  cake, 233
  cherry ice cream, 287
  coconut macaroons, 98

confectionery, sugar-free packaged
  foods, 29
cream, 276
cream tart, 176
date treats, 103
fudge squares, 91
hazelnut cream filling, 81
hazelnut slice, 93
hot, 112
icing, 82
mousse, 267
mousse layer cake, 233
nut clusters, 96
oat biscuits, 92
orange pie, 172
pastry, 162
pear tarts, 178
roll, 185
secrets, 95
swiss roll, 242
Carrot(s)
  and orange soup, 46
  and prunes with tofu dumplings, 127
  cake, 234
  fibre content, 10
  peanut salad, 142
Cereals, sugar-free packaged, 29
Challah, 60
Cheesecake
  cherry, 236
  persimmon, 238
  tofu apple, 239
  yeast, 237
Cherry
  and pineapple jelly, 270
  apple cake, 226
  carob ice cream, 287
  cheesecake, 236
  compôte, 216
  cream, 81
  mango ice cream, 286
  sauce, 255
Chestnut
  and satsuma cream filling, 81
  crème aux marrons, 275
  fudge fingers, 87
Chicken
  fruit, served with yellow split peas, 120
  sweet and sour, 121
Chicory salad, 143
Children's parties
  birthday cakes, 296
  treats for, 295

Chilled almond globes in pastel pink sauce, 200
Chinese cabbage and orange salad, 143
Chocolate, 4, 5
Chutney(s)
fenugreek, 151
French-Canadian, 149
mango, 150
pineapple date, 149
sugar-free, 28
Cinnamon
drops, 97
hazelnut sticks, 100
roll, 187
Clementine cream delight, 194
Coconut
carob macaroons, 98
icing, 82
macaroons, 97
Commission of the Health Association of France, 15
Committee on the Medical Aspects of Food (COMA), 9
Compôte, cherry, 216
Confectionery, 4
Conserve, pineapple, 79
Consumption of sugar, figures, 1
Coronary Prevention Group, 19
Cream(s)
carob, 276
cherry, 81
pineapple-tofu, 273
strawberry, 273
Crème aux marrons, 275
Crohn's disease, 21
Crumble(s)
apple, 212
rhubarb and apple, 212
Curries, sugar-free, 27
Custard, 258
apple, 208
banana, 259

Date(s)
carob treats, 103
delight, 194
dried, fibre content, 9
pineapple chutney, 149
rolls, 182
DDT, 33
Dextrose, 25
Diabetes, diabetics, 1, 6, 16, 20
Diarrhoea, 16, 21

Dietitians, 5
Diverticular disease, 21
Dough, kneading, 55–6
Doughnuts, 65
Dressings
French or vinaigrette, 142
Mediterranean, 142
oil used in, 140
Dried fruit, 29
and fresh fruit salad, 197
minerals in, 30–31
Drop scones, 71

Epilepsy, 16
Equipment, essential, 39–40

Fairy cakes, apricot, 243
Fenugreek chutney, 151
Fibre, 6
and natural sugar content in food, 302
content in food, 9–10
Fig(s)
au fromage frais, 196
dried, fibre content, 9
ginger cake, 246
Fish with sultanas and pine nuts, 122
Food, natural sugar and fibre content in, 302
Fool(s)
gooseberry, 272
mango, 272
Freezing, 36
French-Canadian chutney, 149
French dressing (vinaigrette), 142
Fresh and dried fruit salad, 197
Fresh fruit, as sweeteners, 29–30
Fromage frais, figs au, 196
Frozen strawberry sundaes, 288
Fructose, 25
Fruit
bars, 27
sugar-free packaged foods, 28
cake, 250
chicken with yellow split peas, 120
how to dry, 30–31
ice lollies, 290
juice, 26
loaf, 64
salad, fresh and dried, 197
salad, July, 197
stewed, 214
tarts, 174

Fruit – *cont.*
  tinned in natural juice, 26
  yogurt, 26, 45
Frutti almond tart, 178
Fudge
  carob squares, 91
  chestnut fingers, 87
  pecan, 102

Gallstones, 1, 20
Gateau, hazelnut, 225, 244
Ginger fig cake, 246
Gingerbread men, 88
Glucose, 19, 25, 28
  fibre content, 9
  syrup, 25
Gooseberry fool, 272
Grape(s)
  and pear jelly, 270
  juice, 28
Greek raspberries, 274

Hasty pastry, 150
Hazelnut(s)
  carob cream filling, 81
  carob slice, 93
  cinnamon sticks, 100
  gateau, 225, 244
  pastry, 163
Health Education Council, 9, 17
Heart disease, 1, 19–20
High blood pressure, 1
Honey, 10
  fibre content, 9
Honeydew jelly, 269
Hot carob, 112
Hypoglycaemia, 21

Ice cream
  almond carob, 284
  banana velvet, 282, 283
  cherry carob, 287
  mango cherry, 286
  melon and raspberry, 283
  oat, 286
  peach, 285
  raspberry, 282
  torte, 179
Ice lollies, fruit, 290
Icings
  carob, 82
  coconut, 82
Ingredients, basic, 37–9
Invert syrup, 25

Jams and spreads, sugar-free packaged, 28, 29
Jelly
  honeydew, 269
  pear and grape, 270
  pineapple and cherry, 270
  strawberry, 267
July fruit salad, 197

Ketchup, sugar-free, 27

Lamb, stuffed rolls of, 118
Leeks
  in tomato and lemon sauce, 132
  stuffed, 133
Lemon
  and orange fizz, 110
  and tomato sauce with leeks, 132
  scones, 69
Loaf,
  barley, 70
  fruit, 64
London Food Commission, 33
Lucozade, 6

Macaroons
  carob coconut, 98
  coconut, 97
Maimonides, 22
Mango
  cherry ice cream, 286
  chutney, 150
  fool, 272
  pie delight, 167
Marrons, crème aux, 275
Marzipan, 103
  fruit, 104
  mice, 105
Massachusetts Institute of Technology, 16
Mayonnaise, 141
  sugar-free, 28
Measurements, 37
Mediterranean dressing, 142
Mediterranean half moons, 86
Melon
  and raspberry ice cream, 283
    tart, 284
  bowls, 198
  cool, 111
  fizz, 110
  ice, 290
Meringue, apple, 208

Migraine, theobromine, 91
Milkshake, strawberry, 112
Millet peach delight, 200
Mincemeat, 80
    cake, 247
Minerals, 7
    in dried fruit, 30
Mood and behaviour, 21
Mousse
    apricot, 266
    carob, 267
    pineapple and apple, 265
    strawberry, 265
Muesli, 45
    slices, 90
Muffins, 73
    apple, 74

National Advisory Committee on
    Nutrition Education (NACNE), 9,
    139
National Coaching Foundation, 5
National Commission on Diabetes, 20
Natural sugar and fibre content in
    food, 302
Noodle pudding, 209
Nut carob clusters, 96
NutraSweet, 16

Oat(s)
    carob biscuits, 92
    ice cream, 286
    sesame bars, 90
    snacks, 89
Oatcakes, 72
Obesity, 1, 18–19
Oils used in dressings, 140
Omelette, sweet, 207
Orange
    and carrot soup, 46
    and Chinese cabbage salad, 143
    and lemon fizz, 110
    and strawberry sauce, 255
    carob pie, 172
    cups, 271
    fritters, 206
Organic food, 34–5

Papayalata, 111
Parsnip cake, 235
Passion fruit salmon, 123
Pastel pink sauce, 256

Pastry
    almond, 163
    barley, 162
    carob, 162
    hasty, 158
    hazelnut, 163
    rough puff, 160
    short cut strudel, 159
    sweet seed, 163
    yeast, 164
    yogurt, 158
Peach(es)
    and apple strudel, 169
    custard tart, 173
    ice cream, 285
    ice pops, 290
    millet delight, 200
    poached, 215
    sauce, 256
Peanut(s)
    and sprouts stir-fry, 129
    butter, 28, 78
    carrot salad, 142
    scones, 68
Pear(s)
    and apple pie with crumble topping,
        165
    and grape jelly, 270
    and prune drops, 99
    and spiced melon, 151
    carob tarts, 178
    drink, 111
    pie, 171
    stewed, 214
    stuffed, 217
Pecan
    fudge, 102
    pie, 170
Peppers, stuffed, 130
Persimmon cheesecake, 238
Pesticides, effects on food, 33–4
Phenylketonuria, 16
Phenylalanine, 16
Pies
    apple and pear with crumble
        topping, 165
    mango delight, 167
    orange carob, 172
    pear, 171
    pecan, 170
Pine and almond crescents, 98
Pine nuts and sultanas with fish,
    122

Pineapple
   and apple mousse, 265
   and cherry jelly, 270
   conserve, 79
   date chutney, 149
   drink, 110
   tang cake, 229
   tofu cream, 273
Poached peaches, 215
Polish sweet and sour steak, 119
Pomegranate dip, 195
Poppy seed
   and apple cake, 230
   torte, 245
Prune(s)
   and carob crescents, 101
   and carrots with tofu dumplings, 127
   and pear drops, 99
   fibre content, 9
Pudding
   almond, 209
   apple rice, 211
   apricot sponge, 210
   noodle, 209
   summer, 47

Raisin(s)
   fibre content, 9
   wine, 112
Raspberry(ies)
   and melon ice cream, 283
   Greek, 274
   ice cream, 282
   sauce, 257
Relish, sugar-free, 28
Rhubarb and apple crumble, 212
Ribena, 6
Rice
   apple pudding, 211
   pilav, 134
Roll(s)
   almond rose, 183
   banana and almond, 184
   banana and walnut, 182
   bread, 55
      without Vitamin C, 57
   carob, 185
   cinnamon, 187
   date, 182
Rough Puff Pastry, 160
Royal Bristol Infirmary, 20
Royal College of Physicians, 9, 18, 20
Rye bread, 58

Saccharin, 15–16, 28
Salads
   chicory, 143
   orange and chinese cabbage, 143
   peanut carrot, 142
Salmon passion fruit, 123
Satsuma chestnut cream filling, 81
Sauces
   cherry, 255
   orange and strawberry, 255
   pastel pink, 200, 256
   peach, 256
   raspberry, 257
   savoury apple, 258
   sugar-free packaged foods, 29
   tomato, 118
      and lemon, 132
Savoury apple sauce, 258
Scones, 67
   drop, 71
   lemon, 69
   peanut, 68
Sesame
   oat bars, 90
   squares, 86
Short cut strudel, 159
Singin' Hinny, 72
Sliced apple tart, 181
Snack bars, 'nutritious', 5
Soft drinks, 4, 6, 25–6
   sugar content, 6
Sorbitol, 16
Soup, orange and carrot, 46
Soy sauce, 126
Soya bean curd, 124–5
Spiced melon and pears, 151
Spicy apple tofu cake, 231
Spinach special, 134
Spots and pimples, 21
Spreads
   apricot almond, 78
   sugar-free, 28, 29
   tahini-banana, 79
Sprouts and peanut stir-fry, 129
Steak, Polish sweet and sour, 119
Stewed
   apple, 215
   fruit, 214
   pears, 214
Stir-fry peanut and sprouts, 129
Storing dried fruit, nuts and grains, 32–3
Strawberry
   and orange sauce, 255

cream, 273
hats, 186
ice, 285
ice lollies, 290
jelly, 267
    ring, 268
milkshake, 112
mousse, 265
sundaes, frozen, 288
tart, 174
Strudel
apple, 168
peach and apple, 169
short cut, 159
Stuffed
leeks, 133
pears, 217
peppers, 130
rolls of lamb, 118
Substitutes, 35–6
Sucrose, 2, 20, 25
Sugar
a plant and its power, 12–15
and your health, 17–22
fibre content, 9
how to shake off, 24
spot the, 24–5
Sugar Bureau, 2, 17
Sugar-free packaged foods, 28–9
baby food, 29
biscuits, 28
carob confectionery, 29
cereals, 29
fruit bars, 28
jams and spreads, 28, 29
sauces and relishes, 29
tinned foods, 29
Sugar-free shopping, 25–8
Sultanas
and pine nuts with fish, 122
fibre content, 9
Summer pudding, 47
Sunflower chews, 102
Sunset over Greenland, 201
Sweet omelette, 207
seed pastry, 163
Sweet and sour
chicken, 121
steak, Polish style, 119
tofu, 124
Sweeteners, 29–30
dried fruit, 29
fresh fruit, 29

juice, 30
Swiss roll, 240
carob, 242

Tahini-banana spread, 79
Tarts
apricot, 177
carob cream, 176
carob pear, 178
fruit, 174
frutti almond, 178
melon and raspberry ice cream, 284
peach custard, 173
sliced apple, 181
strawberry, 174
Theobromine and migraine, 91
Tinned foods, sugar-free packaged, 29
Tofu, 124–5
apple cheesecake, 239
dumplings with carrots and prunes, 127
sweet and sour, 124
Tomato
and lemon sauce with leeks, 132
sauce, 118
Tooth decay, 1, 17–18
Torte
ice cream, 179
poppy seed, 245
Trifle, 276

UK Registry for Organic Food
Standards, 35
USA Food and Drug Administration,
15, 16, 17, 18

Vinaigrette (French dressing), 142
Vitamin C (ascorbic acid), 31, 55

Walnut
and banana rolls, 182
cake, 247
crescents, 186
Wheatgerm and apple, 46
Wild Himalayan apricots in rosewater, 199

Yeast
cheesecake, 237
pastry, 164
Yellow split peas served with fruit
chicken, 120
Yogurt
fruit, 26, 45
pastry, 158

Cooking for good health books – in paperback from Grafton Books

Pamela Westland

Low-Fat Cookery	£2.95	☐
Bean Feast	£2.50	☐
High-Fibre Vegetarian Cookery	£2.50	☐
The Complete Grill Cookbook	£1.50	☐

David Canter, Kay Canter and Daphne Swann

The Cranks Recipe Book (illustrated)	£3.95	☐

Cecilia Norman

Microwave Cookery for One	£2.50	☐
Microwave Cookery Course	£2.50	☐
The Pie and Pastry Cookbook	£2.50	☐
Barbecue Cookery	£1.95	☐
The Food Processor Cookbook	£1.95	☐

Mary Cadogan

Low-Salt Cookery	£1.95	☐

Colin Spencer

Colin Spencer's Vegetarian Wholefood Cookbook	£2.50	☐

To order direct from the publisher just tick the titles you want and fill in the order form.

HB481

Cooking for good health books – in paperback from Grafton Books

Kenneth Lo

Cooking and Eating the Chinese Way	£1.95	☐
The Wok Cookbook	£1.95	☐
More Wok Cookery	£1.95	☐

L D Michaels

The Complete Book of Pressure Cooking	£1.95	☐

Franny Singer

The Slow Crock Cookbook	£1.95	☐

Janet Walker

Vegetarian Cookery	£2.50	☐

David Scott

The Japanese Cookbook	£1.95	☐

Marika Hanbury Tenison

Cooking with Vegetables (illustrated)	£1.95	☐
Deep-Freeze Cookery	£1.95	☐

Pamela Westland

Low-Fat Cookery	£2.95	☐
Bean Feast	£2.50	☐
High-Fibre Vegetarian Cookery	£2.50	☐
The Complete Grill Cookbook	£1.50	☐

David Canter, Kay Canter and Daphne Swann

The Cranks Recipe Book (illustrated)	£3.95	☐

To order direct from the publisher just tick the titles you want and fill in the order form.

HB381

Cookery handbooks now available in paperback from Grafton Books

L D Michaels
The Complete Book of Pressure Cooking   £1.95 □

Cecilia Norman
Microwave Cookery for One   £2.50 □
Microwave Cookery Course   £2.50 □
The Pie and Pastry Cookbook   £2.50 □
Barbecue Cookery   £1.95 □
The Food Processor Cookbook   £1.95 □

Franny Singer
The Slow Crock Cookbook   £1.95 □

Janet Walker
Vegetarian Cookery   £2.50 □

Pamela Westland
Low-Fat Cookery   £2.95 □
Bean Feast   £2.50 □
High-Fibre Vegetarian Cookery   £2.50 □
The Complete Grill Cookbook   £1.50 □

Marika Hanbury Tenison
Deep-Freeze Cookery   £1.95 □
Cooking with Vegetables (illustrated)   £1.95 □

Jennifer Stone
The Alcoholic Cookbook   £1.95 □

Barbara Griggs
Baby's Cookbook   £1.95 □

Wendy Craig
Busy Mum's Cookbook   £1.95 □

Carolyn Heal and Michael Allsop
Cooking with Spices   £2.95 □

To order direct from the publisher just tick the titles you want and fill in the order form.

HB681

Health and self-help books – in paperback from Grafton Books

W H Bates
Better Eyesight Without Glasses   £2.50   ☐

Laurence E Morehouse and Leonard Gross
Total Fitness   £2.50   ☐

Constance Mellor
Guide to Natural Health   £1.25   ☐
Natural Remedies for Common Ailments   £1.95   ☐

Sonya Richmond
Yoga and Your Health   £1.25   ☐

Phyllis Speight
Homoeopathy   £1.50   ☐

Dr Richard B Stuart
Act Thin, Stay Thin   £1.50   ☐

Dr Carl C Pfeiffer and Jane Banks
Total Nutrition   £1.50   ☐

Dr Hamilton Hall
Be Your Own Back Doctor   £2.50   ☐

José Silva and Michael Miele
The Silva Mind Control Method   £2.95   ☐

Geneen Roth
Breaking Free from Compulsive Eating   £2.95   ☐
Feeding the Hungry Heart   £2.50   ☐

To order direct from the publisher just tick the titles you want and fill in the order form. **HB881**

International cookery books in paperback from Grafton Books

Elizabeth Cass
Spanish Cooking   £1.25 ☐

Arto der Haroutunian
Complete Arab Cookery   £2.50 ☐
Modern Jewish Cookery   £2.50 ☐

Robin Howe
Greek Cooking   £1.95 ☐
German Cooking   £1.95 ☐
Italian Cooking   £1.95 ☐

Kenneth Lo
Cooking and Eating the Chinese Way   £1.95 ☐
The Wok Cookbook   £1.95 ☐
More Wok Cookery   £1.95 ☐

F Marian McNeil
The Scots Kitchen (illustrated)   £2.50 ☐
The Scots Cellar   £1.95 ☐

David Scott
The Japanese Cookbook   £1.95 ☐

E P Veerasawmy
Indian Cookery   £2.50 ☐

Kenneth Gardnier
Creole Caribbean Cookery   £3.95 ☐

To order direct from the publisher just tick the titles you want and fill in the order form.

HB581

All these books are available at your local bookshop or newsagent, or can be ordered direct from the publisher.

To order direct from the publishers just tick the titles you want and fill in the form below.

Name _____

Address _____

_____

Send to:
Grafton Cash Sales
PO Box 11, Falmouth, Cornwall TR10 9EN.

Please enclose remittance to the value of the cover price plus:

UK 60p for the first book, 25p for the second book plus 15p per copy for each additional book ordered to a maximum charge of £1.90.

BFPO 60p for the first book, 25p for the second book plus 15p per copy for the next 7 books, thereafter 9p per book.

Overseas including Eire £1.25 for the first book, 75p for second book and 28p for each additional book.

_____

Grafton Books reserve the right to show new retail prices on covers, which may differ from those previously advertised in the text or elsewhere.